SCHAUM'S OUTLINE OF

THEORY AND PROBLEMS

OF

FLUID DYNAMICS

•

BY

WILLIAM F. HUGHES, Ph.D.

Professor of Mechanical and Electrical Engineering
Carnegie Institute of Technology

AND

JOHN A. BRIGHTON, Ph.D.

Assistant Professor of Mechanical Engineering
Pennsylvania State University

•

SCHAUM'S OUTLINE SERIES

McGRAW-HILL BOOK COMPANY

New York, St. Louis, San Francisco, Toronto, Sydney

31110

8 9 1 0   SH SH   7 5 4 3 2 1 0 6

Preface

If one casually glances around, most things seem to be solids, but when one thinks of the oceans, the atmosphere and on out into space it becomes rather obvious that a good portion of the earth's surface and of the entire universe is in the fluid state.

Aside from the scientist's interest in the nature of the universe which is mostly gas, the engineer's interest in devices useful to mankind can seldom drift far from fluids. It is indeed difficult to think of any machine, device, or tool which doesn't have some fluid hidden in it somewhere and some fluid mechanics behind its design. Pumps, fans, blowers, jet engines, rockets, gas turbines are primarily fluid machines. Aircraft and ships move through fluids. The atmosphere and the weather are governed by the dynamics of fluids. All machines must be lubricated, and the lubricant is a fluid. Even the vacuum tube in a radio relies on an electron gas for its operation. And, no matter how complex or esoteric the device, the basic concepts of fluid dynamics still apply. After one masters the few basic ideas of fluid mechanics, a whole world of applications is opened.

It would seem unnecessary then to justify the obviously important place of fluid dynamics in modern science and engineering. It forms one of the foundations of aeronautics and astronautics, mechanical engineering, meteorology, marine engineering, civil engineering, bio-engineering and, in fact, just about every scientific or engineering field.

This book may be used as either a text or supplementary text for a first undergraduate course in fluid mechanics. However, one of the unique features is the treatment of a broad spectrum of fluid mechanics topics such as hypersonic flow, magnetohydrodynamics and non-Newtonian fluids not heretofore found in a single book of this type. The coverage of this material and other advanced topics also makes this book ideal for use as a reference and supplementary text for either an intermediate or first year graduate course.

The first few chapters are written primarily for the beginning student, with considerable emphasis on basic ideas of fluid motion. The first three chapters contain rather complete derivations of the conservation equations both in integral and differential form. Many examples are presented in order to convey the very important ideas of a control volume, Bernoulli's equation and the motion of fluids in general. A convenient summary of important equations and a general discussion of problem solving technique, which will be helpful to the beginning student, is provided in Chapter 3.

The level of the book changes from chapter to chapter. Chapters 1 through 5 and Chapter 7 serve as a first introduction to fluid mechanics at the undergraduate level. Chapters 6 and 8 extend to the aerodynamics of subsonic and supersonic flow and are pitched at the advanced undergraduate level.

As the student proceeds through the remaining chapters, he will find that the material becomes more advanced. The second half of the book deals with topics which are of current research interest. For example, the fluid mechanics literature and research efforts of today are largely in the areas of incompressible turbulence, hypersonic flow, magnetohydrodynamics, and non-Newtonian fluids. These chapters are written in such a way that one who is not familiar with these particular subfields may obtain an introduction to the form of the mathematical models, the simplifications and techniques, the nature and peculiarities, and the present state of the art. If one is interested in an in-depth study of one or more of the subfields, the references at the end of the chapters may be pursued. These, along with this book, could serve as the basis for an individual study program.

The authors wish to thank Dr. E. W. Gaylord for his valuable help with Chapter 12, and Mrs. Dorothy C. Wakefield and Mrs. Mary Bathurst for typing the original manuscript.

J. A. BRIGHTON
W. F. HUGHES

University Park, Pennsylvania
Pittsburgh, Pennsylvania
July, 1967

CONTENTS

CONTENTS

Chapter 1

Introduction

1.1 WHAT IS A FLUID

Dynamics, the study of motion of matter, may be divided into two parts—dynamics of rigid bodies and dynamics of non-rigid bodies. The latter is usually further divided into two general classifications—elasticity (solid elastic bodies) and fluid mechanics. Since a large portion of the Earth is in the fluid state, it is rather obvious that engineers and scientists have to know something about fluids. But first, what is a fluid? How does a fluid differ from what we call a solid elastic substance such as a bar of steel?

In simple terms a fluid is a substance which cannot resist a shear force or stress without moving as can a solid. Fluids are usually classified as liquids or gases. A liquid has inter-molecular forces which hold it together so that it possesses volume but no definite shape. A liquid poured into a container will fill the container up to the volume of the liquid regard-less of the container's shape. Liquids have but slight compressibility and the density varies little with temperature or pressure. A gas, on the other hand, consists of molecules in motion which collide with each other tending to disperse it so that a gas has no set volume or shape. A gas will fill any container into which it is placed. For a given mass or system of gas, the pressure, temperature and enclosing volume are related by the gas law, that is, the appropriate equation of state of the gas.

The many applications of fluid mechanics make it one of the most vital and fundamental of all engineering and applied scientific studies. The flow of fluids in pipes and channels makes fluid mechanics of importance to civil engineers. The study of fluid machinery such as pumps, compressors, heat exchangers, jet and rocket engines, and the like, makes fluid mechanics of importance to mechanical engineers. The flow of air over objects, aero-dynamics, is of fundamental interest to aeronautical and space engineers in the design of aircraft, missiles and rockets. In meteorology, hydrology and oceanography the study of fluids is basic since the atmosphere and the ocean are fluids. And today in modern engineer-ing many new disciplines combine fluid mechanics with classical disciplines. For example, fluid mechanics and electromagnetic theory are studied together as magnetohydrodynamics. In new types of energy conversion devices and in the study of stellar and ionospheric phenomena, magnetohydrodynamics is vital.

We see that a good familiarity with fluid mechanics is essential to the modern engineer and scientist, and it is probably obvious that fluid mechanics and its applications is a broad subject with far-flung fields of specialization. What we will do in this book is to present most of the fundamental ideas with many of the applications. Once these fundamentals are mastered more advanced books and research literature may be studied to increase one's understanding of more specialized aspects of fluid mechanics. However, it is essential to be well grounded in the fundamentals which do not change with age, and which can always be relied upon, before going on to more advanced topics.

We will provide an introduction to the subject of fluid mechanics by presenting funda-mental ideas, from the basic mathematical formulation to modern hypersonic flow theory and magnetohydrodynamics.

1

1.2 THE MATHEMATICAL MODEL

In solid rigid body mechanics, we usually ask the question: what is the position in space of a particle as a function of time? From this information all other questions, such as what are the velocity and acceleration, may be answered. If the position vector $\mathbf{r}$ denotes the position of a particle, then $\mathbf{r}(t)$ is the important parameter. Velocity and acceleration are simply $d\mathbf{r}/dt$ and $d^2\mathbf{r}/dt^2$.

However, in a fluid we are not dealing with a single particle. We are concerned with a *continuum*. In fact we don't have to keep track of individual particles or even little blobs of fluid. Rather, it is convenient to ask the question: at some point in space (relative to an arbitrary fixed coordinate system) what is the velocity, acceleration and thermodynamic properties at that point in space as a function of time? As time proceeds the fluid at that point in space is being constantly exchanged for new fluid as the fluid flows past, so that we keep track not of any individual particle of fluid but of history at some point in space regardless of what bit of fluid happens to be there at any particular time. Such a description of the fluid is called an Eulerian description as opposed to a Lagrangian description which is used to keep track of an individual particle as in rigid body dynamics. We will discuss these problems in detail in Chapter 3.

We have mentioned the word continuum. What does this mean in a fluid sense? We assume that the distance between fluid particles (or molecules), or more precisely the mean free path, is very small. By small we mean small compared to any physical dimensions of the problem to which we are applying the principles of fluid mechanics. In aerodynamics, the thickness, say, of a wing is many orders of magnitude greater than the mean free path of the air flowing over the wing. Hence we assume that all mathematical limiting processes (of the calculus) can be taken in a meaningful sense and that any volume of fluid can be continuously subdivided into smaller and smaller volumes while retaining the fluid continuum character. Obviously this division would break down eventually, but we assume that by the time it does the dimensions are so small that they are microscopic and of no concern to us.

However, if such is not the case, as in a rarefied gas flow where the mean free path may be of the same order of magnitude as the physical dimensions of the problem, then the fluid continuum assumption breaks down and we must use a strictly microscopic approach such as free molecule flow theory. We will not be concerned with these rarefied gas theories here and will always be concerned with a homogeneous isotropic continuum which can be treated strictly by macroscopic methods.

The number of basic variables in fluid mechanics is five: three velocity components and two thermodynamic properties. Any two of the thermodynamic properties, such as pressure, temperature, density, enthalpy, entropy, etc., suffice to determine the state and hence all the other properties. The fluid flow field is completely determined once we specify the velocity vector $\mathbf{V}$ and two thermodynamic properties as a function of space and time. Hence we need five independent equations. These are usually the three components of the equation of motion, a continuity equation and an energy equation. Often an equation of state is also introduced in order to allow the writing of the energy equation in terms of three variables (temperature, density and pressure) instead of just two. In that case we have six variables and six equations. In turbulent flow additional unknowns appear for the same number of equations, which prevents a complete theoretical formulation of the problem.

In an incompressible fluid the energy equation is not needed since density is taken as known and only pressure along with velocity need be found in order to completely describe the fluid flow. The temperature is uncoupled then, but an energy equation must be used to find it if this information is needed.

1.3 SOME DEFINITIONS

The flow of fluids may be classified in many different ways. Let us look at some of the different types of flow and relate them to some ordinary everyday experiences and observations. But first a few terms must be defined so that we will have a language in which to talk about fluid flow. Later we will provide more rigorous definitions, but for now, let us give a few simple and somewhat heuristic definitions.

(*a*) **Pressure.** The pressure in a static fluid (one at rest) is defined as the normal compressive force per unit area (normal stress) acting on a surface immersed in the fluid. The pressure might be measured by the force on the face of a unit cube (one with unit dimensions) inserted in the fluid. We have to imagine that the cube does not disturb the fluid, so that the actual pressure at a point in the fluid would be the force acting on a face of the cube divided by the area of that face in the limit as the area becomes infinitesimally small. The pressure at a point is isotropic in a fluid at rest, that is, the force would be the same on all faces of the cube and would be the same regardless of the orientation of the cube in space. Such an isotropic pressure is called hydrostatic pressure. This is the pressure used in thermodynamics (gas laws) and is a thermodynamic property. If the pressure varies from place to place in the fluid a net pressure force would exist on any fixed volume of fluid and must be balanced by a body force such as gravity, or else the fluid will move, the pressure force generating an acceleration in the fluid.

In a dynamical situation (when the fluid moves) there may exist not only pressure forces in the fluid, but shear forces or stresses as well. However, the pressure is still isotropic and defined in the same way as above but must be measured as the normal stress on an area which moves along locally with the fluid. There are sometimes difficulties in moving gases where the normal stresses on a cube are not quite the same in all directions. We can still define a hydrostatic isotropic pressure, but small additional forces in certain directions come about because of fluid viscosity effects. These concepts will be discussed in more detail in the next two chapters.

(*b*) **Viscosity, Friction, and Ideal Flow.** All fluids have viscosity which causes friction. The importance of this friction in physical situations depends on the type of fluid and the physical configuration or flow pattern. If the friction is negligible, we say the flow is ideal. Friction may arise because of viscosity or turbulence.

Fig. 1-1. Flow between parallel plates to illustrate viscosity.
The velocity u is linear across the channel, zero at
the bottom and U at the top. A small element shows
the shear stress.

Roughly speaking, viscosity is a measure of the fluid's resistance to shear when the fluid is in motion (remember a fluid cannot resist shear without moving as can a solid). Imagine two parallel plates of large size, Fig. 1-1, in steady relative motion. Fluid between the plates has a linear velocity profile as shown (if no pressure gradient exists along the plates in the direction of motion). There is no slip between the fluid and plates; that is, at an interface between a fluid and solid, the velocity of the fluid must be the same as the solid. If we consider a small element of the fluid, as shown in Fig.

1-1, the shear stress τ on the top (which is numerically the same as on the bottom in this case) may be written:

$$\tau \;=\; \mu\frac{\partial u}{\partial y} \tag{1.1}$$

where μ, the viscosity, is the proportionality constant between shear stress and velocity gradient. The units of viscosity are clearly lb-sec/ft² in English engineering units. The ratio of viscosity to mass density ρ is called kinematic viscosity and is usually denoted as ν.

The viscosity of a liquid decreases with increasing temperature (as one knows from trying to start an automobile on a cold morning) but gases increase their viscosity with increasing temperature. The viscosity of fluids also depends on pressure, but this dependence is usually of little importance compared to the temperature variation in engineering problems.

Such a simple relationship between shear stress and velocity gradient is known as the Newtonian relationship. In general, fluids which obey such a relationship are known as Newtonian fluids. (A more general expression for Newtonian fluids which allows velocity gradients in three dimensions will be developed later.)

Although the linear Newtonian relationship is only an approximation, it is surprisingly good for a wide class of fluids. For some substances, however, the shear stress may be a function not only of velocity gradient (which is the same as shear strain rate) but also ordinary strain as well. Such substances are known as viscous-elastic. And even for simple viscous fluids, in which the shear stress depends only on velocity gradient, the fluid may not be Newtonian and in fact there may exist a rather complicated nonlinear relationship between shear stress and strain rate. If the fluid stress-strain rate relationship depends on prior working or straining, the fluid is said to be thixotropic (such a substance is printer's ink).

Another type of fluid is one with plastic behavior which is characterized by an apparent yield stress; that is, the fluid behaves as a solid until it yields, then behaves like a viscous fluid. Some greases and sludges behave in this manner. On the other extreme from plastic fluids are fluids called dilatants which flow easily with a low viscosity at low strain rates, but become more like a solid as the strain rate increases (such a substance is quicksand). Fig. 1-2 shows the behavior of these fluids graphically.

Fig. 1-2. Types of viscous and plastic fluids.

Water, air and gases are essentially Newtonian, but considerations of fluids which are visco-elastic or non-Newtonian are very important in fluid mechanics, although generally not so well understood or appreciated.

Internal friction or stresses can be generated, then, by the viscosity in a fluid. In addition, turbulence may generate shear stresses in a fluid, and we will mention turbulence in the next section.

If a fluid has no viscosity and does not flow in a turbulent manner, the fluid is said to be an ideal fluid, or more correctly the flow is said to be ideal. An ideal flow then has no internal friction and hence no internal dissipation or losses. Actually, of course no fluid is ever really ideal, but some fluids, at least in certain regions of flow under certain circumstances, approach ideal conditions very closely and are considered such for analysis. For instance, the flow of air over objects (aerodynamics) is considered ideal flow except in a thin layer called the boundary layer just next to the wing or surface. As we will see, it is convenient to divide real fluid flows into different regions each of which may be considered ideal, viscous, or turbulent.

(c) **Laminar Flow and Turbulent Flow.** The terms laminar flow and purely viscous flow are used synonymously to mean a fluid flow which flows in laminas or layers, as opposed to turbulent flow in which the velocity components have random turbulent fluctuations imposed upon their mean values (Fig. 1-3). A stream of dye or ink inserted in a laminar flow will streak out a thin line and always be composed of the same fluid particles. However, in turbulent flow the dye line would quickly become tangled up and mixed in with the fluid as it flows along, and we would see myriads of threads and clouds ever widening and dispersing as the fluid flows along. A vivid example of laminar flow is a heavy molasses being poured from a bottle.

Streamlines

Laminar   Turbulent

Fig. 1-3.   Laminar and turbulent flow.   The lines indicate the paths of particles.

What determines whether a flow is laminar or turbulent? For a given fluid the velocity and channel configuration or size determine it. As the velocity increases the flow will change from laminar to turbulent, passing through a transition regime. Both laminar and turbulent flow occur in nature, but turbulent flow seems to be the more natural state of affairs.

A simple example of this transition may be seen by observing the smoke rising from a cigarette or smoke stack. For a distance, the smoke rises in a smooth laminar manner. Then, rather abruptly, the smoke begins to mix up, become turbulent, and the smoke column rapidly widens and diffuses. The turbulence aids in the diffusion of the smoke and causes it to diffuse into a widening chaotic stream.

The effects of viscosity are still present in turbulent flow, but they are usually masked by the dominant turbulent shear stresses.

(d) **Surface Tension.** The term surface tension is used loosely to identify the apparent stress in the surface layer of a liquid. This layer behaves like a stretched membrane and can give rise to a pressure difference across a curved liquid surface (that is an air-liquid interface). Actually the surface tension is an energy associated with any fluid-fluid interface and the liquid-air interface is the most common type. Since the liquid surface behaves like a membrane, we see why a liquid may form a miniscus in a capillary, and why raindrops are more or less spherical.

(e) **Compressible and Incompressible Flow.** It is customary to divide fluids into two groups—gases and liquids. Gases are compressible and their density changes readily with temperature and pressure. Liquids, on the other hand, are rather difficult to compress and for most problems one might consider them incompressible. Only in such situations as sound propagation in liquids does one need to consider their compressibility.

In a gas the density is related to temperature and pressure by the gas law (remember for a perfect gas $p = \rho RT$). For a liquid, the density is related to temperature by a coefficient of expansion just as for a solid, and the pressure dependence may be written as

$$dp = \beta \, d\rho/\rho \qquad (1.2)$$

where β is the bulk compression modulus. For water β is about 3×10^5 psi, so that it requires enormous pressures to effect a slight density change. (For adiabatic compression of atmospheric air β is about 20 psi.) For most practical purposes then, liquids are incompressible. And, in fact, under certain flow conditions involving slight pressure changes, gases may be considered incompressible. (This is the case of subsonic aerodynamics where the air is assumed incompressible for low Mach numbers.)

(*f*) **Subsonic and Supersonic Flow.** In compressible flow there is a great distinction between flow involving velocities less than that of sound (subsonic flow) and flow involving velocities greater than that of sound (supersonic). (Sonic speed in air at STP is about 1080 ft/sec or 810 mi/hr.) These differences between subsonic and supersonic flow will be pointed out later, but it is useful to remember that shock waves can only occur in flows which are supersonic.

The Mach number, M, is a measure of this relative speed and is defined as the ratio of the fluid speed to the local speed of sound:

$$M = V/a \qquad (1.3)$$

where V is the fluid speed and a the local sonic speed. When $M < 1$ we have subsonic flow, and when $M > 1$ we have supersonic flow. For flows around objects, where M is less than about 0.3, the flow may be treated as approximately incompressible. Transonic flow occurs when part of a body (airplane or missile, say) has fluid flowing over it at $M < 1$ and another part of the same body has fluid flowing over it at $M > 1$, so that at some point on the body $M = 1$. How can $M < 1$ and $M > 1$ on the same body at the same time? The answer is that the sonic speed and the fluid speed vary over the body. The temperature varies over a body in general and hence the local sonic speed must vary.

(*g*) **Steady Flow.** By a steady flow we mean one in which the velocity components and thermodynamic properties at every point in space do not change with time. Actually if we were to follow an individual fluid particle its properties and velocity might change as it flows along. However, this does not matter. In fluid mechanics we always ask: what is happening at a particular point in space regardless of what fluid particle happens to be there at any particular time? In this sense, then, steady flow means steady in that nothing changes with time at any point in space. A motion picture or snapshot would look the same no matter what time it was made. An important point to understand is that a fluid may have an acceleration at a point in space even in steady flow. A fluid particle may be moving along, but at any particular point in space it behaves just as any other fluid particle when it was at that place.

(*h*) **Types or Classes of Flow.** We have discussed some basic definitions as applied to types of fluid flow. Now we can see what types of flow occur in real physical situations and classify them accordingly. We will see that we may have such classifications as incompressible-laminar, compressible-ideal-supersonic, compressible-laminar, incompressible-turbulent, etc.

1.4 PHYSICAL CLASSIFICATIONS AND TYPES OF FLOW

There are many ways to classify flow, according to the structure of the flow mentioned above, or according to the physical situation or configuration which also allows classification into one of these groups. Let us mention a few of these classifications.

Basically there are two types of fluid configurations, or spatial regions of flow: external and internal flow. By internal flow we mean pipe and channel flow and the like, where the fluid flows within a confining structure. External flow is the flow of a fluid over an object, such as in aerodynamics. Let us examine each of these flow types in more detail.

(a) **External Flow.** The flow region around an object may be divided into three regions. Far from the body the flow is essentially ideal, with friction unimportant. Near the body the fluid develops a shear layer (since the velocity must be zero relative to the body on the surface of the body) where viscosity and/or turbulence is important. This frictional layer is called a boundary layer. The boundary layer may be laminar or turbulent. Behind the body a wake (a third distinct region) develops and is generally a region of high turbulence and low pressure (hence the drag due to the wake). Fig. 1-4 shows the flow over a cylinder with the wake. The wake is due to the separation of the boundary layer from the surface of the body. In fact, the ideal flow region behind the body, but outside the wake, and the wake region are rather well delineated by a shear layer (Fig. 1-4a).

Fig. 1-4.   (a) Boundary layer and separation over a cylinder.
            (b) Ideal flow if no separation occurred.

The boundary layer brought about because of viscosity in the fluid is the cause of the wake. If there were absolutely no viscosity so that the fluid were frictionless in an absolute sense, then there would be no separation and no wake. If there were no wake the flow pattern (which would be ideal) would be symmetrical from front to back of the cylinder and the pressure would be the same on the front as on the back and there would be no drag on an object inserted into a flowing fluid. This absence of drag is contrary to experience and we realize that all fluids must have some internal friction. In the early days of the development of fluid mechanics as a science, it was thought that viscosity was rather negligible and mathematically the flow would be ideal everywhere and hence there would be no drag predicted by theory (Fig. 1-4b). Since this conclusion was contrary to experience it was known as d'Alembert's paradox. It was not until the boundary layer concept was introduced by Prandtl (a German fluid dynamicist) during the early part of this century that it became apparent that there was no paradox at all, but that any amount of viscosity, no matter how small, could bring about a wake and consequent drag.

If a body is streamlined (Fig. 1-5), that is, the trailing edge is faired into a gradual smooth contour, no separation will occur and the boundary layer will hug the body all the way around. Streamlining substantially reduces the drag and most aerodynamic objects, wings, etc., are streamlined. In such cases the flow is ideal completely around the body except for the boundary layer and a thin wake. As we shall see, the boundary layer in such cases may be rather thin and the flow pattern is well described by ideal flow except for the friction drag calculations. In subsonic aerodynamics the lift is determined by the potential (ideal) flow, and the drag essentially by the boundary layer.

Fig. 1-5.   Streamline flow about an object. The gradual taper of the trailing edge prevents separation of the boundary layer.

The boundary layer itself may be laminar or turbulent, depending on the parameters involved. In most practical cases the boundary layer changes from laminar to turbulent along the body. The transition to turbulence usually retards separation, but in partially streamlined bodies separation may not be distinct and the turbulent boundary layer merges into the wake region as shown in Fig. 1-6.

Fig. 1-6.   Subsonic flow with a transition boundary layer with no separation. The boundary layer thickness is exaggerated.

If the velocity is small, then the density variations are small and the flow may be considered incompressible. (This concept will be demonstrated in Chapter 7.) The flow then is as shown in Fig. 1-5 or Fig. 1-6.

If the velocity is increased until the Mach number is greater than about 0.3, then the density variations become important, but the general flow picture is still as shown above. However, when the Mach number is increased to a value greater than one, a shock wave will occur and the flow will be as shown in Fig. 1-7.

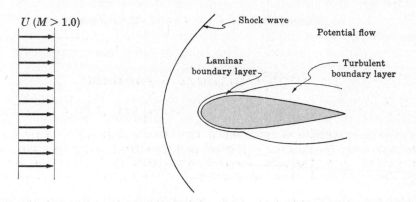

Fig. 1-7.   Supersonic flow around an object.

If the Mach number is increased to a value greater than about six, then dissociation and ionization will occur.

(b) **Internal Flow.** Inside pipes, channels, nozzles, and in fluid machinery the flow of the fluid is confined by walls and is usually referred to as internal flow. Such flow in the main part of a channel may be considered as approximately ideal for gases, but even so a boundary layer (usually turbulent) develops on the walls. In both viscous and turbulent flow the boundary layer thickens downstream so that it eventually extends all the way across the channel or pipe.

Now we are in a position to make topical divisions. These are shown in Fig. 1-8 below with the left column generally going from the least to the most complicated.

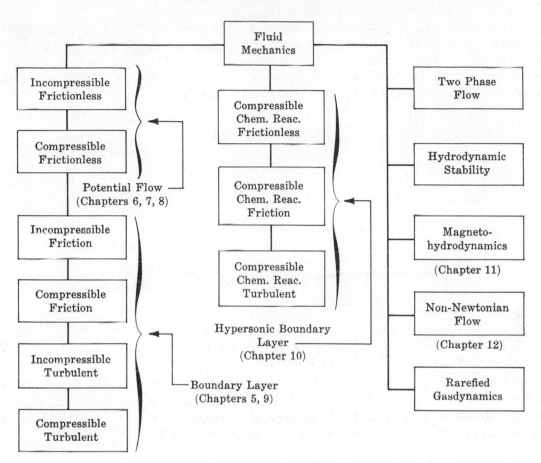

Fig. 1-8. Topical divisions of fluid mechanics.

Supplementary Problems

Below are listed a few simple experiments which illustrate some of the flow behavior of fluids.

1.1. Pour a bit of Karo syrup or molasses into a dish. Pour a little milk over the syrup and try to mix it. What happens? The viscosity is so great that the mixing caused by stirring is laminar and the mixing is rather slow. Turbulent mixing is much faster than laminar mixing. Why? Molecular diffusion also occurs but is rather unimportant in a heavy syrup, compared to the mixing effect.

1.2. Observe the smoke rising from a cigarette. Notice how it begins in a laminar fashion and suddenly becomes turbulent. As the smoke rises the flow becomes unstable and develops into turbulent flow.

1.3. Turn on a water faucet and adjust the flow so that there is a very small laminar trickle. What happens to the water a few inches down the stream? Again the flow becomes unstable and turbulent.

1.4. Increase the flow rate, in the above example. What happens? The water becomes turbulent in the pipe and is turbulent as it leaves the faucet.

1.5. Observe a low lying cloud system on a windy day, especially a heavy rain cloud system. Is the flow turbulent? Is it on a different scale from the water faucet flow?

1.6. Either with a burning cigarette or pipe create a rising column of smoke. Take a pencil and hold it (horizontal) in the stream of smoke. Observe, by looking at the pencil on end, the flow of smoke over the pencil and the separation of the boundary layer from the sides of the pencil. It is best to generate a heavy column of smoke by blowing into the pipe or cigarette.

1.7. Why does the smoke in the preceding problem rise?

Chapter 2

Fluid Statics

2.1 PRESSURE

Before beginning the actual study of fluid dynamics, it is useful to discuss fluid statics, mainly because it allows immediate application of some everyday ideas to real engineering problems without becoming involved in complex notions. The concept of pressure is of particular importance in fluid statics. For example, it is important in determining the force applied to a dam by a body of water or in determining forces on submerged bodies in general. The exploration, recovery of objects and man's survival at large depths in the oceans has received considerable interest in recent years.

Pressure is defined as stress, or surface force per unit area,

$$p \equiv \lim_{\Delta A \to 0} \frac{\Delta F}{\Delta A} = \frac{dF}{dA} \tag{2.1}$$

When we imagine the area going to zero for an actual fluid, a difficulty arises in that we are no longer dealing with a continuum. Thus there is a conflict between the continuum assumption and the usual definition of derivatives and differential quantities. This difficulty or conflict of ideas is present in the development of the differential equations of fluid mechanics, but we resolve it by assuming that the fluid is a continuum to any macroscopic scale of interest.

Let us look at a container of liquid at rest. If we take an imaginary boundary around a small part of the total volume, the net force acting on the fluid mass must be zero since it is not being accelerated. In particular, let us select a small volume as shown in Fig. 2-1.

Since there is no relative motion in the fluid, then the shear stress is everywhere zero. The only surface forces acting on the fluid element are normal (pressure). And the only body force is due to the earth's gravitational field which acts in the negative y direction. Thus summing the forces for the x direction we have

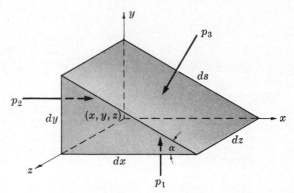

Fig. 2-1. Equilibrium of pressure forces on a fluid element.

$$p_2\, dy\, dz \ - \ p_3\, dz\, ds \sin \alpha \ = \ 0$$

where $ds \sin \alpha = dy$ and thus $p_2 = p_3$. For the y direction[1],

$$p_1\, dx\, dz \ - \ p_3\, dz\, ds \cos \alpha \ - \ \tfrac{1}{2}\rho g\, dx\, dy\, dz \ = \ 0$$

where ρ is the mass density of the fluid and $ds \cos \alpha = dx$, giving

$$p_1 - p_3 - \tfrac{1}{2}\rho g\, dy \ = \ 0$$

---

[1] In this book we will generally use slug units for mass. Thus ρ has units of slug/ft³ and the specific weight γ has units of lb$_f$/ft³ and is given by $\gamma = \rho g$. For a detailed discussion of units and dimensions the reader is referred to Appendix B.

Since the third term is small compared to the first two,

$$p_1 = p_2 = p_3$$

Since the volume element may be chosen with any orientation and the angle α was arbitrary, we have shown that the pressure at a point in a fluid at rest is the same in all directions, that is, isotropic.

2.2 DIFFERENTIAL EQUATIONS OF FLUID STATICS

We will define equilibrium as a state in which each fluid particle is either at rest or has no relative motion with respect to other particles. The significant difference between these two conditions is that in the first there can be no acceleration of the total fluid system, and in the second there can be acceleration. We will consider both cases.

There are two kinds of forces to be considered: (1) body forces—forces acting on the fluid particles at a distance (e.g. gravity, magnetic field, etc.), and (2) surface forces—forces due to direct contact with other fluid particles or solid walls (forces due to pressure and tangential, that is, shear stress).

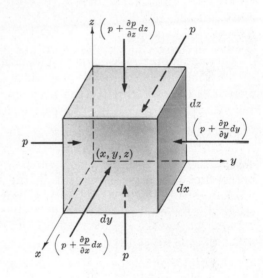

Fig. 2-2

Again, we will look at a container of liquid at rest. This time, however, we shall choose an infinitesimal fluid particle from within the container which is cubical in shape as shown in Fig. 2-2. We assume gravity to act in the negative z direction.

We may assume the pressure over each face is constant since it may be shown that any variations are of second order and do not affect the final result. Summing the forces for the different directions gives

x direction: $p\,dy\,dz - \left(p + \dfrac{\partial p}{\partial x}dx\right)dy\,dz = 0$

y direction: $p\,dx\,dz - \left(p + \dfrac{\partial p}{\partial y}dy\right)dx\,dz = 0$

z direction: $p\,dx\,dy - \left(p + \dfrac{\partial p}{\partial z}dz\right)dx\,dy - \rho g\,dx\,dy\,dz = 0$

Simplifying, $\dfrac{\partial p}{\partial x} = 0, \quad \dfrac{\partial p}{\partial y} = 0, \quad \dfrac{\partial p}{\partial z} = -\rho g$ (2.2)

By equations (2.2) we have $\dfrac{dp}{dz} = -\rho g$ (2.3)

which is an important equation of fluid statics. If the density of the fluid is constant, equation (2.3) may be integrated

$$\int_{p_1}^{p_2} dp = -\rho g \int_{z_1}^{z_2} dz$$

giving $p_2 - p_1 = -\rho g(z_2 - z_1)$ (2.4)

which describes the pressure change with elevation for a fluid in static equilibrium. An independent and simple derivation of equation (*2.3*) may be carried out by considering the forces on a right circular cylinder whose axis is vertical to the earth's surface.

Equation (*2.4*) is valid for an incompressible fluid. Let us consider briefly pressure variations in compressible fluids. Starting with equation (*2.3*) for an ideal gas, we have

$$dp = -\frac{pg}{RT}\,dz$$

where $R =$ gas constant and $T =$ absolute temperature. If we assume an isothermal atmosphere, we may integrate this equation to give

$$\ln\frac{p}{p_1} = -\frac{g}{RT}(z - z_1)$$

or
$$p = p_1 e^{-(g/RT)(z-z_1)} \tag{2.5}$$

2.3 MANOMETRY

A manometer is a device which utilizes displacement of fluid columns to determine pressure differences. Equation (*2.4*) is used to relate the pressure differences to the heights of fluid columns. We may write this equation as

$$p_2 - p_1 = \gamma h = \rho g h \tag{2.6}$$

where
$$h = -(z_2 - z_1) \tag{2.7}$$

Fig. 2-3 shows a single U-tube manometer for measuring pressure difference. The difference in pressures p_A and p_B may be determined as follows. The pressure at point a is given by

Fig. 2-3.   The U-tube manometer.

$$p_a = h_1 \gamma_{H_2O} + (h_3 - h_1)\gamma_{air} + p_A$$

or
$$p_a = h_2 \gamma_{H_2O} + (h_3 - h_2)\gamma_{air} + p_B \tag{2.8}$$

Subtracting,
$$p_A - p_B = (h_2 - h_1)(\gamma_{H_2O} - \gamma_{air}) \tag{2.9}$$

The specific weight of air is small compared to water, which means that the pressure difference is approximately equal to the difference in column heights times the specific weight of water:

$$p_A - p_B = (h_2 - h_1)\gamma_{H_2O} \tag{2.10}$$

Fig. 2-4.   An inclined manometer.

Fig. 2-5.   The two fluid manometer.

Manometers may have different shapes, orientations and use different fluids depending on the application. For example, in order to attain an improved accuracy over the vertical manometer, an inclined manometer as shown in Fig. 2-4 above may be used. Or, a two fluid manometer as shown in Fig. 2-5 above could be used to achieve an improved accuracy. The method of relating pressure differences to fluid column deflections for these two examples is basically the same as that described for the U-tube manometer.

2.4 FLUID FORCES ON SUBMERGED BODIES

The total surface force on a body may be determined by taking the vector sum of the differential surface forces over the entire area,

$$\mathbf{F} = \int_A d\mathbf{F} \tag{2.11}$$

where

$$d\mathbf{F} = p\,d\mathbf{A}$$

and

$$p = p_0 + \gamma h \tag{2.12}$$

where p_0 = pressure at the free surface and h = depth below the free surface.

These equations are all that are needed for establishing the forces on submerged surfaces. In the specific applications then, all that is required is to write the depth h and differential area dA in terms of the same variable of integration. Also, before the equation may be integrated it must be written in scalar form. We shall consider some specific cases.

(*a*) **Horizontal Plane Surface.** Consider a plane horizontal surface at distance h below the surface of a liquid as shown in Fig. 2-6. The force on the surface (one side) is

$$F = \int_A dF = \int_A (p_0 + \gamma h)\,dA = (p_0 + \gamma h)A \tag{2.13}$$

Fig. 2-6. A submerged horizontal plate.   Fig. 2-7. An inclined submerged plate.

(*b*) **Inclined Plane Surface.** Next, consider an inclined submerged surface as shown in Fig. 2-7. Here we have for the force on the plate (which is normal to the plate),

$$F = \int_A dF = \int_A (p_0 + \gamma h)\,dA = p_0 A + \gamma \int_{y_1}^{y_2} wy \sin\theta\,dy$$

$$= p_0 A + \tfrac{1}{2}\gamma w \sin\theta\,(y_2^2 - y_1^2) \tag{2.14}$$

(*c*) **Curved Surface.** For a curved surface, such as shown in Fig. 2-8 below, the force components are

$$F_x = \int_A (p_0 + \gamma h)\,dA_x \tag{2.15}$$

$$F_y = \int_A (p_0 + \gamma h)\,dA_y \tag{2.16}$$

The integration of these equations may not always be the most convenient method for determining the forces on submerged bodies. For example, we may observe that the vertical component of force on any submerged surface is equal to the weight (or equivalent) of fluid directly above that surface plus the force due to pressure at the free surface, and that the horizontal component of force may be determined by considering a plane vertical surface which is the projected area of the surface in question.

Fig. 2-8. A curved submerged plate.

(d) **Buoyancy.** Archimedes' principle states that a submerged body is subject to an upward force equal to the weight of the fluid displaced. Therefore this force (buoyant force) will be equal to the volume of the body which is submerged times the specific weight of the fluid.

It is important that we recognize that the buoyant force can also be computed by summing all of the vertical components of the pressure area products over the submerged surface of the body, i.e.,

$$F_B = \int_A p \, dA_y \tag{2.17}$$

which as we have already noted leads to

$$F_B = \gamma \times \text{volume} \tag{2.18}$$

2.5 ACCELERATING FLUIDS IN THE ABSENCE OF SHEAR STRESS

In the previous sections we have considered fluids at rest. Now we will consider fluids which have a constant acceleration (constant with time) but each fluid particle has no motion relative to its immediate neighbor, so that the fluid moves as a rigid body. For example, consider a container of liquid which has a constant acceleration a upward and to the right as shown in Fig. 2-9. Using the same method as in Section 2.2 it is easily shown that Newton's law for an infinitesimal particle in the container gives

$$\partial p/\partial x = -\rho a_x, \qquad \partial p/\partial y = -(\rho a_y + \gamma)$$

Integrating,

$$p = -[\rho a_x x + (\rho a_y + \gamma)y] + C \tag{2.19a}$$

Fig. 2-9. An accelerating container of fluid. The direction of gravity is in the negative y direction so that a_x and a_y are respectively parallel and perpendicular to the Earth's surface. If a_x and a_y are positive, then the slope is negative as shown.

The shape of the free surface is determined by letting $p = p_0$, yielding a plane surface. Constant pressure surfaces are parallel planes whose slope with respect to the horizontal plane is given by

$$\theta = \tan^{-1} a_x/(a_y + g) \tag{2.19b}$$

where θ is indicated in Fig. 2-9.

Fig. 2-10. A rotating container of fluid. Gravity acts in the negative z direction.

Another example of fluid particles undergoing a constant acceleration is encountered when a fluid body rotates uniformly as a whole without relative motion of its parts. Let ω be the constant angular velocity and ρ the density of the liquid. Choose polar coordinates with z and r as shown in Fig. 2-10. The angular coordinate is ϕ. The centripetal acceleration of a particle at radius r is $-\omega^2 r$ in the r direction. From Newton's law for the z direction,

$$-\rho g r\, dr\, d\phi\, dz + pr\, dr\, d\phi - \left(p + \frac{\partial p}{\partial z} dz\right) r\, dr\, d\phi = 0 \quad\text{or}\quad \frac{\partial p}{\partial z} = -\rho g$$

For the r direction, assuming $\sin \tfrac{1}{2} d\phi \approx \tfrac{1}{2} d\phi$,

$$p\, dz\, r\, d\phi - \left(p + \frac{\partial p}{\partial r} dr\right) dz\, (r + dr)\, d\phi + 2p\, dz\, dr\, (\tfrac{1}{2} d\phi) = -\rho\, dz\, r\, d\phi\, dr\, \omega^2 r$$

which becomes (neglecting higher order terms)

$$\partial p/\partial r = \rho \omega^2 r \tag{2.20}$$

We note that $p = p(r, z)$ and $\quad dp = \dfrac{\partial p}{\partial r} dr + \dfrac{\partial p}{\partial z} dz$

Substituting for $\partial p/\partial r$ and $\partial p/\partial z$,

$$dp = \rho \omega^2 r\, dr - \rho g\, dz$$

Integrating, $\qquad\qquad\qquad p = \tfrac{1}{2}\rho\omega^2 r^2 - \rho g z + C \tag{2.21}$

At $r = 0$ and $z = z_0$ we have $p = p_0$. Then equation (2.21) becomes

$$p - p_0 = \tfrac{1}{2}\rho\omega^2 r^2 + \rho g(z_0 - z) \tag{2.22}$$

At the free surface, where $p = p_0$, we have

$$z = z_0 + \tfrac{1}{2}\omega^2 r^2/g \tag{2.23}$$

which is a paraboloid of revolution.

Note that for constant z, p increases as r^2. A centrifugal pump and a centrifuge make use of this principle. An enclosed mass of liquid is whirled rapidly to create a great difference in pressure between its center and its periphery.

2.6   SUMMARY

In this chapter we have looked at forces acting on fluids which (1) were in static equilibrium (fluids at rest) and (2) were undergoing a constant acceleration. In both cases the absence of relative motion among the fluid particles results in the tangential stresses being everywhere zero. Thus the only forces which were acting on the fluid particles were those due to (1) pressure (normal surface stress) and (2) gravity (a uniform body force).

It was shown that the pressure at a point in a fluid in static equilibrium is the same in all directions. Thus pressure is a scalar function of the spatial coordinates and time.

For a fluid in static equilibrium it was shown that the pressure change with elevation is given by

$$dp/dz = -\gamma = -\rho g$$

and for an incompressible fluid,

$$p_2 - p_1 = -\gamma(z_2 - z_1)$$

which was found useful in establishing pressure from various kinds of manometer readings.

Forces on submerged surfaces may be established by integrating the pressure area product over the entire area for the scalar components of the vector equation:

$$F_x = \int_A p \, dA_x, \qquad F_y = \int_A p \, dA_y$$

where $p = p_0 + \gamma h$. Thus in using these equations for a specific problem, the only remaining consideration is to relate the differential areas and the depth below the surface, h, to some common and convenient variable of integration.

The buoyant force may be calculated in two ways: (1) by integrating the vertical component of pressure area product over the submerged area of the body or (2) by multiplying the volume of fluid displaced by the body times the specific weight of the fluid.

For a fluid undergoing a constant acceleration but having no relative motion among the fluid particles, Newton's laws for an infinitesimal fluid particle gives

$$\partial p/\partial x = -\rho a_x, \qquad \partial p/\partial y = -(\rho a_y + \gamma)$$

where a_x and a_y are the components of the acceleration vector parallel and perpendicular to the earth's surface respectively.

Solved Problems

2.1. The mercury manometer of Fig. 2-11 is connected to the inlet and outlet of a water pump (the left side to the inlet and the right side to the outlet). Assuming that the inlet and outlet are at the same elevation, determine the pressure increase for the pump.

Fig. 2-11

We determine the pressure at point a by computing the pressure due to the column of liquid in the left side as

$$p_a = h_1 \gamma_{Hg} + h_2 \gamma_{Hg} + h_3 \gamma_{H_2O} + p_{in}$$

and in the right side as

$$p_a = h_1 \gamma_{Hg} + h_2 \gamma_{H_2O} + h_3 \gamma_{H_2O} + p_{out}$$

Subtracting,

$$p_{out} - p_{in} = h_2(\gamma_{Hg} - \gamma_{H_2O})$$
$$= \tfrac{6}{12}[62.4(13.6 - 1)] = 393 \text{ psf}$$

We have used the fact that the specific weight of water is 62.4 lb$_f$/ft^3 and the specific gravity of mercury is 13.6.

2.2. In Fig. 2-12 determine the gage pressure at point A.

The absolute pressure at C is the same as at B. The absolute pressure at B is $\gamma_1 h_1 + p_a$ and hence

$$p_A = (p_a + \gamma_1 h_1) + \gamma_2 h_2$$

For convenience we have denoted the specific weights of mercury and water as γ_1 and γ_2 respectively. Then by definition of gage pressure,

$$
\begin{aligned}
p_{A\ gage} &= p_A - p_a = \gamma_1 h_1 + \gamma_2 h_2 \\
&= 62.4(13.6)(15/12) + 62.4(30/12) \\
&= 1216 \text{ psf} = 8.45 \text{ psi}
\end{aligned}
$$

B and C are at the same elevation

Fig. 2-12

2.3. Determine the pressure at point A for the inclined manometer shown in Fig. 2-13.

Fig. 2-13

$$p_B = p_A + \gamma h$$

p_B is atmospheric, so that

$$p_A = p_a - \gamma h = 14.7 - 62.4(13.6)(2.5/12)(1/144) = 13.47 \text{ psi}$$

Note that the level of mercury in the inclined tube is lower than that in the reservoir because a vacuum is being drawn on the reservoir.

2.4. In Fig. 2-14 find the gage pressures at points A, B and C in the pipe filled with flowing water.

Fig. 2-14

Denoting the specific weight of water as γ_1 and the specific weight of mercury as γ_2 we start at point D, work down to level HH, and then up to various points in the tube.

$$p_A = p_a + \gamma_2 h_3 - \gamma_1 h_1 - \gamma_2 h_2$$

But $p_{\text{gage}} = p - p_a$, so that

$$p_{A\,\text{gage}} = \frac{62.4(13.6)}{1728}(5) - \frac{62.4}{1728}(8) - \frac{62.4(13.6)}{1728}(7) = -1.28 \text{ psi}$$

(The number 1728 is the conversion factor to convert the specific weight from lb_f/in^3 to lb_f/ft^3.) Similarly,

$$p_{B\,\text{gage}} = \gamma_2 h_3 - \gamma_1 h_4 - \gamma_2 h_6 = -2.17 \text{ psi}$$

$$p_{C\,\text{gage}} = \gamma_2 h_3 - \gamma_1 h_5 - \gamma_2 h_7 = 0.55 \text{ psi}$$

2.5. Water flows through a nozzle as shown in Fig. 2-15. Determine the height h if the gage pressure at A is 5 psi.

Starting at the free surface B and working around to A, we have

$$p_A = p_a + \gamma_2 h - \gamma_1 (h + 24)$$

$$p_{A\,\text{gage}} = 5 = \frac{62.4(13.6h)}{1728} - \frac{62.4}{1728}(h + 24)$$

from which $h = 12.9$ in.

Fig. 2-15

2.6. Determine the total force of the water acting on the surface of the dam as shown in Fig. 2-16. The dam is 5 ft wide and the water is 10 ft deep.

We integrate the pressure force over the face of the dam to find the total force.

$$F = \int_A dF = \int_A p \, dA = \int_0^{10} 5\gamma y \, dy = 5\gamma y^2/2 \Big]_0^{10} = 15{,}600 \text{ lb}_f$$

We have not considered the atmospheric pressure at the water surface, since it is canceled out by the air pressure on the opposite side of the dam.

Fig. 2-16

Fig. 2-17

2.7. Determine the total force F required to keep the dam gate, shown in Fig. 2-17, from opening. The gate is 5 ft wide.

The sum of moments about the hinge must be zero for static equilibrium. Taking moments,

$$5F - \int_A y p \, dA = 0$$

Thus

$$5F = \int_0^5 y \gamma (7 + y) 5 \, dy = 5(62.4) \left[7y^2/2 + y^3/3 \right]_0^5$$

and $F = 8050 \text{ lb}_f$.

2.8. Determine the total force due to water pressure on the inclined surface shown in Fig. 2-18. The surface is hinged at the top and is 10 ft wide.

Fig. 2-18

The total force is normal to the gate and may be found by integrating the pressure over the surface.

$$F = \int_A dF = \int_A p \, dA = \int_A \gamma h \, dA$$

$$= \int_0^5 \gamma(3 + y \sin 30°)(10 \, dy)$$

$$= 10(62.4)\left[3y + \tfrac{1}{4}y^2 \right]_0^5 = 13,300 \text{ lb}_f$$

Again, since the right hand side of the surface is exposed to the atmosphere, we do not consider the atmospheric pressure in the calculation. The total force could be resolved into x and y components, and the proper location of the resultant force could be found so that the action of this single resultant force would be equivalent to the total pressure force in determining the reactions at the hinge and bottom of the plate. In Problem 2.9 we calculate the reaction force at the base of the plate. After following that calculation it is a simple matter to find the location of the resultant force.

2.9. Determine the total reaction force of the bottom surface on the bottom end of the gate for Problem 2.8. Find the location of the single force F which is equivalent to the total water pressure force.

The sum of the moments about the hinge must be zero. Since the pressure can only exert a force normal to the gate, the reactions at the hinge and bottom will be normal to the plate if we neglect the weight of the plate. Neglecting the weight of the plate, we sum moments about the hinge to obtain

$$F_B \times 5 = \int_A y \, dF = \int_A y(\gamma h) \, dA$$

$$= \gamma \int_0^5 y(3 + y \sin 30°)(10 \, dy) = (10)(62.4)\left[\tfrac{3}{2}y^2 + y^3/6 \right]_0^5 = 36,400 \text{ lb}_f\text{-ft}$$

and $F_B = 7280 \text{ lb}_f$.

If the equivalent resultant force of the pressure, F, is located at $y = y_0$, then $Fy_0 = F_B(5)$ so that

$$y_0 = 5F_B/F = 5(7280)/13,300 = 2.73 \text{ ft}$$

2.10. Determine the total pressure force on the curved surface shown in Fig. 2-19 below. The width of the curved plate is 2 ft.

Force diagram

Fig. 2-19

We can write the general equation for the force of the water on the plate as $\mathbf{F} = \int_A d\mathbf{F}$, but this equation must be written in scalar form before it can be integrated. We write

$$F_x = \int_A dF_x = \int_A p \, dA_x = \int_A (\gamma h) \, 2 \, dy$$

Writing h in terms of y,

$$F_x \;=\; 2\gamma \int_0^1 (1-y)\,dy \;=\; 2(62.4)\Big[\,y - y^2/2\,\Big]_0^1 \;=\; 62.4 \text{ lb}_f$$

Similarly we can find F_y, but we must remember that F_y is defined positive in the positive y direction and the pressure force acts downward in the negative y direction. Hence

$$F_y \;=\; \int_A dF_y \;=\; -\int_A p\,dA_y \;=\; -2\gamma \int_0^1 (1-y)\,dx$$

Writing y in terms of x, we can integrate explicitly:

$$F_y \;=\; -2\gamma \int_0^1 (1-x^2)\,dx \;=\; -86.0 \text{ lb}_f$$

The negative sign indicates that F_y acts downward. The magnitude of the total pressure force is

$$|\mathbf{F}| \;=\; (F_x^2 + F_y^2)^{1/2} \;=\; 106.4 \text{ lb}_f$$

and its direction is given by $\tan\theta = F_y/F_x = -1.38$ or $\theta = -54°$. θ is the inclination of $\mathbf{F}$ to the horizontal. As shown in Fig. 2-19, θ is negative and so the resultant force acts in a downward direction.

2.11. A U-tube accelerometer shown in Fig. 2-20 may be used for measuring the acceleration of an automobile. It is mounted in the vehicle so that the legs are vertical. The open U-tube is partially filled with a liquid of specific weight γ. Under constant acceleration a_x the liquid assumes the configuration shown. Relate the relevant parameters to the value of the acceleration.

The fluid behaves exactly as if it were in an open container of width L. The angle θ given by equation (2.19b) is then

$$\tan\theta \;=\; -h/L \;=\; -a_x/g$$

and we get simply $a_x = gh/L$.

Fig. 2-20

2.12. What is the value of a_x at which the water just begins to run over the rear wall of the container shown in Fig. 2-21? When the container is at rest the water fills it to a depth of 5 ft.

Fig. 2-21

As a_x increases the water rises against the rear wall. As it reaches the top edge, it has risen 5 ft and the front must have lowered by 5 ft. Hence at the onset of spilling, $\tan\alpha = 10/20 = a_x/g$ so that $a_x = g/2 = 16.1$ ft/sec². Note that for convenience we have defined an angle α which is the negative of the angle θ of equation (2.19b).

2.13. Show that when a container of liquid is constantly accelerated at a value **a** in a gravitational field **g**, the pressure distribution in the container is the same as if the container were at rest in a fictitious gravitational field of value $(\mathbf{g} - \mathbf{a})$. That is, assuming gravity acts in the negative y direction, the fictitious field has magnitude $\sqrt{(a_y + g)^2 + a_x^2 + a_z^2}$ and is the vector sum of **g** and the negative of **a** as shown in Fig. 2-22. If a container were falling freely in a gravitational field, then of course the liquid would have zero gage pressure throughout. Explain.

From equation (*2.19a*) we see that the constant pressure surfaces in the fluid are planes. Assuming that there are no variations in the z direction and that gravity acts in the negative y direction, the pressure variation normal to the constant pressure planes may be written by using the rule for differentiation of a variable normal to a constant surface:

$$dp/dh = [(\partial p/\partial x)^2 + (\partial p/\partial y)^2]^{1/2}$$

Carrying out the calculation explicitly, we immediately arrive at

$$dp/dh = \rho\sqrt{(a_y + g)^2 + a_x^2}$$

Fig. 2-22

which may be extended to three dimensions (with **gravity** acting in the negative y direction) to give

$$dp/dh = \rho\sqrt{(a_y + g)^2 + a_x^2 + a_z^2}$$

Integration yields
$$p = p_0 + \rho h\sqrt{(a_y + g)^2 + a_x^2 + a_z^2}$$

The free surface and constant pressure planes are inclined so that they are normal to the vector $(\mathbf{g} - \mathbf{a})$ which may be seen immediately from equation (*2.19b*).

2.14. Discuss the behavior of a tank filled with two immiscible fluids of different densities undergoing constant acceleration as shown in Fig. 2-23. Gravity acts in the negative y direction, and the vector **a** is assumed to have only x and y components.

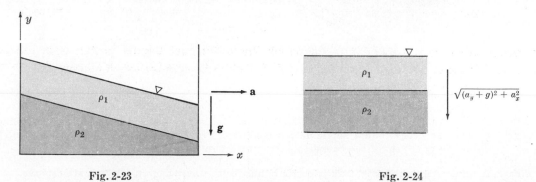

Fig. 2-23   Fig. 2-24

From the previous problem we know that the system behaves as if it were in a gravitational field of $(\mathbf{g} - \mathbf{a})$. Hence the constant pressure surfaces are planes and we can reduce the problem to the system shown in Fig. 2-24 with an equivalent gravitational field and treat it as a simple statics problem just as we did for a two fluid manometer. Alternatively we could solve the equilibrium equation (*2.19a*) and obtain the same result. The slope of the free surface and the interface is the same as for a single liquid.

Supplementary Problems

2.15.   The pressure at the liquid surface in the tank shown in Fig. 2-25 is 4.0 psi larger than atmospheric pressure. Determine the height h if the liquid in the tank is (*a*) water, (*b*) mercury.

Fig. 2-25   Fig. 2-26

2.16.   Determine the pressure change (psi) between the points A and B for flow in the vertical pipe of Fig. 2-26.

2.17.   Determine the manometer reading for Problem 2.16 if the flow is horizontal rather than vertical. The points A and B are at the same elevation but the manometer has the same orientation as in Problem 2.16.

2.18.   An inclined manometer is used to measure the difference in air pressure in a pipe between two points as shown in Fig. 2-27. What is the difference in pressure (psi) for the conditions given in the figure?

Fig. 2-27   Fig. 2-28

2.19.   A bifluid manometer as shown in Fig. 2-28 may be used to determine small pressure differences with a better accuracy than a single fluid manometer. Find the pressure difference $p_A - p_B$ (psi) for a deflection of 2.0 in. of the boundary between the two fluids.

2.20.   A tank as shown in Fig. 2-29 is partially filled with water and open to the atmosphere. A triangular gate is hinged at the bottom and held closed by a force applied at the top. Determine the force.

Fig. 2-29

2.21.   Referring to Fig. 2-30, a skin diver wants to know how far below the water surface he can go
        with a container and still be able to open the access door. Assuming that the pressure inside is
        atmospheric, and the maximum pull the diver can exert is 150 lb, determine the maximum depth.

Fig. 2-30   Fig. 2-31

2.22.   In Fig. 2-31 find the force at O on the solid gate in the shape of a quarter cylinder due to the water.
        The gate is 30 ft long and its weight may be neglected. Also, calculate the force F_N at the bottom
        of the gate.

2.23.   In Fig. 2-32 an object having specific gravity 0.5 is floating in a container of water. If the con-
        tainer and liquid are given an upward acceleration of 10 ft/sec^2, what will be the position of the
        object relative to the water surface?

Fig. 2-32   Fig. 2-33

2.24.   As water rises on the left side of the rectangular gate in Fig. 2-33 it will open automatically. At
        what depth above the hinge will this occur?

2.25.   A U-tube rotates about the line AB as shown in Fig. 2-34. The angular velocity is one revolution
        per second. Determine the pressures at C, D and E. The end at C is closed.

Fig. 2-34   Fig. 2-35

2.26.   A rather novel type manometer employing an inverted straight-sided thick-walled cup floating in
        liquid, as shown in Fig. 2-35, has been suggested as being much more sensitive than a regular
        U-tube manometer for the measurement of pressure. In this proposed manometer the pressure to be
        measured is communicated by a pipe S to the closed chamber C formed by the inverted cup and
        liquid. A container open at the top to the atmosphere holds the liquid in which the cup floats. The
        distance a from the outer water surface to the top of the cup would be used as a measure of the
        pressure. What would be the sensitivity of this manometer, i.e. the change in a with a change in
        pressure?

2.27. Rework Problems 2.8 and 2.9 considering the weight of the gate. Assume the gate to be a uniform steel plate $\frac{1}{4}$ in. thick.

2.28. Rework Problems 2.7 and 2.8, assuming in each case that there is also water, two feet deep, on the right hand side of the gate.

2.29. In Problem 2.7 find the resultant force vector of the water pressure on the gate. That is, what single force can replace the force of the water insofar as the reactions at the hinge and position-holding force F are determined by this resultant force vector?

2.30. A cart of water rolls down an inclined plane as shown in Fig. 2-36. Find the inclination of the free surface, neglecting friction of the wheels and wind resistance effects.

2.31. A vertical cylinder with a tight lid and completely filled with water rotates at an angular velocity ω about its axis. What is the pressure distribution in the cylinder? A small hole in the center of the lid exposes the fluid to the atmosphere.

Fig. 2-36

2.32. In Problem 2.31 the cylinder rotates in a zero gravity field. What is the pressure distribution in the water then?

2.33. In a zero gravity field, a rocket fuel tank containing liquid fuel of density ρ undergoes a constant acceleration **a**. What is the pressure distribution in the tank? Does the shape of the tank matter? Explain.

2.34. A cylinder filled with two immiscible liquids of density ρ_1 and ρ_2, with $\rho_2 > \rho_1$, as shown in Fig. 2-37 rotates with angular velocity ω about its axis. Find the pressure distribution, the shape of the interface between the liquids, and the shape of the free surface.

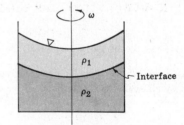

2.35. Does the shape of the U-tube in Problem 2.11 matter? In terms of its performance, what parameters are important?

2.36. What happens in Problem 2.12 when the value of a_x increases? Can the tank be completely emptied by increasing a_x?

Fig. 2-37

2.37. A balloon filled with helium (which is lighter than air) is tethered to the seat inside an automobile. If the windows are all closed, what is the air pressure distribution in the automobile if it accelerates forward at a constant value? Will the balloon tend to slant forward or backward relative to the car? If the balloon is filled with air and hung from the car ceiling, will the answer be the same? Explain.

2.38. One of the problems faced by the designers of the Buick Dynaflow torque-converter was the determination of the maximum tensile stress in the bolts which hold the pump cover to the pump housing as shown in Fig. 2-38 below.

The operation of the Dynaflow unit is as follows: The engine crankshaft is rigidly coupled to the pump housing and drives it at engine speed ω. The pump housing and cover constitute an oil-tight unit, a packing gland being provided around the output shaft which rotates at a speed less than or equal to that of the pump housing. This housing is kept full of oil at a constant "charging" pressure by means of an auxiliary charging pump; for all practical purposes this charging pump delivers oil into the pump housing at its center of rotation.

Attached to the inside of the pump housing are radial blades or vanes (the pump) which circulate the oil as required to the stator (not shown) and to the turbine (not shown) which is fastened to the output shaft.

What tensile stress can be expected in a pump cover bolt? The diameter of the pump housing is D feet, and its angular velocity is ω radians per second.

Fig. 2-38

NOMENCLATURE FOR CHAPTER 2

$\mathbf{a}$ = acceleration

$\mathbf{F}$ = force

g = acceleration due to gravity

h = height of a fluid

p = pressure

R = gas constant

T = temperature

γ = specific weight = ρg

ρ = density

ω = angular velocity

Chapter 3

Mathematical Models of Fluid Motion

3.1 INTRODUCTION AND METHOD

In this chapter we will develop model representations of fluid motion in mathematical form. It must be kept in mind that these models are merely approximations of the actual flow situation, and an understanding of the limitations and proper use of the equations of this chapter is essential. We will carefully derive these mathematical models, emphasizing their physical meaning.

An actual fluid is made up of molecules with empty space between them. However, in general, when one establishes the mathematical models, it is convenient to assume that the fluid is a continuous medium—a continuum. This is the approach we will follow, and in doing so we have immediately begun to abstract about the actual makeup of the fluid and are developing a model representation of the fluid itself. It should be mentioned that while most fluid flow may be treated by the continuum approach, mathematical models taking into account the statistical behavior of the individual fluid molecules have been developed and are necessary for studies of rarefied gases. Examples of the particle approach to fluid motion may be found in books by Chapman and Cowling and by Curtiss and Bird; see references 3 and 4, page 47.

In this chapter we will first derive the basic fluid equations in integral form for a control volume, then obtain the differential equations of fluid flow by applying the integral equations to an elemental volume. As was mentioned in Chapter 1, there are five basic variables in fluid flow, three components of velocity and two thermodynamic properties. Hence there are five basic equations which describe the flow; three components of the momentum equation, the continuity equation, and the energy equation. In general, the energy equation becomes uncoupled in incompressible flow since the density is constant. In turbulent flow the situation is somewhat more complex and a closed set of equations cannot generally be developed. We will not discuss the basic equations of turbulent flow until Chapter 9. Certain constitutive equations, such as an equation of state, may also be used to allow the introduction of an additional thermodynamic property.

3.2 INTEGRAL EQUATIONS

In the study of fluid motion, we are concerned with four basic laws:

- (a) Conservation of mass
- (b) Newton's second law of motion
- (c) Conservation of energy (the first law of thermodynamics)
- (d) Second law of thermodynamics.

These laws apply to a fixed quantity of matter (system) which maintains its identity as it undergoes a change in conditions. In fact, one cannot meaningfully apply the basic laws until a definite system is identified.

It is not usually convenient to identify and follow fixed quantities of matter in the analysis of fluid motion. Rather, it is customary to adopt a field theoretic point of view and identify a definite fixed region or volume in space called a control volume. However, the four basic laws do not apply to fixed volumes but to fixed quantities of matter. Thus our immediate task is to derive equations which apply to control volumes from the known expressions for systems. We ask the question then: what are the properties of the fluid within the fixed control volume at any given time, regardless of the fact that the fluid in the control volume is constantly changing?

We will now proceed to develop the integral equations of fluid motion. The detailed derivations of these equations are presented here in order that one may better understand them in applying them to physical situations. The methods of deriving the control volume equations from the known basic laws follow a basic pattern with slight modifications because of the different physical quantities involved. After the equations are developed they will be applied to solving physical problems which occur in fluid motion.

(a) **Conservation of Mass.** We will focus our attention on the flow field represented by the streamlines of Fig. 3-1. Let us consider a certain quantity of matter at some time t enclosed by the solid line. At some later time $t + \Delta t$, the boundary of the system has a new physical location as represented by the dotted line.

Considering the regions denoted by A, B and C, we have the system occupying the region A at time t and at time $t + \Delta t$ it occupies regions B and A-C. Letting m represent the mass contained in the different regions and at different times with the appropriate subscripts,

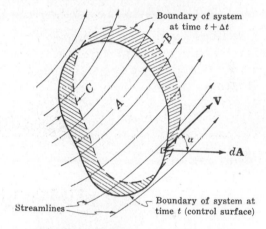

Fig. 3-1.   System moving through a control volume.

$$m_A(t) \; = \; m_A(t + \Delta t) - m_C(t + \Delta t) + m_B(t + \Delta t)$$

Rearranging and dividing by Δt,

$$\frac{m_A(t + \Delta t) - m_A(t)}{\Delta t} \; = \; \frac{m_C(t + \Delta t) - m_B(t + \Delta t)}{\Delta t}$$

Taking the limit as $\Delta t \to 0$, the left side becomes

$$\lim_{\Delta t \to 0} \frac{m_A(t + \Delta t) - m_A(t)}{\Delta t} \; = \; \frac{\partial}{\partial t}(m)_{\text{C.V.}} \; = \; \frac{\partial}{\partial t} \int_{\text{C.V.}} \rho \, d\mathcal{V}$$

where ρ is the mass density, $\mathcal{V}$ indicates volume, and C.V. designates the control volume fixed in space and bounded by the control surface (C.S.). The right side of the equation is

$$\lim_{\Delta t \to 0} \left\{ \frac{m_C(t + \Delta t)}{\Delta t} - \frac{m_B(t + \Delta t)}{\Delta t} \right\} \; = \; \dot{m}_{\text{in}} - \dot{m}_{\text{out}}$$

which becomes

$$\dot{m}_{\text{in}} - \dot{m}_{\text{out}} \; = \; \int_{A_{\text{in}}} \rho V \cos \alpha \, dA \; - \; \int_{A_{\text{out}}} \rho V \cos \alpha \, dA \; = \; - \int_{\text{C.S.}} \rho \mathbf{V} \cdot d\mathbf{A}$$

where $\dot{m}_{\text{in}}$ and $\dot{m}_{\text{out}}$ represent the mass rate of flow in and out of the control volume and $\mathbf{V}$ is the velocity vector. V is the magnitude of the velocity vector and α is the angle between the velocity vector and the outward normal. Then the continuity equation for the control volume becomes

$$\int_{\text{C.S.}} \rho \mathbf{V} \cdot d\mathbf{A} = -\frac{\partial}{\partial t} \int_{\text{C.V.}} \rho \, d\mathcal{V} \tag{3.1}$$

Equation (*3.1*) is the integral form of the continuity equation and physically says that the net rate of mass flow out of the control surface is equal to the time rate of decrease of mass inside the control volume. We will examine equation (*3.1*) by first considering some general simplifications, then some specific examples.

Since the control volume is fixed, the right side of (*3.1*) is zero for steady flow ($\partial \rho / \partial t = 0$) giving

$$\int_{\text{C.S.}} \rho \mathbf{V} \cdot d\mathbf{A} = 0 \tag{3.2}$$

For incompressible flow we have

$$\int_{\text{C.S.}} \mathbf{V} \cdot d\mathbf{A} = 0$$

Considering the steady flow of Fig. 3-2, where the fluid enters section 1 and leaves sections 2 and 3, we have

$$\int_{\text{C.S.}} \rho \mathbf{V} \cdot d\mathbf{A} = 0$$

$$\int_{A_2} \rho \mathbf{V} \cdot d\mathbf{A} + \int_{A_3} \rho \mathbf{V} \cdot d\mathbf{A} + \int_{A_1} \rho \mathbf{V} \cdot d\mathbf{A} = 0$$

Assuming that the velocity is normal to all surfaces where fluid crosses,

Fig. 3-2. Continuity in branching flow.

$$\int_{A_2} \rho_2 V_2 \, dA + \int_{A_3} \rho_3 V_3 \, dA - \int_{A_1} \rho_1 V_1 \, dA = 0$$

If the densities and velocities are uniform over their respective areas,

$$\rho_2 V_2 A_2 + \rho_3 A_3 V_3 - \rho_1 A_1 V_1 = 0 \tag{3.3}$$

For a single pipe with no third exit the equation becomes

$$\rho_2 A_2 V_2 = \rho_1 A_1 V_1 \tag{3.4}$$

The assumptions made in arriving at equation (*3.4*) are (*a*) steady flow, (*b*) velocities normal to the surfaces, (*c*) velocity and density constant over the respective areas, and (*d*) one exit and one inlet to the control volume.

(*b*) **Momentum.** We will now develop the momentum equation for the control volume. This equation is one of the most important mathematical relationships of fluid motion. It enables us to deal with problems involving forces of fluids on solid surfaces and other fluids, such as force on a pipe bend, thrust of a jet engine, lift and drag on an airplane wing, and many others.

The net force $\mathbf{F}$ acting on a particle or system of particles of fixed mass is given by Newton's second law

$$\mathbf{F} = \frac{d\mathbf{M}}{dt} \tag{3.5}$$

where $\mathbf{M}$ is the total linear momentum of the system. If we assume that the force is constant over a time Δt, we may write

$$\mathbf{F} \, \Delta t = \Delta \mathbf{M} \tag{3.6}$$

The right hand side of equation (3.6) is, referring to Fig. 3-1,

$$\Delta\mathbf{M} = \mathbf{M}_A(t+\Delta t) - \mathbf{M}_C(t+\Delta t) + \mathbf{M}_B(t+\Delta t) - \mathbf{M}_A(t)$$

Rearranging and dividing by Δt,

$$\frac{\Delta\mathbf{M}}{\Delta t} = \frac{\mathbf{M}_A(t+\Delta t) - \mathbf{M}_A(t)}{\Delta t} + \frac{\mathbf{M}_B(t+\Delta t) - \mathbf{M}_C(t+\Delta t)}{\Delta t} \qquad (3.7)$$

By taking the limit of equation (3.7) as $\Delta t \to 0$, the first term on the right becomes

$$\lim_{\Delta t \to 0} \frac{\mathbf{M}_A(t+\Delta t) - \mathbf{M}_A(t)}{\Delta t} = \frac{\partial}{\partial t}(\mathbf{M})_{\text{c.v.}} = \frac{\partial}{\partial t}\int_{\text{c.v.}} \rho\mathbf{V}\, d\mathcal{V}$$

and the second term becomes

$$\lim_{\Delta t \to 0}\left[\frac{\mathbf{M}_B(t+\Delta t) - \mathbf{M}_C(t+\Delta t)}{\Delta t}\right] = \lim_{\Delta t \to 0}\left\{\frac{\left[\sum_B \Delta\mathbf{M}(t+\Delta t)\right]_B}{\Delta t} - \frac{\left[\sum_C \Delta\mathbf{M}(t+\Delta t)\right]_C}{\Delta t}\right\}$$

$$= \sum_B \Delta\dot{\mathbf{M}} - \sum_C \Delta\dot{\mathbf{M}} = \left[\sum \Delta\dot{m}\mathbf{V}\right]_{\text{out}} - \left[\sum \Delta\dot{m}\mathbf{V}\right]_{\text{in}}$$

$$= \int_{\text{C.S.}} \mathbf{V}\rho\mathbf{V}\cdot d\mathbf{A}$$

where $\sum_B \Delta\mathbf{M}(t+\Delta t)$ is the momentum associated with the mass that has crossed the boundary into region B in time Δt. $\sum_B \Delta\dot{\mathbf{M}}$ is the time rate at which momentum is crossing the surface into region B at time t. Thus equation (3.6) becomes

$$\mathbf{F} = \frac{\partial}{\partial t}\int_{\text{c.v.}} \mathbf{V}\rho\, d\mathcal{V} + \int_{\text{c.s.}} \mathbf{V}\rho\mathbf{V}\cdot d\mathbf{A} \qquad (3.8)$$

The total force $\mathbf{F}$ is made up of the total surface force $\mathbf{F}_s$ (pressure and shear) and a body force $\mathbf{B}$ which is a force per unit volume. The momentum equation for a control volume becomes

$$\mathbf{F}_s + \int_{\text{c.v.}} \mathbf{B}\, d\mathcal{V} = \frac{\partial}{\partial t}\int_{\text{c.v.}} \mathbf{V}\rho\, d\mathcal{V} + \int_{\text{c.s.}} \mathbf{V}\rho\mathbf{V}\cdot d\mathbf{A} \qquad (3.9)$$

It should be emphasized that this equation is valid only when referred to axes moving without acceleration, since the usual form of Newton's laws holds under these conditions.[1]

For steady flow and negligible body forces, equation (3.9) becomes

$$\mathbf{F}_s = \int_{\text{c.s.}} \mathbf{V}\rho\mathbf{V}\cdot d\mathbf{A} \qquad (3.10)$$

Further, if we assume that the density and velocity are uniform over the areas where the fluid is crossing the control surface, for one entrance 1 and one exit 2, we have

$$\sum F_x = \dot{m}(V_{x_2} - V_{x_1}), \quad \sum F_y = \dot{m}(V_{y_2} - V_{y_1}), \quad \sum F_z = \dot{m}(V_{z_2} - V_{z_1})$$

(c) **Angular Momentum.** Rather than give a rigorous derivation of the angular momentum equation, we will merely write it down and discuss its physical meaning. For a derivation, see reference 2 or 13, page 47.

Let us again write the linear momentum equation (3.9)

$$\mathbf{F}_s + \int_{\text{c.v.}} \mathbf{B}\, d\mathcal{V} = \frac{\partial}{\partial t}\int_{\text{c.v.}} \mathbf{V}\rho\, d\mathcal{V} + \int_{\text{c.s.}} \mathbf{V}\rho\mathbf{V}\cdot d\mathbf{A}$$

[1] For the case of an accelerating control volume without rotation, a term such as $-m\ddot{\mathbf{R}}$ is added to the left side of equation (3.9) where m is the total mass in the control volume and $\ddot{\mathbf{R}}$ is the acceleration relative to the inertial references. The derivation of the complete equation is given in reference 13, page 47.

Then write equation (3.9) with a position vector $\mathbf{r}$ taken as cross product with the vector of each term, giving

$$\int_{C.S.} \mathbf{r} \times d\mathbf{F}_s + \int_{C.V.} \mathbf{r} \times \mathbf{B}\, d\mathcal{V} = \frac{\partial}{\partial t} \int_{C.V.} \mathbf{r} \times \mathbf{V}\rho\, d\mathcal{V} + \int_{C.S.} \mathbf{r} \times \mathbf{V}\rho\mathbf{V} \cdot d\mathbf{A} \qquad (3.11)$$

which is the angular momentum equation. We will now look at the physical interpretation of each term. Refer to Fig. 3-3.

The integrand of the first term $\mathbf{r} \times d\mathbf{F}_s$ gives the moment around the origin attributed to the force $d\mathbf{F}_s$ at the control surface. The integrand of the second term of (3.11) is the moment about the origin due to the body force acting on the infinitesimal volume element $d\mathcal{V}$. The integrand of the third term is the angular momentum of the infinitesimal mass element $\rho\, d\mathcal{V}$. The integration gives the total angular momentum of the mass within the control volume. The last term is the rate of efflux of angular momentum through the control surface.

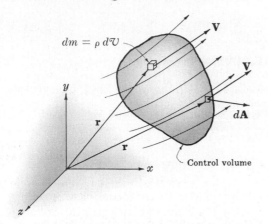

Fig. 3-3. Angular momentum in a control volume.

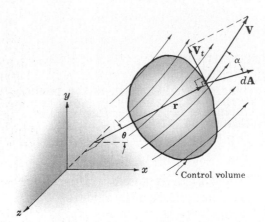

Fig. 3-4. Angular momentum about the z axis.

In applying equation (3.11) the scalar component form is used. For example, if we choose to write the equation for the z axis as shown in Fig. 3-4, we have (for steady flow and negligible body forces)

$$T_z = \int_{C.S.} (\mathbf{r} \times \mathbf{V})_z (\rho \mathbf{V} \cdot d\mathbf{A}) \qquad (3.12)$$

where T_z represents the net torque on the control volume about the z axis and

$$(\mathbf{r} \times \mathbf{V})_z = rV_t, \qquad \rho\mathbf{V} \cdot d\mathbf{A} = \rho V \cos\alpha\, dA$$

where V_t is the component of the velocity vector perpendicular to the z axis and α is the angle between the velocity vector and the area $d\mathbf{A}$. Then

$$T_z = \int_{C.S.} \rho r V_t V \cos\alpha\, dA \qquad (3.13)$$

Let us assume that the entire flow enters the control volume at an area A_1 and leaves at an area A_2, over each of which ρ, V and $\cos\alpha$ are uniform. Define r_2V_{t2} as the mean value of rV_t over A_2 and r_1V_{t1} as the mean value over A_1.

$$r_2V_{t2} = \frac{1}{A_2} \int_{A_2} rV_t\, dA, \qquad r_1V_{t1} = \frac{1}{A_1} \int_{A_1} rV_t\, dA$$

The continuity equation gives, where Q is the volumetric flow rate,

$$\rho_1 A_1 V_1 \cos\alpha_1 = \rho_2 A_2 V_2 \cos\alpha_2 = \rho_1 Q_1$$

Then equation (*3.13*) becomes

$$T_z = \rho_1 Q_1 (r_2 V_{t2} - r_1 V_{t1}) \tag{3.14}$$

Equation (*3.14*) is applicable to the rotor of a turbomachine since the absolute flow in the interior of the rotor is cyclic and we may assume with a fair approximation that ρ, V and $\cos \alpha$ are uniform over the entrance section 1 and the exit section 2 (see Fig. 3-5 and 3-6). In the figures, **v** refers to the rotor (relative velocity), and **V** as usual denotes velocity relative to the earth (absolute velocity). For clarity, only one blade is shown.

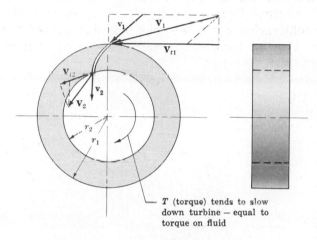

Fig. 3-5. Velocity diagrams for a radial flow turbine runner.

Fig. 3-6. Velocity diagrams for a radial flow impeller.

If we neglect bearing friction, the drag of the fluid on the outside of the rotor, and fluid shearing stresses at 1 and 2, then the external torque T on the shaft equals the resultant external torque on either system. For the turbine, however, T is clockwise, while for the compressor it is counterclockwise. Hence for the turbine,

$$T = \rho_1 Q_1 (r_1 V_{t1} - r_2 V_{t2}) \tag{3.15}$$

and for the compressor or pump impeller (V_{t1} is usually zero here),

$$T = \rho_1 Q_1 (r_2 V_{t2} - r_1 V_{t1}) \tag{3.16}$$

The turbomachines shown here are radial flow devices, i.e. the flow through the rotor is in a radial direction or normal to the axis of rotation. Turbomachines may also be axial flow (flow through the rotor parallel to the axis of rotation) or mixed flow (somewhere intermediate between axial and radial flow).

(*d*) **Energy.** The mathematical statement of the first law of thermodynamics[1] is

$$Q - W = \Delta E \tag{3.17}$$

where Q = heat added to the system

W = work done by the system

ΔE = change in energy of the system.

Again, as in the previous sections, it is strongly emphasized that this law applies to a system. Thus our task, as before, is to determine the mathematical expressions for a control volume.

---

[1]For definitions of heat and work see, for example, references 6 and 7, page 47.

Heat and work of equation (*3.17*) involve an interaction of the system with other systems. Energy, however, is energy associated with the mass of the system and is customarily separated into three parts,

$$E = U + \tfrac{1}{2}mV^2 + mgz$$

where U = internal energy associated with molecular and atomic behavior

$\tfrac{1}{2}mV^2$ = kinetic energy

   mgz = potential energy associated with the location in the earth's gravitational field.

We will write equation (*3.17*) on a unit mass basis,

$$q - w = \Delta e \qquad (3.18)$$

where $q = Q/m$, $w = W/m$, $e = E/m$.

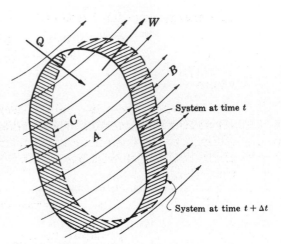

Consider the system at time t as shown in Fig. 3-7. At some later time $t + \Delta t$ the system has moved to another location. The energy equation for the system for this change is

$$Q - W = E_f - E_i$$

where E_f is the final energy of the system and E_i the initial energy. Dividing by Δt,

$$\frac{Q}{\Delta t} - \frac{W}{\Delta t} = \frac{E_f - E_i}{\Delta t} \qquad (3.19)$$

Fig. 3-7. Control volume for energy balance.

Let us evaluate the right hand side of this equation:

$$\frac{E_f - E_i}{\Delta t} = \frac{E_A(t + \Delta t) - E_C(t + \Delta t) + E_B(t + \Delta t) - E_A(t)}{\Delta t}$$

$$= \frac{E_A(t + \Delta t) - E_A(t)}{\Delta t} + \frac{E_B(t + \Delta t) - E_C(t + \Delta t)}{\Delta t}$$

The first term on the right becomes, as $\Delta t \to 0$,

$$\lim_{\Delta t \to 0} \frac{E_A(t + \Delta t) - E_A(t)}{\Delta t} = \frac{\partial}{\partial t}(E)_{\text{c.v.}} = \frac{\partial}{\partial t}\int e\, dm = \frac{\partial}{\partial t}\int_{\text{c.v.}} e\rho\, d\mathcal{V}$$

The last term becomes

$$\frac{E_B(t + \Delta t) - E_C(t + \Delta t)}{\Delta t} = \frac{(\Sigma\, \Delta m\, e)_B\,|_{t+\Delta t}}{\Delta t} - \frac{(\Sigma\, \Delta m\, e)_C\,|_{t+\Delta t}}{\Delta t}$$

where the summation is for the mass crossing the surface, Δm is typical mass, and e is the stored energy associated with the mass Δm. In the limit as $\Delta t \to 0$ the last equation becomes

$$\lim_{\Delta t \to 0} \frac{E_B(t + \Delta t) - E_C(t + \Delta t)}{\Delta t} = \int_{\text{out}} e\, d\dot{m} - \int_{\text{in}} e\, d\dot{m} = \int_{\text{c.s.}} e\rho \mathbf{V} \cdot d\mathbf{A}$$

Thus we have

$$\lim_{\Delta t \to 0} \frac{E_f - E_i}{\Delta t} = \frac{\partial}{\partial t}\int_{\text{c.v.}} e\rho\, d\mathcal{V} + \int_{\text{c.s.}} e\rho \mathbf{V} \cdot d\mathbf{A}$$

Work may be done at the boundary of the system by normal and tangential stresses. We refer to the work done at the boundary of the system due to the normal stresses (hydrostatic pressure) as flow work. This is the work done on element $(\Delta m)_B$, say, in moving it out of region A in time Δt and is equal to $p\,dA\,\Delta x$. However, $dA\,\Delta x$ is the volume of mass element Δm and may be written as $(\Delta m)_B/\rho$. Thus the flow work for both outflow and inflow is

$$\left(\frac{dW}{dt}\right)_{\text{flow work}} = \lim_{\Delta t \to 0}\left(\frac{\Delta W}{\Delta t}\right)_{\text{flow work}} - \lim_{\Delta t \to 0}\left[\frac{\Sigma\,(p/\rho)(\Delta m)_B\,|_{t+\Delta t}}{\Delta t} - \frac{\Sigma\,(p/\rho)(\Delta m)_C\,|_{t+\Delta t}}{\Delta t}\right]$$

$$= \int_{\text{c.s.}} (p/\rho)\rho\mathbf{V}\cdot d\mathbf{A}$$

The energy equation becomes

$$\frac{dQ}{dt} - \frac{dW_S}{dt} = \frac{\partial}{\partial t}\int_{\text{c.v.}} e\rho\,d\mathcal{U} + \int_{\text{c.s.}} (e + p/\rho)\rho\mathbf{V}\cdot d\mathbf{A} \qquad (3.20)$$

where

$$e = u + \tfrac{1}{2}V^2 + gz$$

and (dW_S/dt) is the time rate of work for all work except flow work. Equation (3.20) states that the time rate of heat added to the system minus the work done by the system (other than flow work) is equal to the time rate of change of the stored energy in the control volume plus the net rate of efflux of stored energy and flow work out of the control volume.

Fig. 3-8. A flow device with heat and work.

Let us consider one-dimensional steady flow for the device shown in Fig. 3-8. The shear work done over the cross section of the rotating shaft is called shaft work. The shear work done at all other parts of the boundary is zero, because the velocity is either zero or normal to the shear force. Thus from equation (3.20)

$$\frac{dQ}{dt} - \frac{dW_S}{dt} = \int_{A_1+A_2}\left(\frac{p}{\rho} + u + \frac{V^2}{2} + gz\right)\rho V\,dA$$

Since the flow is one-dimensional p, V, u, ρ are uniform over A_1 and A_2. If in addition to these conditions we neglect z variations over the areas, we have

$$\frac{dQ}{dt} - \frac{dW_S}{dt} = \left(\frac{p_2}{\rho_2} + u_2 + \frac{V_2^2}{2} + gz_2\right)\rho_2 A_2 V_2 - \left(\frac{p_1}{\rho_1} + u_1 + \frac{V_1^2}{2} + gz_1\right)\rho_1 A_1 V_1$$

From the continuity equation we have for one-dimensional steady flow,

$$\rho_1 A_1 V_1 = \rho_2 A_2 V_2 = \frac{dm}{dt} = \text{mass flow rate}$$

which upon substitution into the energy equation gives

$$\frac{dQ}{dt} - \frac{dW_S}{dt} = \left[\left(\frac{p_2}{\rho_2} - \frac{p_1}{\rho_1}\right) + (u_2 - u_1) + \frac{V_2^2 - V_1^2}{2} + g(z_2 - z_1)\right]\frac{dm}{dt} \qquad (3.21)$$

Writing equation *(3.21)* so that each term is referred to unit mass of the flowing fluid,

$$\blacktriangleright \qquad q - w_S = \left(\frac{p_2}{\rho_2} - \frac{p_1}{\rho_1}\right) + (u_2 - u_1) + \frac{V_2^2 - V_1^2}{2} + g(z_2 - z_1) \qquad (3.22a)$$

which is the usual one-dimensional steady flow energy balance of thermodynamics.

By rearranging equation *(3.22a)* and assuming incompressible flow,

$$-w_S = \frac{p_2 - p_1}{\rho} + \frac{V_2^2 - V_1^2}{2} + g(z_2 - z_1) + (u_2 - u_1 - q)$$

In most actual flows, all of the quantities of the preceding equation may be measured by direct means except the internal energy and heat transfer. This is particularly true for flow of liquids in pipes, for example. Thus the usual procedure is to define

$$gH_L = u_2 - u_1 - q$$

so that
$$-w_S = \frac{p_2 - p_1}{\rho} + \frac{V_2^2 - V_1^2}{2} + g(z_2 - z_1) + gH_L \qquad (3.22b)$$

where H_L is referred to as the "loss" or "head loss" and represents the conversion of mechanical energy into thermal energy. As the fluid flows through a pump or pipe it undergoes shearing deformation, since the fluid in contact with a solid surface does not slip. Shearing stresses are set up in the viscous fluid as a result of these deformations. The temperature rises above the value it would have in frictionless flow. The temperature rise tends to increase both $u_2 - u_1$ and the heat transferred to the surroundings.

For a frictionless flow of an incompressible fluid with zero shaft work, *(3.22b)* becomes

$$\frac{p_2 - p_1}{\rho} + \frac{V_2^2 - V_1^2}{2} + g(z_2 - z_1) = 0 \qquad (3.22c)$$

since H_L is then zero. We will want to compare this equation with Bernoulli's equation which will be derived later from the momentum equation. Actually, we can only prove that $(u_2 - u_1 - q)$ is a head loss term by comparing *(3.22a)* with the first integral of the equation of motion for an incompressible fluid, which is identical to *(3.22b)* and which is a generalized Bernoulli equation obtained directly from the momentum equation and discussed in Section 3.3c. It is very important to realize that *(3.22b)*, but not *(3.22a)*, may be derived strictly from the momentum equation. Equation *(3.22a)*, is a general energy equation for compressible flow, but once we say the flow is incompressible and lump $(u_2 - u_1 - q)$ as a frictionless loss term we have removed all true thermodynamic information and are left with only a mechanical energy balance redundant with the equation of motion. For frictionless incompressible flow, *(3.22c)* is identical with the ordinary Bernoulli equation, and the other part of *(3.22b)*, $H_L = 0$, is the first law. That is, $q - \Delta u = 0$ for a unit mass of flowing fluid is the first law of thermodynamics and is independent of *(3.22c)*.

Contained in the general energy equation *(3.22a)* is the first law of thermodynamics and a balance of mechanical energy. Remember that the balance of mechanical energy (the rate of increase of kinetic energy and potential energy is equal to the rate at which the translational forces do work) may be obtained from the momentum equation and is independent of the thermodynamic balance which is known as the first law.

(e) **Second Law of Thermodynamics.** The second law for a control volume is determined by the same procedure as was done for the other basic laws. Rather than going through the entire derivation, only the results will be given. One may refer to references 8 and 10, page 47, for a detailed derivation.

The second law for a system is

$$dS - \frac{dQ}{T} \geqq 0$$

(where S is the entropy of the system), which says that the entropy change, minus the heat transferred to the system divided by the temperature, is equal to or greater than zero. By the same procedure as in the previous sections, the control volume form of the second law is obtained

$$\frac{\partial}{\partial t}\int_{C.V.} s\rho\, d\mathcal{V} + \int_{C.S.} s\rho\mathbf{V}\cdot d\mathbf{A} - \int_{C.S.} \frac{\mathbf{q}}{T}\cdot d\mathbf{A} \geqq 0 \qquad (3.23)$$

where $\mathbf{q}$ is the heat flux vector, which is the rate of heat transfer per unit area. s is the specific entropy, that is, the entropy per unit mass.

If it is assumed that a fluid flows steadily and adiabatically with one inlet and one outlet (e.g. Fig. 3-8), then equation (3.23) becomes

$$s_2 - s_1 \geqq 0$$

If it is further assumed that the process is reversible, then

$$s_2 - s_1 = 0$$

which says that the process is isentropic.

Entropy is a property and is related to other properties. The second law finds particular usefulness in the flow of gases.

3.3 DIFFERENTIAL EQUATIONS

In the previous section the basic laws which apply to a system were used to establish integral equations applicable to a control volume. Now we will use the basic laws to derive the differential equations of fluid dynamics. There are several ways to do this, although three different methods are commonly employed. First, one can formally, by use of the vector calculus, obtain differential expressions from integral expressions. No additional physical reasoning is necessary and the procedure is purely mathematical and rigorous. Second, we may apply the integral relationships to an elemental volume and obtain differential expressions by taking the limit as the volume becomes infinitesimal. The third method is to apply the basic system equations directly to an elemental volume, and in so doing, of course, obtain the basic integral expressions for an elemental volume along the way.

To illustrate the methods we will derive the differential continuity equation by the first method, the momentum equation by the second, and the energy equation by the third.

One important point to remember here is that the coordinates apply to points in space and time, and that coordinates do not denote the location of individual particles. That is, we ask: what are the properties and velocity $\mathbf{V}$ as a function of position and time? For example, $\mathbf{V} = \mathbf{V}(\mathbf{r}, t)$ or $\mathbf{V} = \mathbf{V}(x, y, z, t)$ in cartesian coordinates. Such field coordinates are known as Eulerian, as opposed to Lagrangian which are used in rigid body dynamics. In Lagrangian coordinates, acceleration is simply $\ddot{\mathbf{r}}$ and $\mathbf{r}$ denotes the position of a particle or fixed point on a rigid body. In fluid mechanics one may use Lagrangian coordinates, but such a description is not particularly useful and Eulerian coordinates are used almost exclusively. Clearly then, acceleration cannot be $\ddot{\mathbf{r}}$ in Eulerian coordinates since such a quantity is meaningless; $\mathbf{r}$ is a fixed point in space and its derivatives are meaningless. However, as the fluid flows past any point in question, it does have acceleration which can be written in terms of the fluid velocity. The appropriate expression will be derived presently.

(a) **Continuity (conservation of mass).** Beginning with equation (3.1),

$$\int_{\text{C.S.}} \rho \mathbf{V} \cdot d\mathbf{A} = -\frac{\partial}{\partial t} \int_{\text{C.V.}} \rho \, d\mathcal{V} \tag{3.1}$$

we may formally apply Gauss' theorem to convert the left side to a volume integral. Hence (3.1) may be written

$$\int_{\text{C.V.}} \nabla \cdot (\rho \mathbf{V}) \, d\mathcal{V} + \frac{\partial}{\partial t} \int_{\text{C.V.}} \rho \, d\mathcal{V} = \int_{\text{C.V.}} [\nabla \cdot (\rho \mathbf{V}) + \partial \rho / \partial t] \, d\mathcal{V} = 0 \tag{3.24}$$

Since the control volume is arbitrary the integrand must be zero, so that we obtain the differential form of the continuity equation as

$$\partial \rho / \partial t + \nabla \cdot (\rho \mathbf{V}) = 0 \tag{3.25}$$

which could also be obtained by applying (3.1) directly to an elemental volume.

For steady flow, $\partial \rho / \partial t = 0$ and we have

$$\nabla \cdot (\rho \mathbf{V}) = 0 \tag{3.26}$$

and for incompressible flow
$$\nabla \cdot \mathbf{V} = 0 \tag{3.27}$$

In cartesian coordinates the continuity equation is

$$\frac{\partial \rho}{\partial t} + \frac{\partial}{\partial x}(\rho u) + \frac{\partial}{\partial y}(\rho v) + \frac{\partial}{\partial z}(\rho w) = 0 \tag{3.28}$$

which for incompressible flow is

$$\frac{\partial u}{\partial x} + \frac{\partial v}{\partial y} + \frac{\partial w}{\partial z} = 0 \tag{3.29}$$

In cartesian tensor notation the continuity equation is

$$\frac{\partial \rho}{\partial t} + \frac{\partial}{\partial x_i}(\rho u_i) = 0 \tag{3.30}$$

(b) **Momentum Equation.** We will derive the momentum equation by applying the integral form to an elemental volume. We will use a small cube so that the result will be valid only in cartesian coordinates. The general vector form is best derived by the formal mathematical method, but we will give only the result of that derivation here. Of course, equations for any coordinate system (cylindrical, spherical, etc.) could be derived just as we will for cartesian coordinates by choosing the appropriate elemental volume to begin with.

Before beginning the derivation, let us first review the concept of the stress tensor. We will want to account for the shear stresses and normal stresses (including pressure) in the momentum balance. (After our derivation we will relate these stresses to the velocity components to obtain the final form of the momentum equation.)

Consider a cube of fluid as shown in Fig. 3-9. Stresses are denoted as σ_{ij}. The first subscript denotes the face on which the stress acts, and the second subscript denotes the direction of the stress. (The face is indicated as the plane perpendicular to the axis of the subscript. For instance, the 1 face is perpendicular to the x or x_1 axis.) The idea of positive and negative faces is indicated in Fig. 3-9. The stresses may vary through a fluid so that their gradients may exist. However, the array of stresses σ_{ij} (there are nine of them) may be considered to exist at a point in space and be a function then of $\mathbf{r}$ and t. The stress tensor then may be written as

$$\sigma_{ij} \;=\; \begin{bmatrix} \sigma_{11} & \sigma_{12} & \sigma_{13} \\ \sigma_{21} & \sigma_{22} & \sigma_{23} \\ \sigma_{31} & \sigma_{32} & \sigma_{33} \end{bmatrix} \qquad\qquad (3.31)$$

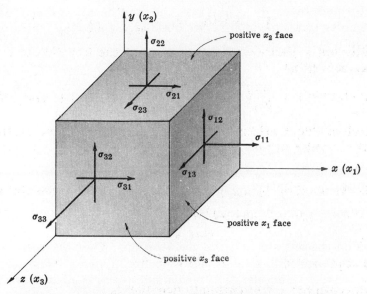

Fig. 3-9.   Stresses at a point in space. The positive faces are shown; the opposite ones are the negative faces. The stresses on the negative faces are equal to but in the opposite direction to those on the positive faces.

The stress tensor must be symmetric, that is, $\sigma_{ij} = \sigma_{ji}$, otherwise if the elemental volume were shrunk to infinitesimal size it would have to rotate with infinite angular velocity. Hence there are six independent components of the stress tensor.

We can now apply the integral momentum equation *(3.9)* to an elemental cube, where the stresses compose the external force $\mathbf{F}_s$. Referring to Fig. 3-10 we can write out the momentum balance for the x direction as

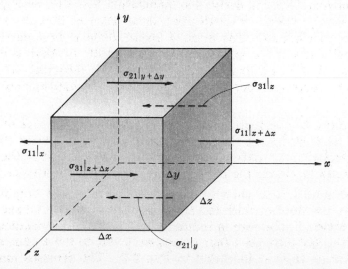

Fig. 3-10.   Elemental cube for momentum equation derivation. Only the forces in the x direction are shown.

$$(\sigma_{11}|_{x+\Delta x} - \sigma_{11}|_x)\Delta y\,\Delta z \; + \; (\sigma_{21}|_{y+\Delta y} - \sigma_{21}|_y)\Delta x\,\Delta z \; + \; (\sigma_{31}|_{z+\Delta z} - \sigma_{31}|_z)\Delta x\,\Delta y \; + \; B_x \Delta x\,\Delta y\,\Delta z$$

$$= \; \frac{\partial}{\partial t}(u\rho)\,\Delta x\,\Delta y\,\Delta z \; + \; \Delta y\,\Delta z\,(\rho u^2|_{x+\Delta x} - \rho u^2|_x)$$

$$+ \; \Delta x\,\Delta z\,(\rho u v|_{y+\Delta y} - \rho u v|_y) \; + \; \Delta x\,\Delta y\,(\rho u w|_{z+\Delta z} - \rho u w|_z)$$

If we divide through by $\Delta x\,\Delta y\,\Delta z$ and take the limit as Δx, Δy and $\Delta z \to 0$, and combine with the continuity (*3.28*) to simplify, we obtain the following. (The y and z components are obtained in a similar manner.)

$$\rho\frac{Du}{Dt} \;=\; \rho\left(\frac{\partial u}{\partial t} + u\frac{\partial u}{\partial x} + v\frac{\partial u}{\partial y} + w\frac{\partial u}{\partial z}\right) \;=\; \frac{\partial\sigma_{11}}{\partial x} + \frac{\partial\sigma_{12}}{\partial y} + \frac{\partial\sigma_{13}}{\partial z} + B_x$$

$$\rho\frac{Dv}{Dt} \;=\; \rho\left(\frac{\partial v}{\partial t} + u\frac{\partial v}{\partial x} + v\frac{\partial v}{\partial y} + w\frac{\partial v}{\partial z}\right) \;=\; \frac{\partial\sigma_{21}}{\partial x} + \frac{\partial\sigma_{22}}{\partial y} + \frac{\partial\sigma_{23}}{\partial z} + B_y \quad (3.32)$$

$$\rho\frac{Dw}{Dt} \;=\; \rho\left(\frac{\partial w}{\partial t} + u\frac{\partial w}{\partial x} + v\frac{\partial w}{\partial y} + w\frac{\partial w}{\partial z}\right) \;=\; \frac{\partial\sigma_{31}}{\partial x} + \frac{\partial\sigma_{32}}{\partial y} + \frac{\partial\sigma_{33}}{\partial z} + B_z$$

or in cartesian tensor notation,

$$\rho\frac{Du_i}{Dt} \;=\; \rho\left(\frac{\partial u_i}{\partial t} + u_j\frac{\partial u_i}{\partial x_j}\right) \;=\; \frac{\partial\sigma_{ij}}{\partial x_j} + B_i \qquad (3.33)$$

The terms on the left side are the acceleration. The $\partial/\partial t$ term is an unsteady term and indicates a change with time at a fixed point in space. The terms other than $\partial/\partial t$ are known as convective acceleration terms and are present because we are working in Eulerian coordinates.

The D/Dt operator is called the substantial or material derivative. In general, D/Dt is a vector operator and consequently the components of D/Dt operating on a vector are *not* the same as D/Dt operating on the scalar components of a vector, *except in cartesian coordinates*. Equations (*3.32*) may be generalized to vector form valid in any coordinate system. Then the acceleration is $\rho\,D\mathbf{V}/Dt$ where

$$\frac{D\mathbf{V}}{Dt} \;=\; \frac{\partial\mathbf{V}}{\partial t} + (\mathbf{V}\cdot\nabla)\mathbf{V} \;=\; \frac{\partial\mathbf{V}}{\partial t} + \nabla(V^2/2) - \mathbf{V}\times\nabla\times\mathbf{V}$$

The vector operator $D\mathbf{V}/Dt$ in various coordinate systems is listed in reference 5, page 47.

To illustrate the physical meaning of convective acceleration, consider a fluid flowing in a converging channel as shown in Fig. 3-11. The velocity at point B is greater than at point A because the area at B is smaller. Thus as a particle moves from A toward B it tends to undergo an acceleration due to area change (convective acceleration). If in addition we impose a time rate of change of mass flow rate (i.e. the mass flow rate at one instant of time is 3 lb/sec, say, and 5 seconds later it is 4 lb/sec), then each point in the flow will undergo a local increase in velocity or local acceleration. Thus local acceleration occurs because the flow is unsteady and convective acceleration occurs because the area changes. It is important to note that the acceleration is a vector, and whether we choose to express it in Eulerian or Lagrangian coordinates does not change its value. In other words, at a point in space at a given time, the fluid at that point has a certain velocity and acceleration, magnitude and direction. Hence $D\mathbf{V}/Dt = \ddot{\mathbf{r}}$ where $\mathbf{r}$ is the Lagrangian coordinate and D/Dt is expressed in terms of Eulerian coordinates.

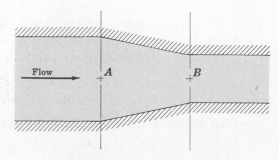

Fig. 3-11. Converging channel.

Most frequently we shall consider steady flows. This means that for the most part the local acceleration will be zero and that particle acceleration will be due to convective effects alone.

(c) **The Momentum Equation for Frictionless Flow.** In frictionless flow, there are no shear stresses and the normal stresses are just the pressure which is isotropic. Since we have defined the normal stresses (σ_{11}, σ_{22} and σ_{33}) as positive if they are tensions, we now set

$$\sigma_{11} = \sigma_{22} = \sigma_{33} = -p$$

so that the equations of motion in cartesian form are

$$\rho\left(\frac{\partial u_i}{\partial t} + u_j\frac{\partial u_i}{\partial x_j}\right) = -\frac{\partial p}{\partial x_i} + B_i \qquad (3.34)$$

or in component form

$$\rho\left(\frac{\partial u}{\partial t} + u\frac{\partial u}{\partial x} + v\frac{\partial u}{\partial y} + w\frac{\partial u}{\partial z}\right) = -\frac{\partial p}{\partial x} + B_x$$

$$\rho\left(\frac{\partial v}{\partial t} + u\frac{\partial v}{\partial x} + v\frac{\partial v}{\partial y} + w\frac{\partial v}{\partial z}\right) = -\frac{\partial p}{\partial y} + B_y \qquad (3.35)$$

$$\rho\left(\frac{\partial w}{\partial t} + u\frac{\partial w}{\partial x} + v\frac{\partial w}{\partial y} + w\frac{\partial w}{\partial z}\right) = -\frac{\partial p}{\partial z} + B_z$$

These equations are known as the Euler equations for frictionless flow. If the flow is incompressible, the density is constant and the three Euler equations plus the continuity equation constitute four equations in four unknowns, u, v, w, and p. The solution is often difficult, however, because the convective acceleration terms make the equations nonlinear.

In general vector form the Euler equations are

$$\rho\left[\frac{\partial \mathbf{V}}{\partial t} + \nabla\left(\frac{V^2}{2}\right) - \mathbf{V}\times\nabla\times\mathbf{V}\right] = -\nabla p + \mathbf{B} \qquad (3.36)$$

An important first integral of the equation of motion can be obtained by integrating *(3.36)* between two points along a streamline. Let ds be an element of length along a streamline. Then

$$\rho\left[\frac{\partial \mathbf{V}}{\partial t}\cdot d\mathbf{s} + \nabla\left(\frac{V^2}{2}\right)\cdot d\mathbf{s} - \mathbf{V}\times\nabla\times\mathbf{V}\cdot d\mathbf{s}\right] = -(\nabla p + \rho\nabla\psi)\cdot d\mathbf{s} \qquad (3.37)$$

Since $\mathbf{V}$ is parallel to $d\mathbf{s}$, the term $(\mathbf{V}\times\nabla\times\mathbf{V})$ is perpendicular to $d\mathbf{s}$ and

$$(\mathbf{V}\times\nabla\times\mathbf{V})\cdot d\mathbf{s} = 0$$

Hence we obtain for frictionless flow,

$$\int_1^2 \frac{\partial \mathbf{V}}{\partial t}\cdot d\mathbf{s} + \frac{V_2^2 - V_1^2}{2} + \int_1^2 \frac{dp}{\rho} + \psi_2 - \psi_1 = 0 \qquad (3.38)$$

Usually this equation is written for steady state and the gravitational potential ψ is gz (where z is the elevation above an arbitrary datum), so that the force of gravity is $-\rho g\hat{z}$ where $\hat{z}$ is a unit vector pointing vertically). Then *(3.38)* becomes

$$\frac{V_2^2 - V_1^2}{2} + \int_1^2 \frac{dp}{\rho} + g(z_2 - z_1) = 0 \qquad (3.39)$$

which is called the generalized Bernoulli or Euler equation. For incompressible flow,

$$\frac{V_2^2 - V_1^2}{2} + \frac{p_2 - p_1}{\rho} + g(z_2 - z_1) = 0 \qquad (3.40)$$

which is the Bernoulli equation, a very important integral form of the equation of motion. Remember, (3.40) is based on steady, frictionless, incompressible flow with gravity being the only body force, and it holds along a streamline.

If we wish to integrate (3.37) between any two points in the flow field (between different streamlines), we can only get the Euler or Bernoulli equation if $\nabla \times \mathbf{V} = 0$. This term is known as the rotation of the fluid, and if $\nabla \times \mathbf{V} = 0$ the flow is said to be irrotational. The criterion for irrotationality will be discussed in Chapter 6.

It is interesting to note that (3.40) is identical with (3.22c) derived from energy considerations. By comparing (3.40) to (3.22b) and (3.22c) we can see that $(u_2 - u_1 - q)$ must be a loss term, and in fact (3.22b) and (3.22c) can be derived from the momentum equation. (3.22b) including w_S may be derived by integrating the generalized form of (3.36), taking into account the viscous terms (which gives rise to H_L) and assuming $\mathbf{B}$ to have a non-conservative part (which gives rise to w_S). This generalized form of the momentum equation will be given by equation (3.48) in part (e) where we discuss the Navier-Stokes equations. We will not carry out the integration here, since it is much simpler to use the integral approach to obtain (3.22b) as we have already done.

Let us now turn to frictional flow, but first a word about stress and strain rates in fluids.

(d) **Stress-Strain Rate Relationships in Fluids.** If we wish to extend our study to viscous fluids, we must first discuss stress and strain rates in more detail.

In a fluid the rate of deformation tensor is written as $\partial u_i / \partial x_j$. The symmetrical part of this tensor is the strain rate tensor, and the antisymmetrical part is the rotation tensor, which is related to $\nabla \times \mathbf{V}$. We denote the strain rate tensor as e_{ij} and the rotation tensor as ω_{ij}. The deformation rate tensor then may be written

$$\frac{\partial u_i}{\partial x_j} = e_{ij} + \omega_{ij} \tag{3.41}$$

In Chapter 6 we will show that the terms of the rotation tensor are related to the angular velocity Ω_i of an infinitesimal fluid particle by

$$\Omega_1 = \omega_{32} = -\omega_{23}, \quad \Omega_2 = \omega_{13} = -\omega_{31}, \quad \Omega_3 = \omega_{21} = -\omega_{12} \tag{3.42}$$

In vector form, the following important relationship may be written

$$\mathbf{\Omega} = \tfrac{1}{2} \nabla \times \mathbf{V} \tag{3.43}$$

The physical angular velocity of the fluid is equal to one-half of the curl of the velocity vector.

The diagonal (normal) components of the strain rate tensor may be identified directly with the true normal strain rate. However, the off-diagonal terms (shear rate components) e_{ij}, $i \neq j$, are equal to one-half the true rate of shear strain components, which we denote as γ_{ij}. The one-half factor is necessary in order to make e_{ij} a true tensor. We can write them $e_{ii} = \gamma_{ii}$ and $e_{ij} = \tfrac{1}{2}\gamma_{ij}$ $(i \neq j)$. The cartesian components of the strain tensor and rotation tensor are listed below. (For a more complete listing see reference 5, page 47.)

$$e_{xx} = \frac{\partial u}{\partial x}; \quad e_{xy} = e_{yx} = \frac{1}{2}\left(\frac{\partial u}{\partial y} + \frac{\partial v}{\partial x}\right)$$

$$e_{yy} = \frac{\partial v}{\partial y}; \quad e_{yz} = e_{zy} = \frac{1}{2}\left(\frac{\partial v}{\partial z} + \frac{\partial w}{\partial y}\right) \tag{3.44}$$

$$e_{zz} = \frac{\partial w}{\partial z}; \quad e_{xz} = e_{zx} = \frac{1}{2}\left(\frac{\partial w}{\partial x} + \frac{\partial u}{\partial z}\right)$$

$$\Omega_x = \omega_{zy} = -\omega_{yz} = \frac{1}{2}\left(\frac{\partial w}{\partial y} - \frac{\partial v}{\partial z}\right)$$

$$\Omega_y = \omega_{xz} = -\omega_{zx} = \frac{1}{2}\left(\frac{\partial u}{\partial z} - \frac{\partial w}{\partial x}\right)$$

$$\Omega_z = \omega_{yx} = -\omega_{xy} = \frac{1}{2}\left(\frac{\partial v}{\partial x} - \frac{\partial u}{\partial y}\right)$$

Now, for a Newtonian fluid, it is assumed that the stress tensor and strain rate tensor are linearly related. The most general relationship can be shown to be of the following form (in cartesian tensor notation)

$$\sigma_{ij} = -p\delta_{ij} + \sigma'_{ij} = -p\delta_{ij} + 2\mu e_{ij} + \delta_{ij}\lambda\phi \qquad (3.45)$$

where ϕ is the fluid dilatation defined as $\nabla \cdot \mathbf{V}$ which is zero for an incompressible fluid. δ_{ij} is the Kronecker delta. λ is a second coefficient of viscosity. Another second coefficient of viscosity is defined as $\zeta = \lambda + \frac{2}{3}\mu$ and is zero for a monatomic gas. Equation (3.45) may be written out as

$$\sigma_{ij} = -p\delta_{ij} + \mu\left(\frac{\partial u_i}{\partial x_j} + \frac{\partial u_j}{\partial x_i} - \frac{2}{3}\delta_{ij}\frac{\partial u_k}{\partial x_k}\right) + \zeta\delta_{ij}\frac{\partial u_k}{\partial x_k} \qquad (3.46)$$

The reader is referred to the references, page 47, for a complete derivation of this expression.

Now this expression for σ_{ij} may be substituted into the momentum equation to yield the full equation of motion for a viscous fluid. These are known as the Navier-Stokes equations of motion.

(e) **The Navier-Stokes Equations.** The Navier-Stokes equations are the complete equations of motion for a viscous Newtonian fluid. Using (3.46), (3.33) becomes

$$\rho\left(\frac{\partial u_i}{\partial t} + u_j\frac{\partial u_i}{\partial x_j}\right) = -\frac{\partial p}{\partial x_i} + B_i + \frac{\partial}{\partial x_j}\left[\mu\left(\frac{\partial u_i}{\partial x_j} + \frac{\partial u_j}{\partial x_i} - \frac{2}{3}\delta_{ij}\frac{\partial u_k}{\partial x_k}\right)\right] + \frac{\partial}{\partial x_i}\left(\zeta\frac{\partial u_k}{\partial x_k}\right) \quad (3.47)$$

or in general vector form,

$$\rho\frac{D\mathbf{V}}{Dt} = \rho\left[\frac{\partial \mathbf{V}}{\partial t} + \nabla\left(\frac{V^2}{2}\right) - \mathbf{V}\times\nabla\times\mathbf{V}\right]$$

$$= -\nabla p + \mathbf{B} + \nabla\times[\mu(\nabla\times\mathbf{V})] + \nabla[(\zeta + \tfrac{4}{3}\mu)\nabla\cdot\mathbf{V}] \qquad (3.48)$$

Usually, the viscosity may be removed from the derivatives with negligible error. For an incompressible fluid $(\nabla\cdot\mathbf{V} = 0)$ these equations reduce to

$$\rho\frac{D\mathbf{V}}{Dt} = -\nabla p + \mathbf{B} + \mu\nabla^2\mathbf{V} \qquad (3.49)$$

which is a very important equation and should become quite familiar to the fluid dynamicist. It is *most important* to remember that D/Dt and ∇^2 are vector operators and may *not* be applied to the velocity components except in cartesian coordinates. Rather, the operations must first be performed, then components taken. The components of this equation in various coordinates are listed in the Appendix and in reference 5, page 47.

Now we can compare the complete Navier-Stokes equations with the Euler equations for frictionless flow. The differences are the additional terms involving the viscosity. If the fluid is incompressible these are all of the form $\partial u_i/\partial x_j$ $(i \neq j)$. Thus for an incompressible fluid, even if μ is not zero, the viscous terms are negligible if derivatives of the form $\partial u_i/\partial x_j$ are small, and the equations reduce to the Euler equations.

Therefore the Navier-Stokes equations reduce to Euler's equations if the viscosity is small or the derivatives of velocities with respect to directions other than the velocity direction are small. The latter approximation is very important in fluid mechanics. It is assumed that for many flows there are two regions: one close to a solid surface where the viscous terms are important (where Navier-Stokes equations must be used), and a region away from the surface where Euler's equations are a good approximation. These two distinct regions are the subjects of two later chapters: "Boundary Layer Flow" (Chapter 5) and "Potential Flow" (Chapter 6). The manner of treating these two subjects is entirely different as a result of the different forms of the equations.

(f) **The Energy Equation.** The energy equation will be derived by considering the balance on a control volume, and then formally obtaining the differential form in a purely mathematical manner. We begin in a manner similar to the integral derivations earlier in this chapter, but we may now consider a control volume immediately without looking at a moving system. Consider the control shown in Fig. 3-12.

We assume the velocity vector **V** and rate of heat flux vector **q** as shown at a point on the surface. **q** is a vector and represents the rate of heat flux by conduction and radiation. The total rate of heat flow into the control volume dQ/dt would be $\quad -\int_{\text{c.s.}} \mathbf{q} \cdot d\mathbf{A} \;=\; -\int_{\text{c.s.}} q_i \, dA_i$.

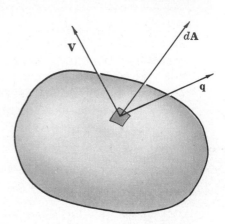

Fig. 3-12.   The control volume for the energy balance.

Work done by the fluid in the volume may be again divided into two parts, reversible work done by the pressure at the control surface and irreversible work done by the shear stresses on the surface. In terms of the stress tensor, the rate of total work done by the fluid in the control volume is (in cartesian tensor form)

$$\frac{dW}{dt} \;=\; -\int_{\text{c.s.}} u_i \, \sigma_{ji} \, dA_j$$

Now we can say that the net rate of increase of total energy (including kinetic, internal and potential) in the control volume is equal to the rate at which heat flows into the control volume, plus the rate of internal heat generation, minus the rate at which the fluid does work on its surroundings. Hence we have

$$\frac{\partial}{\partial t}\int_{\text{c.v.}} \rho e \, d\mathcal{V} \;+\; \int_{\text{c.s.}} \rho e u_i \, dA_i \;=\; -\int_{\text{c.s.}} q_i \, dA_i \;+\; \int_{\text{c.s.}} u_i \sigma_{ji} \, dA_j \;+\; \int_{\text{c.v.}} q''' \, d\mathcal{V}$$

Remember that e, the total energy per unit mass, is given by $e = V^2/2 + u + \psi$ where ψ is the gravitational potential denoted as gz in the integral development earlier. q''' is the internal heat generation rate per unit volume. The stress tensor may be divided into a pressure part and a shear part as $\sigma_{ij} = -p\delta_{ij} + \sigma'_{ij}$. By using Gauss' theorem the energy equation then becomes

$$\int_{\text{c.v.}} \left[\frac{\partial}{\partial t}(\rho e) + \frac{\partial}{\partial x_i}(\rho e u_i) + \frac{\partial}{\partial x_i} q_i + q''' + \frac{\partial}{\partial x_i}(p u_i) - \frac{\partial}{\partial x_i}(u_j \sigma'_{ij}) \right] d\mathcal{V} \;=\; 0$$

Since the volume is arbitrary, the integrand itself must be zero. By expanding the terms and combining with the continuity equation, we get

$$\rho \frac{De}{Dt} \;=\; -\frac{\partial}{\partial x_i} q_i - p \frac{\partial u_i}{\partial x_i} - u_i \frac{\partial p}{\partial x_i} + u_i \frac{\partial \sigma'_{ji}}{\partial x_j} + \Phi + q''' \qquad (3.50)$$

where $\Phi = \sigma'_{ij} \partial u_j / \partial x_i$ is the dissipation function[1] and is the rate at which the shear stresses do irreversible work on the fluid. It is given in terms of u_i in the Appendix. The material derivative here operates on a scalar and we need not be concerned about its vector properties as we were in the equation of motion. The forms of D/Dt in various coordinate systems are listed in the Appendix. Physically the derivative is the rate of change of a property or parameter that one would see if one were riding along with the fluid. If instead of considering a control volume we were to consider a particular fixed particle of fluid, we would use $\partial/\partial t$ instead. The form of D/Dt comes about because we are really writing a balance, instantaneously on a system of fluid (in the control volume) but in Eulerian coordinates.

This equation is useful, but it has hidden in it the momentum equation which may be subtracted out to simplify it. We notice that on the left side are the rates of increase of kinetic and potential energy, and on the right side the third and fourth terms are the rate at which the stresses (including pressure) do work. By taking the vector dot product of $\mathbf{V}$ with the equation of motion (3.33), assuming the body force B_i is the conservative gravitational force $-\rho \, \partial\psi/\partial x_i$, we obtain

$$\rho u_i \frac{D u_i}{Dt} = \rho \frac{D}{Dt}\left(\frac{V^2}{2}\right) = -u_i \frac{\partial p}{\partial x_i} + u_i \frac{\partial \sigma'_{ij}}{\partial x_j} - \rho u_i \frac{\partial \psi}{\partial x_i} \qquad (3.51)$$

which is the mechanical energy equation. Since ψ is constant in time we may add $\rho \, \partial\psi/\partial t$ to the left side (since it is zero) and obtain

$$\rho \frac{D}{Dt}(V^2/2 + \psi) = -u_i \frac{\partial p}{\partial x_i} + u_i \frac{\partial \sigma'_{ij}}{\partial x_j}$$

which may be subtracted out of the energy equation (3.50) to yield

$$\rho \frac{Du}{Dt} = -p \frac{\partial u_i}{\partial x_i} - \frac{\partial q_i}{\partial x_i} + \Phi + q''' \qquad (3.52)$$

which is the final form of the energy equation. u here is the internal energy per unit mass.

Various simplifications of (3.52) may be effected. Let us introduce Fourier's law of heat conduction, $\mathbf{q} = -\kappa \nabla T$, and assume constant thermal conductivity and a perfect gas ($du = c_v \, dT$). Also, $\partial u_i/\partial x_i = \nabla \cdot \mathbf{V}$, and $\nabla \cdot \nabla T = \nabla^2 T$, so that we can write finally

$$\rho c_v \frac{DT}{Dt} = -p \, \nabla \cdot \mathbf{V} + \kappa \nabla^2 T - \nabla \cdot \mathbf{q}_r + q''' + \Phi \qquad (3.53)$$

where $\mathbf{q}_r$ is the radiation heat flux vector. It should be noted that c_v may be a function of temperature and even then occurs outside (*not inside*) the derivative.

Equation (3.53) may be put into other forms. If we introduce the enthalpy $h = u + p/\rho$, the equation may be written

$$\rho \frac{Dh}{Dt} = \frac{Dp}{Dt} + \kappa \nabla^2 T - \nabla \cdot \mathbf{q}_r + q''' + \Phi \qquad (3.54)$$

and for a perfect gas it becomes

$$\rho c_p \frac{DT}{Dt} = \frac{Dp}{Dt} + \kappa \nabla^2 T - \nabla \cdot \mathbf{q}_r + q''' + \Phi \qquad (3.55)$$

An incompressible fluid, we must remember, is not a perfect gas and h depends on T and p. It is best then to start with (3.52) and set $\nabla \cdot \mathbf{V} = 0$. Then we can set $du = c_v \, dT$ and obtain

---

[1]Sometimes the dissipation term is written as $\mu\Phi$, and Φ then is different from ours by a factor μ.

$$\rho c_v \frac{DT}{Dt} \;=\; \kappa \nabla^2 T \;-\; \nabla \cdot \mathbf{q}_r \;+\; q''' \;+\; \Phi \tag{3.56}$$

Sometimes it is useful to use the total equation (*3.50*), particularly for frictionless fluids. Then (*3.50*) becomes (setting $\psi = gz$, using Fourier's law, and introducing the enthalpy):

$$\rho \frac{D}{Dt}(V^2/2 + gz + h) \;=\; \frac{\partial p}{\partial t} + \kappa \nabla^2 T \;-\; \nabla \cdot \mathbf{q}_r \;+\; q'''$$

$$\rho \frac{D}{Dt}(V^2/2 + gz + u) \;=\; -p\nabla \cdot \mathbf{V} \;-\; \mathbf{V} \cdot \nabla p \;+\; \kappa \nabla^2 T \;-\; \nabla \cdot \mathbf{q}_r \;+\; q''' \tag{3.57}$$

Usually $\mathbf{q}_r$ is negligible and q''' is zero except for cases involving such things as resistive heating. It is seldom in fluid dynamics that $\mathbf{q}_r$ and q''' must be considered, but we have included them for completeness.

It is interesting to refer back now to the comparison of equations (*3.22b*), (*3.22c*) and (*3.40*). Equation (*3.22b*) is a true energy equation. But now we know that since the total energy equation [(*3.50*) or (*3.57*)] has momentum hidden in it, equation (*3.22c*) is actually the momentum equation and is identical in meaning to equation (*3.40*), the Bernoulli equation.

(*g*) **The Second Law of Thermodynamics and Entropy Production.** We can make equation (*3.23*) into an equality by introducing the concept of entropy production rate per unit volume, θ. We find, introducing the heat flux vector $\mathbf{q}$,

$$\int_{\text{C.V.}} \theta \, d\mathcal{V} - \int_{\text{C.S.}} \frac{\mathbf{q}}{T} \cdot d\mathbf{A} \;=\; \frac{\partial}{\partial t} \int_{\text{C.V.}} \rho s \, d\mathcal{V} + \int_{\text{C.S.}} \rho s \mathbf{V} \cdot d\mathbf{A} \tag{3.58}$$

Using Gauss' law and the continuity equation, we obtain

$$\theta - \nabla \cdot (\mathbf{q}/T) \;=\; \rho \frac{Ds}{Dt} \tag{3.59}$$

By introducing the energy equation and using the basic thermodynamic relationship

$$\rho \frac{Du}{Dt} \;=\; \rho T \frac{Ds}{Dt} - p \nabla \cdot \mathbf{V} \tag{3.60}$$

which is the Eulerian coordinate form of

$$du \;=\; T \, ds \;-\; p \, d(1/\rho)$$

Equation (*3.59*) can be put into the form (assuming Fourier's law holds, and neglecting radiation)

$$\theta \;=\; \frac{\Phi}{T} + \frac{\mathbf{q} \cdot \mathbf{q}}{\kappa T^2} \;=\; \frac{\Phi}{T} + \kappa \frac{(\nabla T)^2}{T^2} \tag{3.61}$$

which shows the entropy production rate in terms of the coupled irreversibilities of heat currents and viscous dissipation.

3.4   SUMMARY, APPLICATIONS AND PROBLEMS

The derivations of the equations of this chapter have been long and tedious. These equations cannot be treated as "handy formulae". The shotgun approach of picking several equations, plugging in numbers and praying that one will yield the desired result may and probably will be disastrous. Understanding of the meaning of the equations and the limitations or restrictions of the special forms of the equations is of the utmost importance.

The procedure of this chapter was to start with the basic laws, write the corresponding system equations, derive the control volume integral equations, derive the differential equations, and then present some simplified or working forms of these equations. This is summarized in the following:

Basic Laws	→	System Equations	→	Integral (Control Volume) Equations	or	Differential Equations
1. Continuity		1. $\dfrac{d}{dt}(m) = 0$		1. Eq. (3.1)		1. Eq. (3.25)
2. Momentum (linear)		2. $\dfrac{d}{dt}(m\mathbf{V}) = \mathbf{F}$		2. Eq. (3.9)		2. Eq. (3.32), (3.34), (3.48)
3. Momentum (angular)		3. $\dfrac{d}{dt}(m\mathbf{r} \times \mathbf{V}) = \mathbf{r} \times \mathbf{F}$		3. Eq. (3.11)		3. —
4. Energy		4. $\dfrac{d}{dt}(E) = \dfrac{dQ}{dt} - \dfrac{dW}{dt}$		4. Eq. (3.20)		4. Eq. (3.53), (3.54)
5. Second Law of Thermo- dynamics		5. $dS - \dfrac{dQ}{T} \geqq 0$		5. Eq. (3.23)		5. Eq. (3.58), (3.61)

(*a*) **Integral Equations.** All four integral equations for the control volume have the form

$$\text{External effects} = \frac{\partial}{\partial t}\int_{\text{c.v.}} \xi\rho \, d\mathcal{V} + \int_{\text{c.s.}} \xi\rho\mathbf{V} \cdot d\mathbf{\Lambda} \qquad (3.62)$$

where

Basic Law	External Effects	ξ
Continuity	0	1
Linear Momentum	$\mathbf{F}_S + \displaystyle\int_{\text{c.v.}} \mathbf{B}\, d\mathcal{V}$	$\mathbf{V}$
Angular Momentum	$\displaystyle\int_{\text{c.s.}} \mathbf{r} \times d\mathbf{F}_S + \int_{\text{c.v.}} \mathbf{r} \times \mathbf{B}\, d\mathcal{V}$	$\mathbf{r} \times \mathbf{V}$
Energy	$\dfrac{dQ}{dt} - \dfrac{dW}{dt}$	e

We can readily see the similarities in these equations by summarizing them in this manner. Also, we can look back and observe that the methods of deriving the control volume equations were essentially the same.

(*b*) **Special Forms of Integral Equations**

1. Continuity — one-dimensional steady flow:

$$\rho_1 A_1 V_1 = \rho_2 A_2 V_2 \qquad (3.4)$$

2. Momentum — one-dimensional steady flow with the density and velocity uniform over entrance and exit areas:

$$F_x = \dot{m}(V_{2x} - V_{1x}), \quad F_y = \dot{m}(V_{2y} - V_{1y}), \quad F_z = \dot{m}(V_{2z} - V_{1z})$$

3. Angular momentum — velocity uniform over A_1 and A_2, steady flow through a rotor:

$$T_z = \rho_1 Q_1(r_2 V_{t2} - r_1 V_{t1}) \qquad (3.14)$$

4. Energy — one-dimensional, steady flow:

$$q - w_s = (p_2/\rho_2 - p_1/\rho_1) + (u_2 - u_1) + (V_2^2 - V_1^2)/2 + g(z_2 - z_1) \qquad (3.22a)$$

(c) **Differential Equations**

1. Continuity:

$$\frac{\partial \rho}{\partial t} + \nabla \cdot (\rho \mathbf{V}) = 0 \qquad (3.25)$$

which for incompressible flow is

$$\nabla \cdot \mathbf{V} = 0 \qquad (3.27)$$

2. Momentum:

$$\rho \frac{D\mathbf{V}}{Dt} = -\nabla p + \mathbf{B} - \nabla \times [\mu(\nabla \times \mathbf{V})] + \nabla[(\zeta + \tfrac{4}{3}\mu)\nabla \cdot \mathbf{V}] \qquad (3.48)$$

For constant density and viscosity the momentum equation is

$$\rho \frac{D\mathbf{V}}{Dt} = -\nabla p + \mathbf{B} + \mu \nabla^2 \mathbf{V} \qquad (3.49)$$

3. Energy equation:

$$\rho c_v \frac{DT}{Dt} = -p\nabla \cdot \mathbf{V} + \kappa \nabla^2 T - \nabla \cdot \mathbf{q}_r + \Phi + q''' \qquad (3.53)$$

For more detailed equations in other coordinate systems see the Appendix and reference 5, page 47.

(d) **Approach to Solving Problems.** In this chapter we have developed some of the general and important equations of fluid mechanics. After one has attained an understanding of these equations, the next step is to be able to apply them in solving physical problems. While there is no substitute for experience in working problems, a few general guidelines at this point should be helpful.

Let us consider the possible approaches in dealing with real physical problems. In general, there are three:

1. Integral equations – gross effects
2. Differential equations – distributions
3. Start with basic laws and develop equations appropriate to the particular situation.

The integral equations are usually appropriate when one desires to determine the gross effects, e.g. the total force of a flowing fluid on a pipe wall or a rotor vane. The differential equations are usually appropriate when the distributive conditions are desired, e.g. the velocity and pressure distribution (field) around an aerodynamic body. The possibility of developing the equations from basic laws for any particular problem should never be precluded (but could always be obtained from the basic integral or differential equations under the appropriate assumptions). We will find this method particularly appropriate in the development of the boundary layer equations.

The equations of this chapter are the tools which we will use to solve real physical problems (or perhaps to better understand nature). The starting point is the physical problem. And the solution is never (or rarely) an exact description of the real physical situation, but rather an approximation whose accuracy depends on the accuracy of the mathematical model. For example, the procedure for solution may be outlined as follows:

(1) Specific physical problem.

(2) Physical model representation – we represent the real physical problem with a new but simplified problem. For example, we may assume one-dimensional flow, steady flow, fluid obeys ideal gas equation of state, etc. Thus the assumptions make up the model.

(3) Mathematical model — we set down the equations corresponding to the physical model.

(4) Solution — a solution of the equations is obtained for the desired quantities.

(5) Experiment — the final step is to determine the correctness of the model by experiment. This step is very important in fluid mechanics. Experiment will lead to improvements in the model.

References

1. Bird, R. B., Stewart, W. E. and Lightfoot, E. N., *Transport Phenomena*, John Wiley, 1960.

2. Brenkert, K. Jr., *Elementary Theoretical Fluid Mechanics*, John Wiley, 1960.

3. Chapman, S., and Cowling, T. G., *The Mathematical Theory of Non-Uniform Gases*, Cambridge University Press, 1961.

4. Curtiss, C. F. and Bird, R. B., *Molecular Theory of Gases and Liquids*, John Wiley, 1954.

5. Hughes, W. F. and Gaylord, E. W., *Basic Equations of Engineering Science*, Schaum Publishing Co., 1964.

6. Jones, J. B. and Hawkins, G. A., *Engineering Thermodynamics*, John Wiley, 1960.

7. Keenan, J. H., *Thermodynamics*, John Wiley, 1941.

8. Landau, L. D., and Lifshitz, E. M., *Fluid Mechanics*, Addison-Wesley, 1959.

9. Pai, S. I., *Viscous Flow Theory*, Vols. I and II, Van Nostrand, 1956.

10. Reynolds, W. C., *Thermodynamics*, McGraw-Hill, 1965.

11. Sabersky, R. H., and Acosta, A. J., *Fluid Flow*, Macmillan Co., 1964.

12. Schlichting, H., *Boundary Layer Theory*, McGraw-Hill, 1955.

13. Shames, I. H., *Mechanics of Fluids*, McGraw-Hill, 1962.

14. Sommerfeld, A., *Dynamics of Deformable Media*, Academic Press, 1950.

Solved Problems

3.1. Consider the steady flow of a compressible fluid through a pipe bend as shown in Fig. 3-13. Determine the force of the fluid on the pipe between sections 1 and 2.

Fig. 3-13

First, choose a control volume for the fluid as shown by the dotted line. Equation (*3.9*) for steady flow is

$$\mathbf{F}_s + \int_{\text{C.V.}} \mathbf{B}\, d\mathcal{V} \;=\; \int_{\text{C.S.}} \mathbf{V}\rho \mathbf{V}\cdot d\mathbf{A}$$

It will be assumed that the pressures and velocities are uniform over the areas A_1 and A_2. The surface forces for the x and y directions respectively are

$$F_{sx} \;=\; p_1 A_1 - p_2 A_2 \cos\theta + F_{px}$$
$$F_{sy} \;=\; -p_2 A_2 \sin\theta + F_{py}$$

where p is the pressure and F_{px} and F_{py} are the unknown forces of the pipe wall on the fluid. The only body force is due to gravity and is equal to the weight of the fluid between sections 1 and 2. For many problems the weight is negligible compared to other forces, particularly for gases; it will be neglected here. The momentum flux terms become

$$\int_{\text{C.S.}} V_x \rho \mathbf{V}\cdot d\mathbf{A} \;=\; \rho_2 A_2 V_2^2 \cos\theta - \rho_1 A_1 V_1^2$$

$$\int_{\text{C.S.}} V_y \rho \mathbf{V}\cdot d\mathbf{A} \;=\; \rho_2 A_2 V_2^2 \sin\theta$$

Then the equations become

$$F_{px} \;=\; p_2 A_2 \cos\theta - p_1 A_1 + \rho_2 A_2 V_2^2 \cos\theta - \rho_1 A_1 V_1^2$$
$$F_{py} \;=\; p_2 A_2 \sin\theta + \rho_2 A_2 V_2^2 \sin\theta$$

The components of the force of the fluid on the pipe, say, R_x and R_y, would be opposite F_{px} and F_{py} and therefore we have

$$R_x \;=\; p_1 A_1 - p_2 A_2 \cos\theta + \rho_1 A_1 V_1 (V_1 - V_2 \cos\theta)$$
$$R_y \;=\; -p_2 A_2 \sin\theta - \rho_2 A_2 V_2^2 \sin\theta$$

3.2. Consider the steady flow of a water jet impinging on a stationary vane as shown in Fig. 3-14 below. Determine the force required to hold the vane in place. Assuming the jet follows the surface of the vane in a smooth manner and has the same shape and area at the exit, then the momentum equation can be written for the control volume shown in Fig. 3-14.

The jet will be exposed to atmospheric pressure over the entire surface plus an additional force where the jet makes contact with the vane. This additional force is precisely the force required to turn the fluid jet. The atmospheric pressure on the jet side will be canceled by the atmospheric pressure on the opposite side. Thus we have

$$F_x \;=\; \rho A V^2 \cos \theta \,-\, \rho A V^2, \qquad F_y \;=\; \rho A V^2 \sin \theta$$

which is also equal to the force required to hold the vane in place.

Fig. 3-14   Fig. 3-15

3.3. In Problem 3.2 consider that the vane moves in the positive x direction at some velocity V_v which is less than the jet velocity V_j. Fig. 3-15 shows the moving vane. Find the force necessary to keep the vane moving at constant velocity, that is, to prevent it from accelerating.

We must write the momentum equation in a frame of reference at rest with respect to the vane. Thus all velocities must be the velocities relative to the vane. The velocity of the fluid relative to the vane entering the control volume is $V_j - V_v$, and if we neglect friction of the vane Bernoulli's equation tells us that the velocity leaving relative to the vane is the same, $V_j - V_v$ at the angle θ. Since the velocity is the same, the cross sectional area of flow A must be the same. The momentum equation gives

$$F_x \;=\; \rho A (V_j - V_v)^2 \cos \theta \,-\, \rho A (V_j - V_v)^2, \qquad F_y \;=\; \rho A (V_j - V_v)^2 \sin \theta$$

which gives the net force required to keep the vane from accelerating. Since the vane is in equilibrium, the force of the fluid on the vane must be $-F_x$ and $-F_y$ and hence the reaction force of the vane on the fluid is simply F_x and F_y.

Alternatively, we could have taken the control surface just on the inner surface of the vane so that it included only fluid. Then the analysis is exactly the same but we get immediately that the force on the fluid (exerted by the vane) is F_x and F_y.

3.4. A vane shown in Fig. 3-16 moves at a constant velocity $u = 30$ fps and receives a jet of water which leaves a nozzle at a velocity $V = 100$ fps. The nozzle has an exit area of 0.04 ft². Find the total force on the moving vane.

Fig. 3-16   Fig. 3-17

Take the control volume around the vane as shown in Fig. 3-17. The velocities relative to the control volume are $V - u = 100 - 30 = 70$ fps in the x direction entering and $V - u = 70$ fps leaving in the direction shown. Thus the force on the fluid is determined from the steady flow momentum equation. For the x direction we have

$$F_x \;=\; \dot{m}(V_{2x} - V_{1x})$$

where the mass flow rate, $\dot{m}$, relative to the control surface is $\dot{m} = \rho A (V - u) = \rho A (100 - 30)$. The x components of velocities entering and leaving relative to the control volume are $V_{1x} = V - u$ and $V_{2x} = -(V - u) \cos 60°$. Substituting into the momentum equation,

$$F_x = \rho A(V - u)\{-(V - u)\cos 60° - (V - u)\}$$
$$= -\rho A(V - u)^2\{\cos 60° + 1\} = -(62.4/32.2)(0.04)(100 - 30)^2(\cos 60° + 1) = -569 \text{ lb}_f \text{ on fluid}$$

or $F_x = 569$ lb$_f$ on vane.

For the y direction we have $\qquad F_y = \dot{m}(V_{2y} - V_{1y})$

The velocities entering and leaving in the y direction are $V_{1y} = 0$ and $V_{2y} = (V - u)\sin 60°$. Substituting into the momentum equation,

$$F_y = \rho A(V - u)\{(V - u)\sin 60° - 0\}$$
$$= \rho A(V - u)^2 \sin 60° = (62.4/32.2)(100 - 30)^2 \sin 60° = 329 \text{ lb}_f \text{ on fluid}$$

or $F_y = -329$ lb$_f$ on vane.

The magnitude of the force on the vane is

$$|\mathbf{F}| = \{F_x^2 + F_y^2\}^{1/2}$$
$$= [(569)^2 + (-329)^2]^{1/2} = 658 \text{ lb}_f$$

The direction of the force is $\tan\theta = -329/569 = -0.578$ or $\theta = -30°$, the negative sign indicating that the force acts downward. Finally, the forces on the vane are as shown in Fig. 3-18.

Fig. 3-18

3.5. A water jet having a velocity of 100 fps strikes a vane moving at a velocity of 40 fps as shown in Fig. 3-19. Determine (a) the power transmitted to the vane and (b) the absolute velocity of the jet leaving the vane.

Fig. 3-19

Fig. 3-20

(a) The power transmitted to the vane is equal to the product of force in the direction of motion of the vane and the velocity of the vane. Thus,

$$\text{Power} = F_x V_v$$

The force of the fluid on the vane may be determined from the momentum equation for a control volume that moves at a velocity equal to that of the vane as shown in Fig. 3-20.

The momentum equation for the control volume is

$$F_x = \dot{m}(V_{2x} - V_{1x}) \text{ on fluid}$$

F_x here is also the force exerted on the vane by the external mounting as was explained in Problem 3.3. The mass flow rate relative to the control surface is $\dot{m} = \rho A(V - V_v)$. The velocities for the x direction entering and leaving the control volume are $V_{1x} = V - V_v$ and $V_{2x} = (V - V_v)\cos 60°$. Substituting,

$$F_x = \rho A(V - V_v)\{(V - V_v)\cos 60° - (V - V_v)\} = \rho A(V - V_v)^2\{\cos 60° - 1\}$$
$$= (62.4/32.2)(100/12 - 40/12)^2(\cos 60° - 1) = -6.48 \text{ lb}_f \text{ on fluid}$$

or $F_x = 6.48$ lb$_f$ on vane. Thus the power $= 6.48(40) = 259$ ft-lb$_f$/sec $= 0.472$ horsepower.

(b) The velocity leaving the vane may be found by adding the velocity of the fluid relative to the vane to the velocity of the vane. Thus the absolute velocity of the fluid leaving the vane in the x direction is

$$V_{2x} = V_{x\text{ relative}} + V_v = (100 - 40)\cos 60° + 40 = 70 \text{ fps}$$

The velocity of the fluid leaving the vane in the y direction is

$$V_{2y} = (100 - 40) \sin 60° = 51.9 \text{ fps}$$

The absolute velocity of the fluid leaving the vane is

$$|\mathbf{V}_2| = (V_{2x}^2 + V_{2y}^2)^{1/2}$$

$$= [(70)^2 + (51.9)^2]^{1/2} = 87.2 \text{ fps}$$

The direction of fluid leaving the vane is given by $\tan \theta = 51.9/70 = 0.741$ or $\theta = 36.6°$. The velocity vector diagram for the fluid leaving the vane is shown in Fig. 3-21.

$\mathbf{V} = 87.2$ fps　$V_{2y} = 51.9$ fps　$36.6°$　$V_v = 40$ fps　$V_{2x \text{ relative}} = 30$ fps

Fig. 3-21

3.6.　Determine the force of the water jet on the inclined plate as a function of the angle θ as shown in Fig. 3-22.

$V_j = 100$ fps　$A_1 = 1.0 \text{ in}^2$　θ　Plate

Fig. 3-22

Control surface　2　V_2　y　x　1　V_1　3　V_3

Fig. 3-23

Consider the control volume as shown in Fig. 3-23 where the fluid is entering at section 1 and leaving at sections 2 and 3. The mass flow rate of the fluid entering the control volume is equal to the mass flow rate of the fluid leaving the control volume, giving

$$\rho A_1 V_j = \rho A_2 V_2 + \rho A_3 V_3 \quad \text{or} \quad A_1 V_j = A_2 V_2 + A_3 V_3$$

Next we write Bernoulli's equation along a streamline between sections 1 and 2 and between sections 1 and 3, yielding

$$p_1/\rho + \tfrac{1}{2}V_j^2 = p_2/\rho + \tfrac{1}{2}V_2^2$$

and

$$p_1/\rho + \tfrac{1}{2}V_j^2 = p_3/\rho + \tfrac{1}{2}V_3^2$$

where all elevation changes have been neglected. If it is assumed that the pressures at sections 1, 2 and 3 are all equal to atmospheric pressure, then Bernoulli's equation gives $V_j = V_2 = V_3$. Using the result that the velocities are equal, we have from the continuity equation $A_1 = A_2 + A_3$.

Now we write the steady flow momentum equation in the x direction along the plate neglecting any shear stress where the fluid comes in contact with the plate. Referring to Fig. 3-24 we have for F_x, the force of the plate on the fluid,

$$F_x = 0 = \rho A_2 V_2^2 - \rho A_3 V_3^2 - \rho A_1 V_j^2 \cos \theta$$

V_2　y　x　θ　$V_j \sin \theta$　θ　V_j　V_3

Fig. 3-24

which simplifies to $A_1 \cos \theta = A_2 - A_3$. Now adding this equation to the expression obtained from continuity, we obtain

$$A_2 = \tfrac{1}{2}(1 + \cos \theta)A_1 \quad \text{and} \quad A_3 = \tfrac{1}{2}(1 - \cos \theta)A_1$$

Next, we write the momentum equation in the y direction normal to the plate. We have for F_y, the y component of the force of the plate on the fluid,

$$F_y = \rho A_1 V_j^2 \sin \theta$$

which for the numbers given becomes

$$F_y = (62.4/32.2)(1.0/144)(100)^2 \sin \theta = 135 \sin \theta \text{ lb}_f$$

3.7. A converging two-dimensional channel shown in Fig. 3-25 has a linear area variation. The flow rate of an incompressible fluid is constant at $Q = 10$ ft³ per sec per unit width of the channel. What is the acceleration as a function of the distance x? What is the acceleration at a point 1 ft from the beginning of the converging section?

Fig. 3-25

We assume the flow to be quasi-one-dimensional and neglect variations across the channel. Then, from continuity, the flow rate Q is given by

$$Q = uA = u(2 - x/5)$$

where u, the velocity in the channel, is a function of x given by the above equation since Q is a constant. Then the acceleration is given by

$$a_x = \frac{\partial u}{\partial t} + u \frac{\partial u}{\partial x}$$

but since the flow is steady, $\partial u/\partial t = 0$, and by differentiating the expression for u we can find $\partial u/\partial x$ which is simply du/dx since u depends only on x. We obtain

$$a_x = u \frac{du}{dx} = \left(\frac{5Q}{10 - x}\right)\left[\frac{5Q}{(10 - x)^2}\right] = \frac{(5 \times 10)^2}{(10 - x)^3} = \frac{2500}{(10 - x)^3} \text{ ft/sec}^2$$

where x is measured in feet. At $x = 1$ ft, $a_x = 3.43$ ft/sec².

3.8. In the preceding problem, suppose the flow is unsteady and increasing at a rate of 2 ft³ per sec² (per unit width of the channel). What is the acceleration now at the instant when $Q = 10$ ft³ per sec per ft of channel width?

The acceleration is given by $a_x = \partial u/\partial t + u\,\partial u/\partial x$, and $u\,\partial u/\partial x$ is the same as in the preceding problem. But now $\partial u/\partial t$ is not zero. We find it as

$$\frac{\partial Q}{\partial t} = \frac{\partial u}{\partial t}(2 - x/5) = 2 \text{ ft}^3/\text{sec}^2/\text{ft}$$

Hence $\partial u/\partial t = 10/(10 - x)$ ft/sec², which is 1.11 ft/sec² at $x = 1$ ft. Then the value of a_x is found by adding $\partial u/\partial t$ and $u\,\partial u/\partial x$ to give $1.11 + 3.43 = 4.54$ ft/sec² as the acceleration at the station $x = 1$ ft.

3.9.   A jet engine shown in Fig. 3-26 is being tested statically on a test stand. The inlet velocity is 500 fps and the exhaust gases leave at a velocity of 3500 fps. The air at the inlet and the exhaust gases at the exit are at atmospheric pressure. The fuel-to-air ratio is 1/50 and the inlet and exhaust areas are both 2 ft². The density of air entering is 0.0024 slugs/ft³. Determine the force T_x required to hold the jet engine stationary.

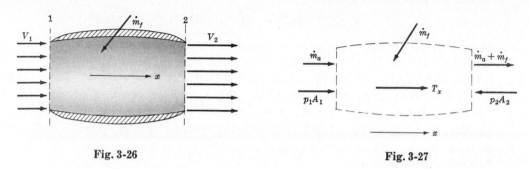

Fig. 3-26   Fig. 3-27

Consider a control volume around the fluid inside the engine between sections 1 and 2 as indicated in Fig. 3-27. The steady flow momentum equation is

$$F_x = (\dot{m}_a + \dot{m}_f)V_{2x} - \dot{m}_a V_{1x}$$

where F_x is the total external force acting on the engine and includes the pressure forces and the mounting stand reaction T_x. $\dot{m}_a$ is the mass flow rate of air and $\dot{m}_f$ is the mass flow rate of fuel. By continuity, $\dot{m}_a$ must be the same at the inlet and outlet. We will assume that the fuel has negligible momentum in the x direction when it enters the engine. Then we can write

$$p_1 A_1 - p_2 A_2 + T_x = (\dot{m}_a + \dot{m}_f)V_{2x} - \dot{m}_a V_{1x}$$

But since the inlet and outlet areas are the same and we assume p_1 and p_2 are both atmospheric, we have

$$T_x = (\dot{m}_f + \dot{m}_a)V_{2x} - \dot{m}_a V_{1x} = (\dot{m}_f/\dot{m}_a + 1)\dot{m}_a V_{2x} - \dot{m}_a V_{1x}$$

Assuming the inlet air to be at standard conditions with $\rho_1 = 0.0024$ slugs/ft³, the air mass flow rate is $\dot{m}_a = \rho_1 A_1 V_1 = (0.0024)(2)(500) = 2.40$ slugs/sec. Then we have for T_x,

$$T_x = (1/50 + 1)(2.40)(3500) - (2.40)(500) = 7300 \text{ lb}_f$$

The static thrust on the engine would be equal and opposite in direction to T_x.

3.10.   Consider a three-stage rocket for space exploration. The first two stages will carry the third stage rocket to such a distance from the earth for launching that gravitational attraction will be negligible during its travel. Frictional resistance will be negligible also. This third stage rocket will be launched from the second stage rocket just as the second stage rocket attains its maximum height, at which time, of course, its velocity with respect to the earth will be zero. The engine of the final rocket is so designed that the velocity of the exhaust jet with respect to the rocket is maintained at a constant value of V_0 ft/sec. What is the final velocity of the third stage rocket in terms of relevant parameters?

In Fig. 3-28 consider a control volume in the shape of a cylinder which extends from the earth out far beyond the third stage rocket. The control volume will contain the third stage rocket, its fuel, and all the material exhausted from the third stage rocket. Then the momentum of the rocket plus fuel plus

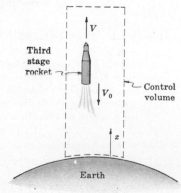

Fig. 3-28

all exhausted material remains constant. The control volume has no external force acting on it. Hence, if M = mass of third stage rocket, m = instantaneous mass of fuel in the rocket, the mass of fuel in the rocket is changing at a rate dm/dt which is a negative number since m is decreasing. If V is the velocity of the rocket, then the z component of momentum of the rocket plus fuel in the rocket at time t is $(M+m)V$ and the z component of momentum of the exhausted fuel is $\int_0^t -\dfrac{dm}{dt}(V-V_0)\,dt$, so that the momentum balance becomes

$$0 = \frac{d}{dt}[(M+m)V] - \frac{dm}{dt}(V-V_0) = (M+m)\frac{dV}{dt} + V_0\frac{dm}{dt}$$

where V is the absolute velocity of the rocket in the z direction. But $m = m_0 + (dm/dt)t$ where m_0 is the original mass of fuel at time $t = 0$ when the third stage is fired, and dm/dt is assumed a constant which we write simply as $\dot{m}$. Hence we have

$$0 = (M + m_0 + \dot{m}t)\frac{dV}{dt} + V_0\dot{m}$$

which can be integrated from $V = 0$ at $t = 0$ to $V = V_f$ when the fuel is exhausted and $m = 0$. V_f is the final velocity of the third stage rocket. The fuel is finally consumed at time $t = m_0/(-\dot{m})$. Remember $\dot{m}$ is negative.

$$\int_0^{V_f} dV = -\int_0^{-m_0/\dot{m}} \frac{V_0\dot{m}}{M + m_0 + \dot{m}t}\,dt \quad \text{and} \quad V_f = V_0 \ln\frac{M+m_0}{M}$$

3.11. A simplified two-dimensional boundary layer of water over one side of a flat plate is shown in Fig. 3-29. At the leading edge the velocity is uniform and equal to U. Downstream at the trailing edge the velocity profile is as shown. Find the shear force of the fluid on the plate by using an overall control volume approach.

Fig. 3-29

We choose a rectangular control volume as shown. We write

$$\mathbf{F} = \int_{\text{C.S.}} (\rho\mathbf{V})\mathbf{V}\cdot d\mathbf{A}$$

where $\mathbf{F}$ is the total force on the fluid. But we assume the pressure to be uniform throughout the flow and if we write the momentum equation in a direction parallel to the plate (x direction), F_x is the shear force exerted by the plate on the fluid. Across the surface 2-3 fluid flows with a small velocity normal to the plate and with a component parallel to the plate of nearly U. Hence F_x per unit width of the plate is

$$F_x = \underbrace{-\rho U^2 h}_{1\text{-}2} + \underbrace{\int_0^h (\rho U^2 y^2/h^2)\,dy}_{3\text{-}4} + \underbrace{\dot{m}U}_{2\text{-}3}$$

where $\dot{m}$ is the mass flow rate per unit width through surface 2-3 and is given by $\dot{m} = \rho U h - \rho U h/2 = \rho U h/2$. Hence

$$F_x = -\rho U^2 h + \rho U^2 h/3 + \rho U^2 h/2 = -\rho U^2 h/6$$

The fact that F_x is negative indicates that it is a retarding force on the fluid (acting in the negative x direction). The force of the fluid on the plate is equal and opposite to F_x.

3.12. A centrifugal pump shown in Fig. 3-30 pumps water at a rate of 1.0 ft³/sec. The water enters the impeller in an axial direction. The diameter of the impeller is 10 in. and the vanes are 1.0 in. high and radial at the outside diameter. Determine the power input to the rotor which turns at 1000 rpm.

Fig. 3-30

The power input is the product of the torque T of the shaft on the rotor and the angular velocity ω of the rotor. Power $= T\omega$. The angular velocity is given and the torque can be determined from the angular momentum equation for steady flow. We have for the torque about the axis of rotation,

$$T_z = \int_{C.S.} (\mathbf{r} \times \mathbf{V})_z \, \rho \mathbf{V} \cdot d\mathbf{A}$$

where the control surface is taken around the impeller as shown in Fig. 3-31 so that the torque appearing in the equation is the torque exerted on the rotor by the drive shaft. Assuming the velocities are uniform over the inlet and outlet surfaces, we have

$$T_z = \rho_1 Q_1 (r_2 V_{t2} - r_1 V_{t1})$$

where $\rho_1 Q_1 = \dot{m}$ is the mass rate of flow. Since the flow at the impeller inlet is in the axial direction, the tangential component of velocity there, V_{t1}, is zero. We need only, then, to determine the

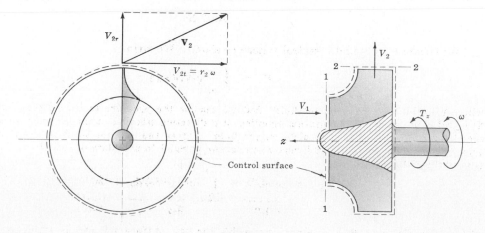

Fig. 3-31

tangential component of velocity at the exit. Assuming there is no slippage at the impeller exit, that is, the fluid follows exactly the contour of the vanes, then the tangential velocity at the exit is $V_{t2} = r_2\omega = (10/12)(1000 \times 2\pi/60) = 87.3$ ft/sec and the torque is $T_z = (62.4/32.2)(1.0)(10/12)(87.3) = 141$ lb$_f$-ft. The power required $= 141(1000 \times 2\pi/60) = 14,800$ ft-lb$_f$/sec or 27 horsepower.

3.13. Water flows horizontally out of a pipe through a 1/8 in. slit as shown in Fig. 3-32. The total flow rate is 1 ft³/sec and the velocity varies linearly from a maximum at one end of the slit to zero at the other end. Determine the moment about the axis of the connecting vertical pipe resulting from the flow out of the slit.

First determine an expression for the velocity distribution. Let u_{max} be the maximum velocity at the inlet as shown in Fig. 3-32. Then we have

$$u = u_{max}(1 - x/6)$$

along the pipe. The value of u_{max} can be determined from the continuity equation. The total flow rate Q is given by

$$Q = \int_A u\,dA = \int_0^6 u_{max}(1 - x/6)(\tfrac{1}{8}/12)\,dx = 1$$

Fig. 3-32

and $u_{max} = 32$ ft/sec. Next the reaction moment of the connecting pipe on the horizontal pipe can be determined by considering the control volume as shown in Fig. 3-33. Since $\mathbf{r}$ is perpendicular to $\mathbf{V}$ and $d\mathbf{A}$ is parallel to $\mathbf{V}$ we have, where M is the moment exerted by the connecting pipe,

$$M = \int_{C.S.} (\mathbf{r} \times \mathbf{V})\rho\mathbf{V} \cdot d\mathbf{A} = \int_{C.S.} (ru)\rho u\,dA$$

and since $r = 2 + x$ and $u = 32(1 - x/6)$, we have

$$M = (32)^2\rho \int_0^6 (2 + x)(1 - x/6)^2(\tfrac{1}{8}/12)\,dx$$

which, when evaluated with $\rho = 62.4/32.2$ slugs/ft³, gives $M = 145$ lb$_f$-ft. This is the moment about the axis of the connecting pipe, which would be important in determining stresses in the pipe. The sign of the moment is positive as shown in Fig. 3-33. The moment exerted on the vertical connecting pipe by the horizontal pipe is equal and opposite in sign to M.

Fig. 3-33

Supplementary Problems

3.14. One method of producing a vacuum is to discharge water through a venturi, and connect the system to be evacuated with the throat of the venturi as shown in Fig. 3-34. How much water must discharge through the venturi tube to produce a vacuum of 20 inches of mercury?

Fig. 3-34　　　　　　　　　　　　　　　　　　**Fig. 3-35**

3.15. A circular pipe of radius a ft and length L ft is attached to a smoothly rounded outlet of a liquid reservoir by means of flanges and bolts as shown in Fig. 3-35. At the flange section the velocity is uniform over the cross section with magnitude V_0. At the outlet, which discharges into the atmosphere, the velocity profile is parabolic because of the friction in the pipe. What force must be supplied by the bolts to hold the pipe in place?

3.16. In the previous problem find the upstream pressure at the flange if the shear stress (due to viscous friction) on the wall is τ_0 lb/in².

3.17. Determine the force of the water jet on the inclined plate of Problem 3.6 if the plate is moving at a velocity V_p (which is less than the jet velocity) in the same direction as the water jet.

3.18. A ship is propelled at a constant speed of 25 mph by hydraulic jet propulsion. The total drag force is 3000 lb. The diameter of the jet exit section of the exhaust nozzle is 2 ft. Calculate the absolute velocity of the jet.

3.19. The water jet pump of Fig. 3-36 has a jet area $A_j = 0.05$ ft² and a jet velocity $V_j = 90$ ft/sec which entrains a secondary stream of water having a velocity $V_s = 10$ ft/sec in a constant area pipe of total area $A = 0.6$ ft². At section 2 the water is thoroughly mixed in such a way that the velocity is uniform. Neglect wall shear. Determine the pressure at section 2. The pressure at the nozzle is 10 psi.

Fig. 3-36

3.20. A fluid is flowing steadily in a circular pipe. The velocity profile is parabolic in shape, being zero at the pipe wall and increasing to a maximum velocity V_c along the centerline of the pipe. Radial and circumferential components of velocity are zero.

(1) In terms of V_c and other appropriate quantities, find expressions for

     (a) quantity of fluid flowing

     (b) axial momentum of the fluid

     (c) kinetic energy of the fluid

as the flow passes through any given cross-section of the pipe.

(2) For a constant density fluid, find the error (percent) involved in using the expressions

     (a) $\rho A V^2$ for momentum

     (b) $\rho A V^3/2$ for kinetic energy

where ρ is the fluid density, A is the cross-sectional area of the pipe, and V is the mass rate of flow divided by the product ρA.

The velocity profile is given by the equation $u = V_c [1 - (r/R)^2]$ where R is the radius of the pipe.

3.21. Water enters a pipe from a large reservoir and on issuing out of the pipe strikes a 90° deflector plate as shown in Fig. 3-37. If a horizontal thrust of 200 lb is developed on the deflector, what is the horsepower developed by the turbine?

Fig. 3-37   Fig. 3-38

3.22. Water flows steadily up the vertical pipe and enters the annular region between the circular plates as shown in Fig. 3-38. It then moves out radially, issuing out as a free sheet of water. (a) If we neglect friction entirely, what is the flow of water through the pipe if the pressure at A is 24.7 psi? (b) Determine the force in the pipe wall at section A. Neglect the weight of the pipe.

3.23. A vehicle is moving at a velocity $V = 100$ ft/sec along level ground under the action of a constant force $F = 1000$ lb. At time $t = 0$, mass begins leaving the vehicle through a hole in the bottom. Assuming the mass leaves the vehicle vertically at a rate of 10 lb/sec and the vehicle continues to move under the action of the constant force F, determine the velocity of the vehicle after 20 sec. Initial mass of the vehicle is 2000 lb.

3.24. A container for water in the form of a wagon (Fig. 3-39) is being driven along a frictionless, level tract by a jet of water. The jet of water has a horizontal velocity of 30 ft/sec and the cross-sectional area of the jet is 2 in². The jet of water overtakes the wagon, hits the far end of it, and is deflected

Fig. 3-39

down into the body of the wagon. No water is spilled; all of it falls down into the wagon. At time zero, the wagon has a velocity of 10 ft/sec and the mass of the wagon and the water which is in it at that instant is 100 lb. Calculate the time required for the wagon to accelerate from a velocity of 10 ft/sec to a velocity of 20 ft/sec. Assume that the jet of water follows the wagon and falls into it during all this time.

3.25.   Work Problem 5.22, page 100, using the basic principles outlined in Chapter 3.

3.26.   When water is flowing steadily through the turbine sketched in Fig. 3-40, the turbine delivers 75 horsepower. The water flow rate is 1200 lb/sec.

    The inlet pipe to the turbine is 12 in. inside diameter and the discharge pipe is 16 in. inside diameter. The rest of the piping system is not shown and the inlet and outlet pressures are not known. The change in elevation of the piping shown is not known.

    A manometer connected across the inlet and outlet, as shown in the sketch, contains mercury. Calculate the difference in height, h, between the mercury columns under steady flow conditions and state whether the right leg or left leg of mercury is higher.

Fig. 3-40   Fig. 3-41

3.27.   A pipe has a contraction as shown in Fig. 3-41. At a certain time the velocity of water entering, V_1, is 30 ft/sec and is changing at a rate of 2 ft/sec². Determine the pressure gradient (dp/dx) at $x = 1$ ft at the time when $V_1 = 30$ ft/sec, assuming the velocity is uniform over any cross-section.

3.28.   Derive the momentum equation (in terms of stresses) in cylindrical coordinates by applying the integral form to the appropriate elemental volume.

3.29.   Repeat Problem 3.28 for spherical coordinates.

3.30.   Go through the details of the derivation of the forms of the energy equation.

3.31.   In Problem 3.8 find the acceleration if the flow rate is decreasing instead of increasing (at the rate given).

3.32.   A cylinder with a closed top has a tube, exposed to atmospheric pressure, extending some distance into the incompressible fluid within the tank of Fig. 3-42. The fluid discharges from a nozzle of area A_2 a distance h_1 from the bottom of the tube. If the cross-sectional area of the cylinder is A_1, find the flow rate Q as a function of time.

3.33.   Rework Problem 3.11 by choosing a control volume such that the upper surface lies on a streamline.

Fig. 3-42

3.34.   A cylinder is placed in a uniform flow of incompressible fluid of density ρ (Fig. 3-43). Velocity profiles are measured upstream and downstream as shown. Find the drag force on the cylinder per unit length. *Hint.* Take a large control volume about the cylinder.

Downstream a distance of 10 diameters, the velocity data is:

y/D	u/U
0	0.5
0.5	0.6
1.0	0.8
1.5	0.9
2.0	1.0

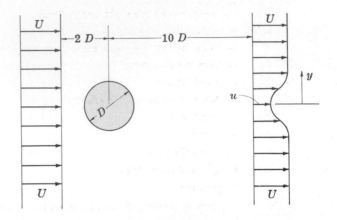

Fig. 3-43

3.35.   A connecting rod bearing is to be lubricated by feeding oil of specific gravity 0.8 into the center of the crankshaft at atmospheric pressure. From there, the oil flows through a small drilled passage to the connecting rod bearing. At what minimum rpm of the crankshaft will there be positive oil pressure at the connecting rod bearing when the crank arm is in a vertical position as shown in Fig. 3-44?

Fig. 3-44

Fig. 3-45

3.36.   A water pump shown in Fig. 3-45 pumps water from a reservoir up to a height H. The motion of the pump piston is sinusoidal. At very high piston velocities it is found in practice that the water cavitates in front of the piston, allowing the water to drop back to the reservoir. This is undesirable and requires the pump to be primed in order to get it going again.

Find the maximum frequency of the piston such that the cavitation does not occur when the piston is at bottom dead center. Cavitation is defined as the condition when the pressure in the fluid drops to zero absolute, or at least tends to this value.

This maximum frequency you find then will be a limiting value, and if it is surpassed the pressure on the face of the piston tries to drop below zero absolute; the result is cavitation and separation of the fluid.

NOMENCLATURE FOR CHAPTER 3

A = area

a   = acceleration vector

B   = body force vector per unit volume

D/Dt = substantial derivative

e = total energy per unit mass ($e = u + V^2/2 + gz$)

e_{ij} = strain rate tensor

E = total energy

g = local acceleration of gravity

H_L = head loss

m = mass

$\dot{m}$ = mass flux

M   = momentum vector

p = pressure

q = heat transfer per unit mass of flowing fluid

q   = heat flux vector, (directed rate of heat transfer per unit area)

q$_r$ = radiation heat flux vector

q''' = internal heat generation rate per unit volume

Q = total heat transferred to system; volumetric flow rate

r = radial coordinate

s = entropy per unit mass

S = entropy of system

t = time

T = absolute temperature

T_z = torque about z axis

u = velocity in x direction, internal energy per unit mass

u_i = velocity in x_i direction ($i = 1, 2, 3$)

U = internal energy for system, velocity of a free stream

v = velocity in y direction

V   = velocity vector

V_t = tangential velocity

$\mathcal{V}$ = volume

w = velocity in z direction

W = work done by system

w = work done by a unit mass of flowing fluid

x_i = coordinates (x_1, x_2, x_3)

x, y, z = coordinates — correspond to (x_1, x_2, x_3)

α = angle between normal to surface and velocity vector

δ_{ij} = Kronecker delta, $\delta_{ij} = \begin{Bmatrix} 1; & i = j \\ 0; & i \neq j \end{Bmatrix}$

θ = entropy production rate per unit volume

κ = thermal conductivity

μ = viscosity

ν = kinematic viscosity

ρ = density

σ_{ij} = stress tensor, σ'_{ij} = shear part of stress tensor

Φ = dissipation function

ω_{ij} = rotation tensor

Chapter 4

Dimensional Analysis and Similitude

4.1 SIMILITUDE IN FLUID DYNAMICS

In fluid mechanics a great many important results may be obtained from dimensional arguments. The relevant parameters in any physical situation may be combined into independent dimensionless groups which characterize the flow. These dimensionless parameters are often precisely defined and given names in fluid dynamics.

These dimensionless parameters, or Π's as they are called, may be obtained by the method of dimensional analysis or directly from the governing differential equations as a consequence of their being put into dimensionless form.

Consider any fluid flow problem; for example, the flow over a solid object. The flow pattern and properties are determined by the geometrical shape of the object and the relevant fluid properties. We say that two flows are similar if they are geometrically similar and if all the relevant dimensionless parameters are the same for both flows. Consider a model (as in a wind tunnel) and a prototype. How do we relate measurements made on the model to the prototype? The answer is: by the methods of similitude, that is, by making the geometry similar and the Π's the same for both.

The meaning of similar flow and model-prototype correlation can be understood by considering the dimensionless form of the governing equations. Clearly, if all the relevant differential equations are made dimensionless, the size of the object is irrelevant if the shape is geometrically similar. However, the dimensionless parameters (which appear as dimensionless coefficients in the dimensionless differential equations) must be made the same for both flows. These parameters depend on the fluid properties and a characteristic physical dimension (used as a reference base) of the object. Hence in similar flows the describing differential equations are identical for the model and prototype. Measurements might then be made of any dimensionless variable, say, dimensionless pressure, on the model. The appropriate dimensionless pressure for the model would have the same value as for the prototype and by converting back to dimensional form, data taken on the model can be directly related to the prototype.

In summary, two flows are similar if the dimensionless parameters and variables are all the same regardless of the size of the flow pattern, if geometrical similarity is maintained.

In practice, it is not always possible to make all the dimensionless parameters the same, at the same time, for model and prototype. In such cases some compromise must be made; however, in most important flows sufficient similarity may be achieved to make the method useful. Often, only certain of the dimensionless parameters are important for a given flow, and the fact that all the parameters cannot be made the same does not matter.

We will, in the next section, examine the basic differential equations of fluid mechanics and see what the dimensionless differential equations look like. But first, there is another method used to find the dimensionless parameters for any given problem: dimensional analysis.

Dimensional analysis, or the Buckingham Pi Theorem as it is called, is a method of finding the relevant dimensionless parameters without knowing the relevant differential equations. This method requires that one know all the relevant variables in any given problem. Then these variables are combined together in as many independent dimensionless groups or Π's as possible. A systematic method of obtaining these Π's is given in Problem 4.8, page 70. The advantage of this system is that one need not know the governing equations or laws for complex problems, but then one must know all the variables and only those relevant variables must be introduced into the problem. Any extraneous variables or the omission of one relevant one will destroy the analysis. These restrictions are rather severe and it is usually safer to begin with the governing equations. At any rate, once these parameters are found, experimental data can be obtained and correlated in dimensionless form.

The number of Π's for a given problem is fixed and is usually, but not always, equal to the total number of variables minus the number of fundamental dimensions. In mechanics there are three fundamental dimensions which are independent. The actual choice is arbitrary, but the three most commonly chosen ones are mass, length and time, and in compressible flow the temperature enters so that there are four fundamental dimensions.

A basic set of Π's must be chosen so that they are independent. Actually, many Π's may be formed by multiplying or dividing other Π's, but the number of independent Π's for a given problem is fixed. Hence there is not a unique set of Π's for a problem; but in fluid mechanics there are certain dimensionless parameters which are customarily studied and have physical significance.

After a set of Π's is found they can be expressed in functional form, that is, any one Π can be written as a function of all the other Π's. This functional form cannot be found by dimensional analysis, but only by either solving the governing equations or by experimentation. In experimental work it is very convenient to express the results in dimensionless form as plots of Π's. Hence correlations among Π's may be determined. Aside from removing the scale of the experiment as a parameter, the dimensionless form reduces the number of variables by at least three. Dimensional analysis is a vital tool in all engineering and scientific experimentation.

4.2 PARAMETERS OF INCOMPRESSIBLE FLOW

In incompressible flow only the equations of motion and continuity are necessary to describe the flow. There are four dependent variables, the three velocity components and the pressure, which appear in four equations. In addition, there are the fluid properties, viscosity and density, and the gravitational potential which enter into the Π formulation.

If we introduce the following dimensionless variables, independent and dependent, (denoted by asterisks), the equations may be written in dimensionless or normalized form. Let

$$p^* = p/\rho V_0^2, \quad \mathbf{V}^* = \mathbf{V}/V_0, \quad t^* = t/t_0 = tV_0/L, \quad \mathbf{r}^* = \mathbf{r}/L, \quad \psi^* = \psi/gL \qquad (4.1)$$

where the subscript zero indicates a characteristic value and L is a characteristic dimension. For example, if we were to consider the external flow over a cylinder, L could be the diameter and V_0 the free stream velocity. ψ is the gravitational potential. In terms of these variables the equation of motion in vector form is

$$\frac{\partial \mathbf{V}^*}{\partial t^*} + \nabla^*(V^{*2}/2) - \mathbf{V}^* \times (\nabla \times \mathbf{V}^*) = -\nabla^* p^* + \frac{1}{N_R} \nabla^{*2} \mathbf{V}^* - \frac{1}{F_r} \nabla^* \psi^* \qquad (4.2)$$

and continuity is

$$\nabla^* \cdot \mathbf{V}^* = 0 \qquad (4.3)$$

Here N_R is the Reynolds number $\rho L V_0/\mu$ and F_r is the Froude number V_0^2/gL, where ρ is the mass density and μ is the absolute or dynamic viscosity. Both numbers are dimensionless and represent the two parameters which must be set equal in order to achieve similarity.

The total number of relevant Π's for a given geometry would be the two numbers N_R and F_r, the dimensionless independent variables r^* and t^* (if the problem is time independent) and one dependent dimensionless variable such as p^* or $\mathbf{V}^*$. The total number of variables and parameters is ten (including the components of $\mathbf{r}$ and $\mathbf{V}$ and the gravitational potential and the viscosity) so that the total number of independent Π's would be seven. Such is the case. N_R and F_r together with t^*, the three components of $\mathbf{r}^*$, and one other dimensionless dependent variable such as p^* or one component of $\mathbf{V}^*$ make seven. Once all these seven Π's are specified the others follow from the equations since the other Π's are not independent.

Now equations (4.2) and (4.3) are entirely dimensionless so that flow over objects of different sizes which are geometrically similar should have the same solutions in terms of these dimensionless variables if the two characteristic parameters of the fluid, the Reynolds number N_R and the Froude number F_r, are the same.

These numbers have physical significance. The Reynolds number is a measure of the ratio of the inertia to viscous force. When the Reynolds number is small, $N_R \ll 1$, the viscous forces dominate and when $N_R \gg 1$ the inertia forces dominate. The Froude number F_r is a measure of the ratio of inertia to the gravity force. By examining equation (4.2) we see that when both N_R and F_r are $\gg 1$ the inertia must be balanced by the pressure forces.

In a large class of flows the Froude number is rather large and gravity is unimportant and only the Reynolds number becomes of interest in modeling. One exception is in marine modeling of ships where gravity waves are very important. Unfortunately, in modeling of incompressible flow it is usually possible to make only either the Reynolds or Froude number the same for model and prototype.

In modeling we can set

$$N_{R_m} = \left(\frac{\rho L V_0}{\mu}\right)_m = \left(\frac{\rho L V_0}{\mu}\right)_p = N_{R_p} \qquad (4.4)$$

where the m and p represent model and prototype respectively, or we can set

$$F_{r_m} = \left(\frac{V_0^2}{gL}\right)_m = \left(\frac{V_0^2}{gL}\right)_p = F_{r_p} \qquad (4.5)$$

but these two conditions cannot be satisfied simultaneously. In aerodynamics the Reynolds number is important and condition (4.4) can be satisfied without regard to (4.5) (since gravity is unimportant and F_r is very large). However, in marine ship modeling the situation is more complex and two experiments must be run, one with the N_R numbers equal (to determine viscous drag) and one with the F_r numbers equal (to determine the gravity wave drag).

In terms of the Buckingham Pi Theorem then, we would have N_R and F_r and we could write the dependent dimensionless variables as functions of N_R and F_r and the dimensionless independent variables. For example,

$$p^* = f(N_R, F_r, \mathbf{r}^*, t^*)$$

or any steady function of p^* such as lift could be computed as a function of only N_R and F_r, the variable $\mathbf{r}^*$ being integrated out. As we will see, the dimensionless lift and drag on an object will be functions only of the Reynolds number (for a given geometry, of course).

There is one other important point to understand now in connection with showing the equivalence of the Buckingham Pi Theorem method and the equation normalization method. In the latter we have a set of characteristic parameters, such as N_R and F_r, which appear as coefficients in the governing equations. For a given geometry we say that any dimensionless dependent variable depends only on these characteristic parameters and the dimensionless independent variables, as we have pointed out above in the case of pressure. Now, on the other hand, if we had started out from scratch without any equations and asked: for a given flow what variables are important and relevant in determining some aspect of the flow behavior over the body?, we would have had to pick all the relevant variables and properties of the flow (such as V_0, L, μ, p, $\mathbf{r}$, t, etc.) and combine them into an appropriate set of dimensionless quantities. Even if we are able to pick all the relevant variables and properties, we are still faced with the task of combining them in the most convenient manner and then giving them physical interpretation. For example, suppose we ask again: what is the pressure distribution in steady flow over a body and what does it depend on? We would get for a given shape,

$$p = f(L, V_0, \mathbf{r}, \mu, \rho, g) \tag{4.6}$$

There are nine variables and hence they must reduce to six dimensionless ones. These are p^*, N_R, F_r, $\mathbf{r}^*$. $\mathbf{r}^*$ is a vector and has three scalar components, each of which is an independent variable. F_r may of course be unimportant in the problem of interest. p^* is the pressure above the pressure in the free stream of the flow. If we need to know the absolute pressure, we would have to introduce an additional parameter, the pressure p_0 in the free stream and we would have as a result an additional dimensionless parameter, $p_0/\rho V_0^2$. This is not usually necessary since we are mainly interested in the pressure excess in an aerodynamic problem.

4.3 PARAMETERS OF COMPRESSIBLE FLOW

In compressible flow additional parameters enter. In addition to motion and continuity we need the energy equation and an equation of state. We introduce the following dimensionless variables

$$\rho^* = \rho/\rho_0, \quad T^* = T/T_0, \quad M_0 = V_0/a_0, \quad a_0 = \sqrt{kRT_0}, \quad \Phi^* = L\Phi/V_0^2\nu\rho_0 \tag{4.7}$$

in addition to those of the previous section. Here a_0 is the ordinary sonic speed, Φ is the viscous dissipation function, k is the ratio of specific heats c_p/c_v, R is the gas constant, T is the absolute temperature, and ν is the kinematic viscosity μ/ρ.

The dimensionless equations then become

Continuity:
$$\frac{\partial \rho^*}{\partial t^*} + \nabla^* \cdot (\rho^* \mathbf{V}^*) = 0 \tag{4.8}$$

Motion:
$$\rho^* \left[\frac{\partial V^*}{\partial t^*} + (\mathbf{V}^* \cdot \nabla)\mathbf{V}^* \right]$$
$$= -\nabla^* p^* + \frac{1}{N_R}\nabla^{*2}\mathbf{V}^* + \left(\frac{1}{N_R'} + \frac{1}{3N_R} \right)\nabla^*(\nabla^* \cdot \mathbf{V}^*) - \frac{\rho^*}{F_r}\nabla^*\psi^* \tag{4.9}$$

Energy:
$$\rho^* \frac{DT^*}{Dt^*} = \frac{k(k-1)M_0^2\Phi^*}{N_R} - p^*\nabla^* \cdot \mathbf{V}^*[k(k-1)M_0^2] + \frac{k}{N_R P_r}\nabla^{*2}T^* \tag{4.10}$$

State:
$$p^* = \frac{1}{kM_0^2}\rho^* T^* \tag{4.11}$$

In addition to the dimensionless coefficients N_R and F_r which have appeared already in the incompressible analysis, three new dimensionless groups appear. These new numbers are the Mach number M_0 which is the ratio of the characteristic speed V_0 to the characteristic sonic speed a_0, the Prandtl number P_r which is the ratio of the kinematic viscosity ν to the thermal diffusivity α, and k. Thus

$$M_0 = V_0/a_0 \quad \text{and} \quad P_r = \nu/\alpha = \mu c_p/\kappa$$

where μ is the viscosity, c_p the specific heat at constant pressure, κ the thermal conductivity, and α is the thermal diffusivity defined as $\kappa/\rho c_p$.

The Prandtl number plays an important role in convective heat transfer since, physically, the product $N_R P_r$ is a measure of the ratio of heat transfer by convection to heat transfer by thermal conduction. For most gases P_r is of order unity and for liquids P_r may vary between 0.1 and 0.001. The value of N_R must be small if heat conduction is to be important in a fluid. Usually in nature N_R is quite large, much greater than unity, so that convection dominates. However, in some situations of engineering interest N_R may be less than unity and both conduction and convection become important modes of heat transfer. Such is the case in a thin film of lubricating oil in a bearing, for example.

Many other combinations of the variables are possible to form other dimensionless groups, but they are not independent of the ones already mentioned. In certain engineering problems it is convenient to introduce other dimensionless groups. Sometimes the term Φ^* is written as $\kappa B_r/N_R P_r \Phi^*$, where B_r is the Brinkman number defined as $B_r = \mu V_0^2/\kappa T_0$. Further, the ratio of B_r/P_r is sometimes called the Eckert number E_c. Clearly then the form of the Π's is not independent and we can choose only one of M_0, B_r or E_c in addition to N_R, P_r and k (the ratio of specific heats c_p/c_v) in the energy equation. There is a second Reynolds number, N'_R, based on the second coefficient of viscosity but it is not important except for certain problems such as sound attenuation and dispersion.

To summarize, we model as follows for incompressible and compressible flow.

N_R the same: viscous flow and subsonic aerodynamics.

M_0 and k the same: high speed compressible and supersonic flow.

N_R and M_0 the same: compressible boundary layer.

P_r the same: heat conduction.

N_R, M_0, and P_r the same: compressible boundary layer with heat conduction.

N_R and F_r the same: marine ship modeling.

Usually only one number can be held the same for model and prototype at the same time, so that several experiments may be necessary to model various effects of interest and such modeling may become rather complex and will not be discussed further here. Often, however, two parameters can be simultaneously made the same, as for example k and M_0. If air is used for the model and prototype, k is the same and by appropriate scaling M_0 can be made the same.

4.4 ADDITIONAL PARAMETERS INVOLVED IN FREE CONVECTIVE HEAT TRANSFER IN FLUIDS

The equation of motion may be complicated by one other factor, the buoyancy effects. These effects give rise to free convection if thermal gradients exist which cause density gradients. We assume here that the fluid is essentially incompressible, with a temperature coefficient of volume expansion β.

The equation of motion is

$$\rho[\partial \mathbf{V}/\partial t + (\mathbf{V} \cdot \nabla)\mathbf{V}] = -\rho\beta g(T - T_0) + \mu\nabla^2\mathbf{V} \tag{4.12}$$

where the compressibility effects have been neglected. In such problems there is usually no reference velocity and we define a new dimensionless velocity, time and temperature as

$$\mathbf{V}^\dagger = \mathbf{V}L\rho/\mu, \quad t^\dagger = t\mu/\rho L^2, \quad \Theta = (T - T_0)/(T_1 - T_0) \tag{4.13}$$

where $T_1 - T_0$ is a characteristic temperature difference of the system, so that (4.12) becomes

$$\partial \mathbf{V}^\dagger/\partial t^\dagger + (\mathbf{V}^\dagger \cdot \nabla^*)\mathbf{V}^\dagger = -\nabla^{*2}\mathbf{V}^\dagger + \Theta G_r \tag{4.14}$$

G_r is the Grashof number, $g\rho_0^2\beta(T_1 - T_0)L^3/\mu^2$.

In free convection the Reynolds number is unimportant and does not enter. In the energy equation, dissipation is usually neglected and compressibility effects are unimportant so that in dimensionless form

$$\frac{D\Theta}{Dt^\dagger} = \frac{1}{P_r}\nabla^{*2}\Theta \tag{4.15}$$

Hence in free convection, only the Grashof and Prandtl numbers are important.

References

1. Birkhoff, G., *Hydrodynamics*, Dover Publications, 1955.

2. Bridgman, P. W., *Dimensional Analysis*, Yale University Press, 1931.

3. Buckingham, E., On Physically Similar Systems, *Physical Review*, Vol. 4, Ser. 2, p. 345, 1914.

4. Langhoar, H. L., *Dimensional Analysis and the Theory of Modeling*, John Wiley, 1951.

Solved Problems

4.1. In incompressible time dependent flow oscillating with period τ due to a body immersed in a fluid, what are the parameters which characterize the flow?

For incompressible flow, only the Reynolds number appears as a dimensionless coefficient. If we solve for a dimensionless period τ^* defined as $\tau V_0/L$, we can write

$$\tau^* = \tau V_0/L = f(N_R)$$

The dimensionless number $\tau V_0/L$ is known as the Strouhal number. Such oscillations occur in the shedding of Karman vortices in the wake and will be discussed in Chapter 5.

4.2. In problems involving surface tension T_s, what new parameters enter?

The equations of motion are the same as for flow without surface tension effects but the boundary conditions are different. At a liquid-air interface the pressure force must be balanced by the surface tension, and is not necessarily zero as it must be at a free surface without surface tension. A finite pressure difference, remember, can exist across an interface (if it has curvature) and be balanced by surface tension. Consider a two dimensional case as shown in Fig. 4-1. From equilibrium considerations,

$$2T_s(d\theta/2) = pR\,d\theta$$

where R is the radius of curvature of the surface and $\sin\theta \simeq \theta$ for small θ. Then we can write

$$T_s = p^*R^*(\rho_0 V_0^2 L)$$

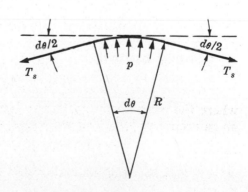

Fig. 4-1

having introduced the dimensionless pressure and radius of curvature as $p^* = p/\rho_0 V_0^2$ and $R^* = R/L$. We define a dimensionless surface tension T_s^* as

$$T_s^* = T_s/\rho_0 V_0^2 L$$

so that

$$T_s^* = p^* R^*$$

The dimensionless parameter $\rho_0 V_0^2 L/T_s$ is called the Weber number.

4.3. In a shallow liquid, small surface disturbances propagate as shown in Fig. 4-2. On what parameters does the infinitesimal surface wave speed depend? What dimensionless groups are relevant?

Consider a wave as shown. The speed a can depend on the depth h and the value of gravity g. The only dimensionless group that can be formed is

$$\Pi = a^2/gh$$

Here, since the number of variables is three and the number of fundamental units (length and time) are two, we have one Π. Since there is only one Π in the problem, we must say that it is a constant:

$$\Pi = a^2/gh = \text{constant}$$

Fig. 4-2

It happens here that the constant is unity and $a = \sqrt{gh}$, but this result could not be determined from dimensional analysis.

Another point to remember here is that the density of the fluid does not enter. However, one might not know this in the beginning and its introduction could lead to irrelevant Π's and possible incorrect conclusions. It is always a problem to know just what variables are relevant if we do not begin with the basic governing equations.

4.4. When a valve is closed suddenly in a pipe with flowing water, a water hammer wave is set up. Such waves can generate enormous pressures causing damage to the pipe. Using dimensional analysis, find the maximum pressure generated by this phenomenon.

We take as the relevant parameters: the maximum pressure p_{max}, the density ρ, the initial flow velocity U_0, and the bulk modulus β (since the wave must be a compression wave of some sort). There are two possible independent Π's here. We may pick them as

$$p_{max}/\beta \quad \text{and} \quad U_0^2\rho/\beta$$

Hence we can write

$$p_{max}/\beta = f(U_0^2\rho/\beta)$$

This is as far as we can go with dimensional analysis. Actually it turns out that $p_{max}/\beta = (U_0^2\rho/\beta)^{1/2}$ so that $p_{max} = \sqrt{\rho\beta}\, U_0$, but this fact cannot be obtained except by solution of the relevant differential equations.

As in the previous problem, we can say something about the speed of propagation of this water hammer wave. The wave speed a depends on the density ρ and bulk modulus β (if one is fortunate enough to guess this correctly), so that the only Π that can be formed is $a^2\rho/\beta$ and it must be a constant. Again, the actual speed is $\sqrt{\beta/\rho}$.

4.5. In subsonic aerodynamics, how can we model lift on an airfoil?

The lift on a body may be found by integrating the appropriate component of the normal pressure force on the body over its surface. The pressure is found from the equation of motion. In steady flow the dimensionless pressure depends on the location of the body, **r***, and on the Reynolds number; however, usually the Reynolds number dependence is slight, and if the flow is streamlined, as in a true airfoil, the Reynolds number dependence may be neglected. For a given geometrical shape the pressure may be integrated over the body to eliminate the **r*** dependence as we find the lift L. However, even for a given geometrical shape, the angle of attack θ (the relative angle at which the free stream flow approaches the body) affects the lift.

Referring to Fig. 4-3, it follows that

$$L = -\int_A p\,\hat{\mathbf{y}} \cdot d\mathbf{A}$$

where $\hat{\mathbf{y}}$ is a unit vector in the y direction, and hence

$$L^* = \frac{L}{\rho V_0^2 A_0} = -\int p^*\hat{\mathbf{y}} \cdot d\mathbf{A}^* = f(\theta)$$

where A_0 is a characteristic area of the airfoil and $A^* = A/A_0$. Therefore the lift may be written

$$L = C_L(\theta)\,\rho V_0^2 A_0^2/2$$

Fig. 4-3

where C_L is known as the lift coefficient. The factor 2 is introduced by convention so that $\rho V_0^2/2$ may be interpreted as dynamic pressure. In experiments the lift coefficient is usually determined as a function of θ for a given shape airfoil.

4.6.   In subsonic aerodynamics, how do we model drag?

The drag is caused mainly by skin friction, although if the body is not streamlined a wake will occur and the low pressure in the wake will dominate the skin friction (viscous drag due to the boundary layer). In the flow over an airfoil there is also an induced drag which is brought about by the effective angle of attack changing due to the downwash. The lift, which must be at right angles to the local effective free stream flow, then has a component in the main free stream direction (that is, opposite to the direction of motion of the body through the fluid).

The induced drag D may be formulated in terms of a pressure integral, and as for lift we can write

$$D = C_D\,\rho V_0^2 A_0/2$$

when $C_D(\theta)$ is the drag coefficient.

If we consider bodies which are not streamlined and in which the major portion of drag is due to viscous drag and the low pressure wake, the flow is highly sensitive to the Reynolds number (unlike lift and induced drag) and we can write that the integrated skin friction and wake drag must be a function of Reynolds number (for a given geometrical shape). Of course we could still have an angle of attack dependence, but we assume now that the angle of attack is held constant as the Reynolds number is varied. Actually the angle of attack is not a useful variable then, since the body is not streamlined and the angle of attack is not very meaningful. A different angle of attack is considered a different geometry. Then the drag can be written in dimensionless form as

$$D^* = \frac{D}{\rho V_0^2 A_0/2} = f(N_R) = C_D(N_R)$$

so that we retain the concept of drag coefficient but say that it may not be a constant for a given geometry but depends on N_R. In the general case we can say for any airfoil with separating boundary layer or not,

$$C_D = f(N_R, \theta)$$

4.7.   In a pipe the pressure drop depends on the wall friction which in turn depends on whether the flow is laminar or turbulent. If the flow is laminar the wall friction depends on the viscosity. If the flow is turbulent the wall friction depends on the Reynolds number and the roughness of the wall. How can this pressure drop be modeled?

The calculation of pressure drop, Δp, in a pipe of length L must be based on the equation of motion. Hence the dimensionless pressure drop per unit length along the pipe must depend on the Reynolds number and pipe roughness, which can be represented as the ratio of the mean height of surface asperities to the diameter, ϵ/D. Hence

$$\frac{\Delta p^*}{L^*} = h(N_R, \epsilon/D)$$

if we define the dimensionless length L^* as L/D, where D is the pipe diameter and h is a function of N_R and the roughness of the pipe. In terms of pressure p,

$$\frac{\Delta p^*}{L^*} = \frac{\Delta p}{\rho V^2} \frac{D}{L} = h(N_R, \epsilon/D)$$

Now the head loss in feet is H_L (in engineering units), so that we can write

$$H_L = \frac{\Delta p}{\rho g} = \frac{\Delta p^*}{L^*} \frac{V^2 L}{Dg}$$

and

$$H_L^* = H_L \frac{Dg}{V^2 L} = h(N_R, \epsilon/D) = f/2$$

The function $(N_R, \text{roughness})$ is written as $f/2$ where f is the friction factor, a dimensionless number which depends on the Reynolds number and also on roughness if the flow is turbulent. Finally,

$$H_L = \frac{fL}{D} \frac{V^2}{2g}$$

Experimental data for friction factors are of vital importance in pipe flow problems.

4.8. Solve Problem 4.7 using the detailed Buckingham Pi method. Consider the flow of a fluid in a pipe. Determine the important Π parameters for such a flow.

First we have to guess the important physical quantities. We will assume that they are the following. M, L and T indicate dimensions of mass, length and time, respectively.

Physical Quantity	V	D	ρ	μ	ϵ	dp/dx
Dimension	LT^{-1}	L	ML^{-3}	$ML^{-1}T^{-1}$	L	$ML^{-2}T^{-2}$

where ϵ is some average height of the wall roughness and dp/dx is the pressure change per unit length in the flow direction.

We have 6 physical quantities involving 3 primary dimensions and therefore there will be a maximum of three Π terms. We will now determine the Π terms taking 4 physical quantities at a time.

$$V^{x_1} D^{y_1} \rho^{z_1} \mu = (LT^{-1})^{x_1} L^{y_1} (ML^{-3})^{z_1} ML^{-1}T^{-1} = M^0 L^0 T^0$$

Then $L \rightarrow x_1 + y_1 - 3z_1 - 1 = 0$, $M \rightarrow z_1 + 1 = 0$, $T \rightarrow -x_1 - 1 = 0$

from which $z_1 = -1$, $x_1 = -1$, $y_1 = -1$. Thus

$$\Pi_1 = \mu/\rho VD \quad \text{or} \quad \Pi_1 = \rho VD/\mu$$

By the same procedure we can take

$$D^{x_2} \rho^{y_2} \mu^{z_2} \epsilon = M^0 L^0 T^0 \qquad \text{and} \qquad V^{x_3} \rho^{y_3} D^{z_3} dp/dx = M^0 L^0 T^0$$

and obtain $$\Pi_2 = \epsilon/D, \qquad \Pi_3 = \frac{(dp/dx)D}{\rho V^2}$$

Then we have $\Pi_3 = h(\Pi_1, \Pi_2)$ and

$$\frac{(dp/dx)D}{\rho V^2} = h(\rho VD/\mu, \epsilon/D) = h(N_R, \epsilon/D)$$

where h indicates a functional relationship.

The functional relation among these quantities is determined experimentally. These results are shown graphically in Chapter 5 and are called the Moody or Stanton diagram.

The usefulness of dimensionless quantities is readily apparent in this example. An enormous amount of experimental work would have been required if we were to vary each of the five physical quantities independently, whereas by reducing the number to three dimensionless quantities a complete experimental program can be reasonably performed.

It is customary to write the head loss in a pipe of length L as $H_L = \Delta p/\rho g$ where Δp is the pressure drop in the pipe. Then $\Delta p/L = dp/dx$ and we can write, using the results above,

$$H_L^* = H_L \frac{Dg}{V^2 L} = \frac{(dp/dx)D}{\rho V^2} = \text{a function of } (N_R, \epsilon/D) = f/2$$

where f is the friction factor, defined by the above equation. In terms of f then, we can express the head loss as $H_L = (fL/D)(V^2/2g)$.

4.9. An airfoil of surface area 1 ft^2 is tested for lift L in a wind tunnel. At an angle of attack of 5° with standard air of density 0.0024 slugs/ft^3 at a speed of 100 ft/sec, the lift is measured as 7.0 pounds. What is the lift coefficient C_L? For a prototype wing of area 100 ft^2, what is the lift L_p at an air speed of 100 mph at the same angle of attack, 5°?

C_L may be computed from the data taken on the model.

$$C_L = \left(\frac{L}{A\rho V_0^2/2}\right)_m = \frac{7.0}{1(0.0024)(100)^2/2} = 0.58$$

Then for the prototype C_L is the same and we find the lift L_p as

$$L_p = (C_L A\rho V_0^2/2)_p = 0.58(100)(0.0024)(100 \times 88/60)^2/2 = 1500 \text{ lb}$$

4.10. Discuss the modeling of a pump or fan for an incompressible fluid.

The modeling is essentially the same for a centrifugal or axial flow machine. The important parameters which describe the performance of a machine are the power input P, the head H produced across the machine, and the efficiency η. For a given geometrical design the performance is characterized by the following related variables: ρ, fluid density; ω, angular velocity of the rotor; D, mean diameter of the rotor; μ, fluid viscosity; Q, fluid flow rate.

P, gH and η are not independent but are functions of the variables listed above. It is convenient to introduce the head as gH instead of H since the product gH represents the shaft work per unit mass of fluid and is independent of g. Hence we can write

$$P = f_1(\rho, \omega, D, Q, \mu)$$

$$\eta = f_2(\rho, \omega, D, Q, \mu)$$

$$gH = f_3(\rho, \omega, D, Q, \mu)$$

We apply the Buckingham II Theorem to each equation and obtain a convenient set of II's as

$$P/\rho\omega^3 D^5 = f_4(Q/\omega D^3, \rho\omega D^2/\mu)$$

$$\eta = f_5(Q/\omega D^3, \rho\omega D^2/\mu)$$

$$gH/\omega^2 D^2 = f_6(Q/\omega D^3, \rho\omega D^2/\mu)$$

It is important to note here that the II's ($P/\rho\omega^3 D^5$, $gH/\omega^2 D^2$ and η) are not independent and are determined once the other II's are known.

From experimental data it is known that viscosity and hence the II $\rho\omega D^2/\mu$ is rather unimportant in determining the performance of a pump or fan. Hence it can be neglected and we obtain finally for a given design configuration,

$$gH/\omega^2D^2 = f_7(Q/\omega D^3), \quad P/\rho\omega^3D^5 = f_8(Q/\omega D^3), \quad \eta = f_9(Q/\omega D^3)$$

Experimental data are usually expressed as a plot of the Π's gH/ω^2D^2, $P/\rho\omega^3D^5$ and η versus $Q/\omega D^3$ for a given machine.

Supplementary Problems

4.11.   A model of a subsonic wing is tested in a laboratory wind tunnel and the following data taken.

Lift (pounds)	0	10	12	14	12	8
Angle of attack, θ	0°	5°	10°	15°	20°	25°

The model is tested with standard air at a speed of 100 ft/sec. The total area of the model wing is 1 ft^2.

Plot the lift coefficient C_L vs. θ. For a prototype wing of area 100 ft^2, what would be the lift for an air speed of 100 mi/hr and an angle of attack of 5°?

4.12.   A new type of interior finish has been developed for oil pipelines. This finish is applied to a sample 12″ I.D. pipe for testing. A 100 ft length of the sample pipe is tested with water (at room temperature) with varying flow rates. The following data were taken:

Pressure drop across pipe (ft of water)	0.011	0.078	0.28	15.3
Flow rate (gal/min)	172	475	950	7860

Plot the friction factor f (as defined in Problem 4.7) vs. the Reynolds number. For a real pipe of 12″ I.D., what pressure drop in psi would occur per mile of pipe for a flow rate of 5000 gal/min of crude oil? Convert the pressure drop into feet of oil and into feet of water.

4.13.   A model of a hemispherically shaped dome cover is to be tested in a wind tunnel for lift and the lift coefficient C_L determined. The real dome is subjected to 100 mph gales in the Arctic at temperatures of −40°F. If the model is to be made 1 ft in diameter and the real dome is 50 ft in diameter, what should be the wind tunnel speed if standard air is used? Does the speed matter? Could you achieve Reynolds number modeling here?

4.14.   A nonretractable streamlined landing gear for a small plane is to be modeled $\frac{1}{3}$ scale for drag in a small wind tunnel. The wind tunnel uses standard air. The frontal projected area of the model is 0.5 ft^2. If we wish to determine the drag on the prototype operating at 100 mph, the cruising speed, at what speed should the wind tunnel be operated? Operating at the proper speed, the wind tunnel gives a drag of 20 pounds. What would be the drag on the actual gear at the cruising speed? What is the drag coefficient C_D?

4.15.   In Fig. 4-4 is shown a weir which is a notch in a dam or barrier in an open channel and which is used for measuring the flow rate. The notch may be of varying shape and the height H of water in the notch is a measure of the flow rate. Show that for a triangular notch as in the figure, if the water is fairly deep and the effects of surface tension and viscosity are neglected the flow rate Q can be approximated by $Q = C\sqrt{g}\,H^{5/2}$ where C is a constant. From experiment it has been found that C can be represented by $C = 0.44 \tan \frac{1}{2}\theta$.

Fig. 4-4

4.16. The flow of a liquid through a pipe may be measured by a flat plate orifice inserted in the pipe as shown in Fig. 4-5. A pressure gage on each side of the plate gives the pressure drop across the orifice, and from this data the flow rate may be calculated for a given fluid. If we assume that the flow rate depends on Δp across the orifice, the fluid density ρ, the pipe diameter D, and the orifice diameter D_0, show that the flow rate may be expressed as $Q = CD_0\sqrt{2\Delta p/\rho}$. Is C a constant? Explain.

Fig. 4-5

4.17. In astronomical and cosmological calculations where the distances and times involved are so large compared to our ordinary units, it is sometimes convenient to employ a special system of units.

For one such system of units the following universal constants are taken as unity for simplicity in making calculations: velocity of light, $c = 1$; mass of the sun, $M = 1$; Newtonian gravitational constant, $K = 1$. (K is defined as follows: Two masses attract each other according to the gravitational law $F = KM_1M_2/r^2$. F is usually given in dynes, the masses in grams, and r in centimeters.)

It is desired to determine the fundamental units of M, L and T in this new system where the given universal constants are unity, and to relate these new units to our ordinary system of units of grams, cm, sec, etc. That is, how many cm make up the new astronomical unit, and how many sec make the new astronomical unit of time? Do the same for mass.

Data: Mass of sun, 1.98×10^{33} grams

Velocity of light, 10^{10} cm/sec

Gravitational constant (K), 6.67×10^{-8} gm^{-1} cm^3 sec^{-2}

Note: What about the force; will it still be dynes even in the new system of units?

4.18. Discuss the modeling of a propeller. Assume the thrust depends on the diameter D, the fluid density ρ and viscosity μ, the velocity V of the propeller through the fluid, and the angular velocity ω of the propeller.

4.19. The propeller of a ship 800 ft long is 10 ft in diameter and rotates at 100 rpm. If a model ship 8 ft long is to be tested in a towing tank, discuss the conditions of the propeller test in order to achieve meaningful modeling.

4.20. A small ship 100 ft long is designed to move at 20 mph through fresh water. Find the kinematic viscosity of a liquid suitable for similitude tests with a model 5 ft long.

4.21. Analyze a turbine using an analysis similar to that of Problem 4.10. The results are the same except that the terms must be interpreted in terms of the performance of a turbine instead of a pump.

4.22. A pump tested at 1000 rpm delivers 5 ft^3/sec of water against a head of 200 ft. The power necessary to run the pump is 200 hp. Calculate the efficiency of the pump. A geometrically similar pump of three times the diameter is made to run at 500 rpm. Find the flow rate, head and power for the same efficiency.

4.23. A rather well-known cookbook gives the following table for turkey baking.

Weight of turkey, lb	6-10	10-16	18-25
Time required per pound, min/lb	20-25	18-20	15-18

From dimensional analysis considerations you should be able to obtain this information from just one bit of experimental information. That is, from only the information that a 6-10 pound turkey takes 20-25 min/lb to bake, you should be able to construct the table and extrapolate to heavier turkeys or fill in a more complete table.

Hint. Consider two geometrically similar turkeys, both at an initial temperature T_0 and to be baked to a temperature T_c in an oven at temperature T_s. A dimensionless temperature may be defined as $\theta = (T - T_0)/(T_s - T_0)$, and a dimensionless time may be defined as $\tau = \alpha t/L^2$ where α is the thermal diffusivity of turkeys, L is the characteristic dimension, say the length, and t is time. It can be shown (do it) that the following formula is valid:

$$(\text{baking time}) \times (\text{weight of turkey})^{-2/3} = \text{constant}$$

4.24. In experiments on heat leakage through the walls of home freezers, a test was made on a specially insulated box about $3 \times 3 \times 4$ ft in size. With the box initially at $70°F$ an incandescent light bulb was used to maintain a constant flow of heat to the interior of the box. The outside surface of the box was maintained at $70°F$. Data on the temperature rise of the inside surface over the outside surface are given below.

(a) Plot the data on temperature rise versus time in terms of dimensionless groups so that it can be applied to other problems of a similar nature. One group should contain temperature but not time and the other group should contain time but not temperature.

(b) Determine the temperature difference that should be expected at the end of 15 minutes under conditions exactly the same as those of the test except with a wall thickness only one-half as great.

Data:

Time, hours	0	0.5	1.0	2.0	3.0	5.0	10
Temperature difference, °F	0	15.9	22.5	30.0	35.5	42.0	48.3

Rate of heat flow per unit area = 6.09 BTU/hr-ft²

Thickness of insulation = 2 in.

Conductivity of insulation = 0.0209 BTU/ft-hr-°F

Thermal heat capacity of insulation = 4.85 BTU/ft³-°F

NOMENCLATURE FOR CHAPTER 4

a = sonic speed

B_r = Brinkman number = $\mu V_0^2/kT_0$

C_D = drag coefficient

C_L = lift coefficient

c_p = specific heat at constant pressure

c_v = specific heat at constant volume

D = drag force, diameter

E_c = Eckert number = B_r/P_r

f = friction factor

F_r = Froude number = V_0^2/gL

G_r = Grashof number
= $g\rho_0^2\beta(T_1 - T_0)L^3/\mu^2$

g = acceleration due to gravity

k = ratio of specific heats = c_p/c_v

L = characteristic length, lift force

M = Mach number = V/a

N_R = Reynolds number = LV_0/ν

p = pressure

R = gas constant

r = position vector

T = absolute temperature

t = time

V = velocity vector

$(\ )_0$ = free stream value

$(\ )^*$ = dimensionless variable

$(\ )^\dagger$ = dimensionless variable

α = thermal diffusivity = $\kappa/\rho c_p$

β = volume coefficient of thermal expansion

Θ = dimensionless temperature

κ = thermal conductivity

μ = absolute viscosity

ν = kinematic viscosity

Π = dimensionless group

ρ = density

Φ = dissipation function

ψ = gravitational potential

P_r = Prandtl number = $\nu/\alpha = \mu c_p/\kappa$

Chapter 5

Boundary Layer Flow
and Flow in Pipes and Ducts

5.1 INTRODUCTION

One of the most important advances in fluid mechanics was contributed by Prandtl in 1904. He suggested that fluid motion around objects could be divided into two regions: a thin region close to the object where frictional effects are important, and an outer region where friction may be neglected. This chapter is concerned primarily with the region where friction is important (the boundary layer), while Chapter 6 is concerned with flows of negligible friction (potential flow).

In this chapter we will look at the basic character of flow with friction. We will examine the methods of determining (1) the size of the boundary layer, (2) the resulting velocity distribution, (3) the pressure distribution, and (4) the force of a fluid on a solid surface.

It is convenient to split the main topics in terms of "external flows" and "internal flows". External flows occur around solid objects, and internal flows occur inside objects such as pipes and channels. While the differential equations describing these flows are essentially the same, the boundary conditions are different so that the resulting flows are entirely different.

The less complicated flows will be studied first. This means that laminar flows will be considered first, then turbulent flows. While some space in this chapter is devoted to turbulent flow, Chapter 9 considers this subject in much greater depth.

Before considering the details of the equations and solutions of boundary layer flows, we will make some general observations of engineering importance concerning the physical character of the boundary layer which is illustrated in Fig. 5-1.

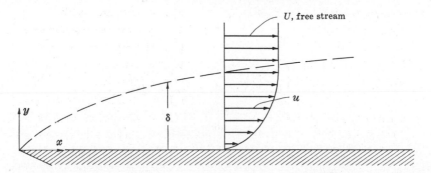

Fig. 5-1. Velocity distribution in the boundary layer.

There is no precise dividing line between the potential flow region where friction is negligible and the boundary layer, but it is customary to define the boundary layer as that region where the fluid velocity (parallel to the surface) is less than 99% of the free stream velocity which is described by potential flow theory. The thickness of the boundary layer, δ, grows along a surface (over which fluid is flowing) from the leading edge. At the leading edge of a flat plate the thickness is zero, but on the front of a blunt body such as a cylinder there is a finite thickness even at the stagnation point.

The flow within the boundary layer begins as laminar flow, but as the layer grows along a surface a transition region occurs and the flow in the boundary layer may become turbulent if the surface is long enough. The laminar-transition-turbulence sequence occurs in all flows, if the surface is long enough, regardless of whether the free stream is laminar or turbulent, but as the degree of turbulence in the free stream increases, the transition from laminar to turbulent flow in the boundary layer occurs earlier, that is, closer to the leading edge.

It can be shown that even in flows where the pressure varies along the surface, such as flow over a curved surface, the pressure variation normal to the surface is negligible through the boundary layer. It is assumed then that the pressure distribution in the boundary layer is imposed by the potential flow free stream pressure gradient just outside the boundary layer. In many problems the boundary layer is so thin that the potential flow solution may be computed neglecting the boundary layer entirely and that solution used to find the pressure distribution for the boundary layer calculations. This approach is employed in aerodynamics to find the flow over streamlined bodies such as airfoils (see Chapter 6).

The shape of the velocity profile and the rate of increase of the boundary layer thickness, δ, depend on the pressure gradient, $\partial p/\partial x$. For example, if the pressure increases in the direction of flow, the boundary layer thickness increases rapidly and the velocity profiles will appear as shown in Fig. 5-2. If this adverse pressure gradient is large enough, then separation will occur followed by a region of reversed flow. (The separation point is defined as the point where $\partial u/\partial y|_{y=0} = 0$). If the pressure decreases in the direction of flow, the boundary layer thickness increases slowly. u is the velocity parallel to the wall (in the x direction) and y is the coordinate normal to the wall.

Fig. 5-2.   Velocity profiles for flow on a flat plate where $\partial p/\partial x > 0$.

The effect of a pressure gradient is very important in establishing the flows in diffusers and nozzles and around objects. The diffuser, illustrated in Fig. 5-3, has a positive pressure gradient. Thus the boundary layer grows rapidly and if the diffuser angle of divergence is too large, separation will occur. This separation results in a diffuser of poor performance since the resulting pressure recovery would not be as large as that of a diffuser operating without separation. The design of diffusers is one of compromise of length and angle. If the angle is too large, separation will occur and if the angle is too small, an excessive length is required to obtain a given pressure, resulting in large friction losses.

The nozzle, in contrast, involves flow with a decreasing pressure in the direction of flow (favorable pressure gradient). As a result, the boundary layer remains relatively small as shown in Fig. 5-3 below. Separation is not a problem in nozzle flows and the design problems for nozzles are somewhat simpler.

(a) Subsonic diffuser

(b) Subsonic nozzle

Fig. 5-3. Comparison of diffuser and nozzle flows.

The potential flow solution for the flow past an object as shown in Fig. 5-4 predicts a decreasing pressure over the front portion of the body and an increasing pressure over the rear portion. Again, there results a relatively thin boundary layer over the front portion and a thick boundary layer and possible separation over the rear portion. In many flows one finds that the boundary layer is so small over the entire body that a solution neglecting viscosity completely (i.e. a potential flow solution) gives accurate results for the pressure distribution. Such is the case for flow over streamlined airfoils, for example. However, if the body is blunt in the rear and the wake becomes appreciable because of boundary layer thickening or separation, the potential flow solution is incorrect except over the front portion of the body where the boundary layer is thin.

Fig. 5-4. External flow effect of pressure gradient of boundary layer growth.

5.2 EXTERNAL FLOWS

(a) Flow Over a Flat Plate

The flow over a flat plate is characteristic of external flows in general. This flow is shown in Fig. 5-1. The boundary layer thickness is zero at the leading edge and increases with distance along the plate surface. The early portion of the boundary layer is laminar but may be followed by a transition region where the flow changes from laminar to turbulent. This transition region actually consists of bursts of turbulence which spread until they intermingle to result in a fully turbulent region as shown in the top view of Fig. 5-5. These turbulence bursts do not have fixed locations but continually move. Thus we see that while the fully laminar flow region may be steady and two-dimensional, the transition region and the fully turbulent regions are unsteady and three-dimensional.

Fig. 5-5. Boundary layer flow over a flat plate.

The exact solution to the appropriate equations describing the laminar boundary layer is difficult and only a few simple problems can be treated easily. The solution to the flow over a flat plate cannot be expressed in closed form and an infinite series expression, known as the Blasius solution, is necessary.

Several approximate methods for treating laminar boundary layer flow have been developed. Below we will discuss one, the momentum-integral method which is of great importance in many types of boundary layer calculations.

The chief results of the Blasius solution and integral method for the flat plate are then discussed and compared.

(b) von Karman Momentum-Integral Equation

Consider the control volume for flow over a flat plate as shown in Fig. 5-6. We will write the momentum equation for this control volume for the x direction; see equation (3.9). We have

$$F_{s_x} = \int_{\text{C.S.}} \rho V_x \mathbf{V} \cdot d\mathbf{A}$$

$pW\delta \longrightarrow \qquad \left(p + \frac{\partial p}{\partial x}\, dx \right)(\delta + d\delta)W$

$\tau_0 W\, dx$

(a) **Forces on control volume**

$\dot{m}$

$W \int_0^\delta \rho u\, dy \longrightarrow \qquad W\left[\int_0^\delta \rho u\, dy + \frac{\partial}{\partial x}\left(\int_0^\delta \rho u\, dy \right) dx \right]$

(b) **Mass flux**

$-WU\frac{\partial}{\partial x}\left(\int_0^\delta \rho u\, dy \right) dx$

$W \int_0^\delta \rho u^2\, dy \longrightarrow \qquad W\left[\int_0^\delta \rho u^2\, dy + \frac{\partial}{\partial x}\left(\int_0^\delta \rho u^2\, dy \right) dx \right]$

(c) **Momentum flux**

Fig. 5-6.   Development of boundary layer integral equations.
W is the width of the plate (in the z direction).

The surface forces are

$$F_{s_x} \;=\; pW\delta \;-\; \left(p + \frac{\partial p}{\partial x}\,dx\right)(\delta + d\delta)W \;-\; \tau_0 W\,dx$$

where W is the width of the plate, δ is the boundary layer thickness, and τ_0 is the shear stress on the wall defined as $\tau_0 = \mu\,\partial u/\partial y|_{y=0}$. Neglecting second order terms and simplifying,

$$F_{s_x} \;=\; \left[-\delta\frac{\partial p}{\partial x}\,dx \;-\; \tau_0\,dx\right]W$$

Before we determine the momentum flux terms, we will consider the mass flux. As shown in Fig. 5-6(b) there will be mass flux across three faces. The mass flux $\dot m$ across the top surface then is

$$\dot m \;=\; W\int_0^\delta \rho u\,dy \;-\; W\left[\int_0^\delta \rho u\,dy \;+\; \frac{\partial}{\partial x}\left(\int_0^\delta \rho u\,dy\right)dx\right]$$

$$\;=\; -W\frac{\partial}{\partial x}\left(\int_0^\delta \rho u\,dy\right)dx$$

where u is the x component of velocity. The x momentum flux $\dot M_x$ of the fluid crossing the top surface is

$$\dot M_x \;=\; \dot m U \;=\; -WU\frac{\partial}{\partial x}\left(\int_0^\delta \rho u\,dy\right)dx$$

where U is the free stream velocity (in the x direction), and the total momentum flux is

$$\int_{\text{C.S.}} \rho V_x \mathbf{V}\cdot d\mathbf{A} \;=\; W\left[\int_0^\delta \rho u^2\,dy \;+\; \frac{\partial}{\partial x}\left(\int_0^\delta \rho u^2\,dy\right)dx\right]$$

$$-\;WU\frac{\partial}{\partial x}\left(\int_0^\delta \rho u\,dy\right)dx \;-\; W\int_0^\delta \rho u^2\,dy$$

Simplifying, $\quad \displaystyle \int_{\text{C.S.}} \rho V_x \mathbf{V}\cdot d\mathbf{A} \;=\; W\frac{\partial}{\partial x}\left[\int_0^\delta \rho u(u-U)\,dy\right]dx \;-\; W\frac{\partial U}{\partial x}\int_0^\delta \rho u\,dy$

So that finally the complete momentum equation becomes

$$\tau_0 \;+\; \delta\frac{\partial p}{\partial x} \;=\; \frac{d}{dx}\int_0^\delta \rho u(U-u)\,dy \;-\; \frac{\partial U}{\partial x}\int_0^\delta \rho u\,dy \qquad (5.1)$$

If the external pressure gradient is zero (and hence U is a constant), the equation becomes

$$\tau_0 \;=\; \frac{d}{dx}\int_0^\delta \rho u\,(U-u)\,dy \qquad (5.2)$$

An approximate boundary layer thickness may be obtained for incompressible laminar flow by assuming a reasonable velocity distribution and substituting into equation (5.2). Let us choose a third degree polynomial velocity distribution as

$$u/U \;=\; \tfrac{3}{2}(y/\delta) - \tfrac{1}{2}(y/\delta)^3 \qquad (5.3)$$

The coefficients are determined by satisfying the boundary conditions that $u = 0$ at $y = 0$, $u = U$ at $y = \delta$, and $\partial u/\partial y = 0$ at $y = \delta$. Then we determine τ_0 as

$$\tau_0 \;=\; \mu\frac{\partial u}{\partial y}\bigg|_{y=0} \;=\; \frac{3}{2}\mu\left(\frac{U}{\delta}\right) \qquad (5.4)$$

where μ is the fluid viscosity. Substituting the velocity distribution of equation (5.3) into equation (5.2) and integrating, we have

$$\frac{3}{2}\mu\left(\frac{U}{\delta}\right) \; = \; \frac{39}{280}\rho U^2 \frac{d\delta}{dx}$$

Separating variables and integrating,

$$\delta/x \; = \; 4.64/\sqrt{Ux/\nu} \; = \; 4.64/\sqrt{N_{R_x}} \tag{5.5}$$

where ν is the kinematic viscosity and N_{R_x} is the Reynolds number based on the length x. Now we can combine equations (5.4) and (5.5) to obtain

$$\tau_0 \; = \; 0.323\rho U^2/\sqrt{N_{R_x}} \tag{5.6}$$

The skin friction coefficient C_f is defined as $C_f = \tau_0/(\frac{1}{2}\rho U^2)$, so that we find the approximate value of C_f as

$$C_f \; = \; 0.646\sqrt{\nu/Ux} \; = \; 0.646/\sqrt{N_{R_x}}$$

This value of C_f is based on the third degree polynomial approximation for the velocity profile. In the next section we will find a more exact value of C_f and compare the two.

The same procedure may be used to determine the rate of boundary layer growth for turbulent flow. However, in turbulent flow it is necessary to use an empirical velocity distribution and wall shear stress. Blasius found that for smooth surfaces,

$$\tau_0 \; = \; 0.0225\rho U^2(\nu/U\delta)^{1/4}$$

The power law velocity distribution discussed on page 82 will be used, where

$$u/U \; = \; (y/\delta)^{1/7}$$

Substituting the above shear stress and velocity distribution into equation (5.2),

$$\delta/x \; = \; 0.376(Ux/\nu)^{-1/5} \; = \; 0.376(N_{R_x})^{-1/5}$$

where it is assumed that the boundary layer is turbulent from the leading edge. The shear stress is in terms of the distance x:

$$\tau_0 \; = \; 0.0286\rho U^2(\nu/Ux)^{1/5} \; = \; 0.0286\rho U^2(N_{R_x})^{-1/5}$$

(c) Prandtl Boundary Layer Equations and the Blasius Solution

If we consider incompressible laminar flow at large Reynolds number over a flat plate, the Navier-Stokes equations reduce to

$$u\frac{\partial u}{\partial x} + v\frac{\partial u}{\partial y} \; = \; -\frac{1}{\rho}\frac{\partial p}{\partial x} + \nu\frac{\partial^2 u}{\partial y^2} \tag{5.7}$$

where

$$\frac{\partial p}{\partial y} \; \ll \; \frac{\partial p}{\partial x} \tag{5.8}$$

and u and v are the x and y components of velocity respectively and the flow is assumed to be incompressible with a constant viscosity. These equations may be derived by an order of magnitude analysis of the complete Navier-Stokes equations. The reader may refer to reference 9, page 92, for the details.

The continuity equation is

$$\frac{\partial u}{\partial x} + \frac{\partial v}{\partial y} \; = \; 0 \tag{5.9}$$

Thus the problem reduces to two equations and two unknowns, u and v. The pressure gradient $\partial p/\partial x$ is determined from the flow outside the boundary layer where the viscous effects can be neglected. This problem is taken up in the next chapter.

Consider flow over a flat plate with zero pressure gradient. The equations for this flow are

$$u\frac{\partial u}{\partial x} + v\frac{\partial u}{\partial y} = v\frac{\partial^2 u}{\partial y^2}, \qquad \frac{\partial u}{\partial x} + \frac{\partial u}{\partial y} = 0$$

with boundary conditions: $u = v = 0$ at $y = 0$; $u = U$ at $y = \infty$. It is assumed that the velocity curves at different axial locations are similar in shape (which is indeed the situation here) and thus may be written as

$$u/U = g(y/\delta)$$

where $g(\ )$ is a functional notation.

Further, we let

$$\eta = y\sqrt{U/vx}, \quad u = \partial\psi/\partial y, \quad v = -\partial\psi/\partial x, \quad \psi = \sqrt{vxU}\,f(\eta)$$

where ψ is known as the stream function and f is an unknown function to be found. Then in terms of the stream function ψ, the momentum equation becomes

$$\frac{\partial\psi}{\partial y}\frac{\partial^2\psi}{\partial y\,\partial x} - \frac{\partial\psi}{\partial x}\frac{\partial^2\psi}{\partial y^2} = v\frac{\partial^3\psi}{\partial y^3}$$

And in terms of f we have the ordinary differential equation

$$f\frac{d^2f}{d\eta^2} + 2\frac{d^3f}{d\eta^3} = 0$$

and the boundary conditions: $f - f' = 0$ at $\eta = 0$; $f' = 1$ at $\eta = \infty$. This equation was solved by Blasius [see reference 2, page 92] by a series expansion. The result is shown in Fig. 5-7.

Since the skin friction coefficient is defined by $C_f = \tau_0/(\frac{1}{2}\rho U^2)$ where $\tau_0 = \mu\,\partial u/\partial y|_{y=0}$ we find C_f as

$$C_f = 2\sqrt{v/Ux}\,\frac{d^2f}{d\eta^2}\bigg|_{\eta=0}$$

From the Blasius solution, $d^2f/d\eta^2|_{\eta=0} = 0.332$ and we have

$$C_f = 0.664\sqrt{v/Ux} = 0.664/\sqrt{N_{R_x}}$$

Comparing this value of C_f to the one obtained previously by the integral method, we see that the third degree polynomial approximation leads to an error in C_f of only about 2.7%, which points out the value of the approximate methods.

Fig. 5-7. Velocity distribution for laminar flow along a flat plate with zero pressure gradient [ref. 2, page 92].

(d) Turbulent Boundary Layers

There is no completely analytical solution for the mean velocity distribution in turbulent flows even for such simple situations as flow over a flat plate and fully-developed pipe flow. The purpose of this section will be to present the semi-empirical methods for describing mean velocity and pressure distributions in turbulent flows. In all of the methods that follow, the results will apply only to two-dimensional flow.

(i) *Power Laws*

The power laws come from Blasius' resistance formula for smooth straight pipes. They apply as well, however, to other channel flows and two-dimensional boundary layers. We shall assume that the walls are smooth and that the pressure gradient is negligible.

If we assume that the skin friction coefficient, C_f, can be expressed as a power function of Reynolds number, (based on δ), we have

$$C_f = \frac{\text{constant}}{(U\delta/\nu)^m} \tag{5.10}$$

where U is the centerline velocity for pipe flow and the free stream velocity for boundary layer flow. δ is the radius for pipe flow and boundary layer thickness for flow over a flat plate. Then from the definition of C_f and equation (5.10),

$$U/u_\tau = (\text{constant})(u_\tau\delta/\nu)^{m/(2-m)} \tag{5.11}$$

where we have introduced the friction velocity u_τ defined as $\sqrt{\tau_0/\rho}$. We assume that the velocity, u, at any distance from the wall, y, may be expressed by an equation similar to (5.11), obtaining

$$u/u_\tau = (\text{constant})(u_\tau y/\nu)^{m/(2-m)} \tag{5.12}$$

If we further assume that the mean velocity profiles are similar and combine equations (5.11) and (5.12), we obtain

$$u/U = (y/\delta)^{m/(2-m)} \tag{5.13}$$

It is found that by taking $m = \frac{1}{4}$, equation (5.13) expresses the variation of friction coefficients in pipes for $3000 < U\delta/\nu < 70,000$. This then is the advantage of introducing the power law distribution. Ideally one would hope for no change in the exponent m. And, since it varies but weakly with Reynolds number, it is found to be useful in many engineering calculations.

For pipe flow the equations become

$$\left.\begin{aligned} C_f &= 0.0466(U\delta/\nu)^{-1/4} \\ u/u_\tau &= 8.74(u_\tau y/\nu)^{1/7} \\ u/U &= (y/\delta)^{1/7} \end{aligned}\right\} \begin{aligned} &\text{Pipe flow} \\ &3000 < N_R < 70,000 \end{aligned}$$

For increasing values of Reynolds number the exponent m for the above equation decreases [see reference 9, page 92].

(ii) *Law of the Wall*

If we assume that there is a region close to the wall where viscosity is important and that the wall shear stress is the important constraint on the flow (i.e. pressure gradient can be neglected), we may write the following functional relationship for the velocity distribution:

$$u = F(\tau_0, y, \mu, \rho)$$

By dimensional analysis we have

$$u/u_\tau = f(yu_\tau/\nu) \tag{5.14}$$

Equation (5.14) is the expression for the "law of the wall". It says that if one plots yu_τ/ν vs. u/u_τ for many different flows there will be a single curve. This has been verified experimentally for a variety of flows. For example, the results hold well for smooth surfaces and moderate pressure gradients even at large distances from the wall (but not for the outermost portion of the boundary layer). The effect of large adverse pressure gradients is to cause deviations from the law of the wall to occur closer to the wall. Some experimental results are shown in Fig. 5-8.

Fig. 5-8. Velocity distribution for the law of the wall. u_τ is the friction velocity, $\sqrt{\tau_0/\rho}$.

Fig. 5-9. Velocity distribution for velocity defect law.

(iii) *Velocity Defect Law*

We now assume that the viscosity is no longer important for the outer portion of the boundary layer. We assume that the velocity defect $(U - u)$ depends on the shear stress at the wall and the distance δ to which the effect has diffused from the wall. Then

$$U - u = G(\tau_0, y, \delta, \rho)$$

and by dimensional analysis we have

$$(U - u)/u_\tau = g(y/\delta) \tag{5.15}$$

The velocity defect law is satisfied experimentally for zero pressure gradient flows for the outer portion of the boundary layer. It is independent of wall roughness. The results are shown in Fig. 5-9.

(iv) *Logarithmic Forms of Law of the Wall and Velocity Defect Law*

It has been observed that there is an intermediate region of overlap where both the law of the wall and the velocity defect law hold simultaneously. In this region of overlap where both laws are valid it can be shown that the functions f and g mentioned above must be logarithmic. That is, equation (5.14) becomes

$$u/u_\tau = C_1 \ln (yu_\tau/v) + C_2 \tag{5.16}$$

and equation (5.15) becomes

$$(U - u)/u_\tau = C_3 \ln (y/\delta) + C_4 \tag{5.17}$$

The constants C_1, C_2, C_3 and C_4 are determined experimentally and there are slight variations in these quantities as reported in the literature. Clauser [ref. 3, page 92] gives

$$C_1 = 2.44, \quad C_2 = 4.9, \quad C_3 = -2.44, \quad C_4 = 2.5$$

Comparison with experiment is shown in Fig. 5-8 and 5-9.

(e) Drag and Lift

Whenever an object is placed in a moving fluid (or moves through a stationary fluid) it will experience a force in the direction of the motion of the fluid relative to the object (drag force, D) and it may experience a force normal to the flow direction (lift force, L). These forces may be expressed as

$$D = C_D(\rho V^2/2)A \qquad (5.18)$$

$$L = C_L(\rho V^2/2)A \qquad (5.19)$$

Here A is the characteristic area which is usually the surface area or the projected area normal to the flow direction. Equations (5.18) and (5.19) define the drag coefficient C_D and the lift coefficient C_L. In all except a few cases these coefficients must be experimentally determined and they generally depend on the Reynolds number.

The drag and lift forces are caused by the sum of the tangential and normal forces at the surface of the body. The drag due to tangential stresses is called friction, skin friction or viscous drag. This kind of drag is most important where the surface area parallel to the flow direction is large compared to the projected area normal to the flow. For example, skin friction drag accounts for all of the drag on a flat plate aligned with the flow.

The drag due to normal stresses is called form or pressure drag. Pressure drag is more important and often dominant for bluff bodies. In Chapter 6 it is seen that if the fluid passing the object were frictionless, and thus there were no boundary layer, the drag force would be zero. However, the fluid is not frictionless and a boundary layer exists. The boundary layer grows more rapidly for an adverse pressure gradient and if the pressure gradient is large enough, separation may occur. The large boundary layer or wake over the rear portion of the body results in a lower pressure than would be obtained for frictionless flow. This reduced pressure on the rear portion of the body, then, results in a net force in the direction of flow. This is shown in Fig. 5-10.

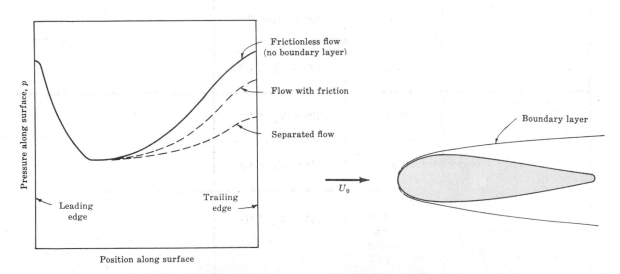

Fig. 5-10.   Effect of boundary layer on pressure distribution along the surface of an object.

We see that in order to reduce pressure drag it is necessary to reduce the magnitude of the adverse pressure gradient over the rear portion of the body and to prevent separation if possible. This means that there should be a long gradual taper over the rear portion of the body. However, if the body is too long, the gain by reducing the pressure drag may be offset by the increase in skin friction drag. The problem of the design of a body for minimum drag is one of compromise between skin friction drag and pressure drag.

Table 5.1. Drag Coefficients

Object	C_D	Reynolds No. Range	Characteristic Length	Characteristic Area
Flat Plate (Tangential)	$1.33(N_R)^{-1/2}$	laminar	L	Plate surface area
	$0.074(N_R)^{-1/5}$	$N_R < 10^7$		
Flat Plate (Normal)	L/d 1 1.18 5 1.2 10 1.3 20 1.5 30 1.6 ∞ 1.95	$N_R > 10^3$	d	Plate surface area
Circular Disk (Normal)	1.17	$N_R > 10^3$	d	
Sphere	$24(N_R)^{1/2}$	$N_R < 1$	d	Projected area
	0.47	$10^3 < N_R < 3 \times 10^5$		
	0.2	$N_R > 3 \times 10^5$		
Hollow Hemisphere	0.34	$10^4 < N_R < 10^6$	d	Projected area
	1.42	$10^4 < N_R < 10^6$		
Solid Hemisphere	0.42	$10^4 < N_R < 10^6$	d	Projected area
	1.17	$10^4 < N_R < 10^6$		
Circular Cylinder	L/d 1 0.63 5 0.8 10 0.83 20 0.93 30 1.0 ∞ 1.2	$10^3 < N_R < 10^5$	d	Projected area
Square Cylinder	2.0	$3.5(10)^4$	d	Projected area

Drag coefficients for bodies of given shapes depend primarily on the Reynolds number. And, although the free stream turbulence intensity and surface roughness usually have only minor effects on drag, under certain conditions they may be very important. Table 5.1 above gives the drag coefficients for several different body shapes. For a more complete listing of drag coefficients the reader may refer to Hoerner [ref. 5, page 92].

Lift is explained, in principle, by the frictionless flow analysis of Chapter 6.

We will consider the flow past a circular cylinder in order to demonstrate some of the ideas previously expressed concerning the causes of drag. The drag coefficient for a circular cylinder is shown in Fig. 5-11. The flow is shown in Fig. 5-12.

Fig. 5-11. Drag coefficients for circular cylinders.

(a) Low Reynolds no. flow ($N_R < 1.0$)

(c) Separated flow – Laminar boundary layer ($N_R < 5(10)^5$)

(b) Flow with Karman vortices ($N_R > 1.0$)

(d) Separated flow – Turbulent boundary layer ($N_R > 5(10)^5$)

Fig. 5-12. Flow past a circular cylinder.

The character of the flow is determined by the Reynolds number. For example, for a very low Reynolds number ($N_R < 1$) the flow does not separate and skin friction is important. For the very low Reynolds number the drag is proportional to the velocity and the drag coefficient decreases as the Reynolds number increases. As the Reynolds number is increased, the flow will tend to separate. The separation takes place in a periodic way in the form of shedding of Karman vorticies. A further increase in Reynolds number will result in a fully separated flow. The laminar boundary layer over the front portion of the cylinder is thin because of the favorable pressure gradient. As a result the pressure distribution can be accurately determined from a frictionless flow analysis (Chapter 6). However, an adverse pressure gradient exists over the rear portion, resulting in a rapid growth of the boundary layer and separation. Pressure drag is much greater than skin friction and the drag coefficient is relatively constant for this case.

The boundary layer becomes turbulent at a certain Reynolds number. As a result, there is a sudden decrease in drag coefficient because the point of separation is delayed, resulting in a lower pressure drag and thus lower total drag.

5.3 INTERNAL FLOW

(a) Entrance Flows

Internal flows differ from external flows in that in the entry region of an internal flow there is a boundary layer and a uniform free stream which accelerates according to the rate of growth of the boundary layer. A second, and more important, difference exists when the flow becomes fully developed. Here the velocity varies over the entire channel and there is no free stream or well defined boundary layer.

Consider laminar flow in the entry region of a tube as shown in Fig. 5-13. The velocity is uniform at the entrance. The boundary layer grows with distance from the entrance until the flow becomes fully developed. From the continuity equation it is seen that the frictionless core must accelerate. Then by writing Bernoulli's equation along a streamline in this free stream region it is seen that the pressure must decrease. The laminar development length X_L for the flow to become fully developed was found by Boussinesq to be

$$X_L = 0.03 N_R D$$

Fig. 5-13.   Flow in the entry region of a pipe for laminar flow.

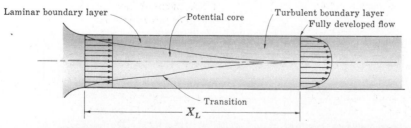

Fig. 5-14.   Flow in the entry region of a pipe for turbulent flow.

Fig. 5-14 shows the flow in the entry region for the case where the Reynolds number is large enough for the flow to be turbulent ($N_R > 2300$). There are several ways of setting criteria for fully developed flow. For example, one may define fully developed flow on the basis of pressure drop, mean velocity distribution or turbulence quantities. The actual lengths for these are substantially different. The pressure gradient generally takes on the fully developed value after three or four diameters of entrance length. The mean velocity requires from 30 to 60 diameters of entrance length before it becomes fully developed. And the turbulence quantities require a much greater length. Strictly speaking, the criterion for establishing fully developed flow should be that the rate of change of all mean quantities (except pressure) with respect to the coordinate in the flow direction is zero. However, the criterion used most frequently in the literature is the point where the mean velocity profiles are not changing with distance in the flow direction.

(b) Fully Developed Flows

(i) Transition

Flow in a pipe may be well ordered and smooth (laminar) or it may assume a chaotic fluctuating motion (turbulent) superimposed on the mean flow. The character of the flow is determined by wall roughness and Reynolds number. This is demonstrated by the classic Reynolds experiment. A stream of dye is introduced into the flow in a glass tube. For small values of flow rate the dye forms a smooth line. As the flow is increased, a point is reached at which the dye breaks up into jagged pattern indicating turbulent motion. The Reynolds number for the transition from laminar to turbulent flow is approximately 2300. However, for special conditions transition has been known to occur at Reynolds numbers as high as 40,000.

(ii) Laminar Flow

Consider fully developed laminar flow between parallel walls as shown in Fig. 5-15. The velocity will be a maximum at the center and zero at the walls. Also, the velocity distribution will be symmetric about the y axis.

The equation of motion for the x direction for this case becomes

$$0 = -dp/dx + \mu(d^2u/dy^2)$$

Integrating once gives $\mu(du/dy) = (dp/dx)y + C_1$

and using the condition that at $y = 0$, $du/dy = 0$, we have $C_1 = 0$. Since $dp/dx =$ constant for fully developed flow and $\tau = \mu(du/dy)$, we have

$$\tau = (dp/dx)y$$

Thus the shear stress is a linear function of y. This result applies for turbulent flow also.

If we integrate again and apply the condition that $u = 0$ at $y = h$, we have

$$u = \frac{1}{2\mu}\frac{dp}{dx}(y^2 - h^2) \tag{5.20}$$

Fig. 5-15. Fully developed laminar flow between parallel walls.

Fig. 5-16. Fully developed laminar flow in a pipe.

Next consider fully developed laminar flow in a circular tube as shown in Fig. 5-16. Such flow is known as Poiseuille flow. Again by applying the equation of motion and boundary conditions and integrating directly, we obtain

$$u \;=\; \frac{1}{4\mu}\frac{dp}{dx}(r^2 - R^2) \tag{5.21}$$

(iii) *Friction Factor and Head Loss*

Pressure losses will occur in internal flows as a result of friction. These losses, which are important to the engineer, may occur in straight pipes or ducts (major losses) or in sudden expansions, valves, elbows, etc. (minor losses).

The energy equation for a control volume between two points in a flow channel is

$$V_1^2/2 + p_1/\rho + gz_1 \;=\; V_2^2/2 + p_2/\rho + gz_2 + u_2 - u_1 - q$$

or

$$V_1^2/2g + p_1/\rho g + z_1 \;=\; V_2^2/2g + p_2/\rho g + z_2 + H_L \tag{5.22}$$

where $H_L = (u_2 - u_1 - q)/g$ is the head loss and u here is the specific internal energy. This H_L term actually represents the decrease (loss) in mechanical energy between points 1 and 2 and in general contains both major and minor losses.

We will now consider the methods of determining the losses. There is no way of determining the losses for turbulent flow by a purely analytical method. Thus the results are highly empirical in nature.

First, let us look at the method of determining the major losses. Our analysis will be restricted to fully-developed, incompressible turbulent flow in a constant diameter tube.

By observing equation (5.22) we see that pressure changes result from velocity changes, elevation changes and friction losses. For the constant area, incompressible case being considered, we have $V_1 = V_2$ and we assume $z_1 = z_2$. Thus equation (5.22) becomes $H_L = (p_1 - p_2)/\rho g$.

The pressure change is known to depend on (1) pipe diameter D, (2) average velocity V, (3) length L, (4) viscosity μ, (5) density ρ, and (6) wall roughness ϵ. Thus

$$\Delta p \;=\; F(D, V, L, \mu, \rho, \epsilon)$$

From dimensional analysis we get four dimensionless parameters, or,

$$\frac{\Delta p}{\rho V^2} \;=\; G(\rho VD/\mu, \epsilon/D, L/D)$$

Experiments show that two of the parameters may be combined to give

$$\frac{\Delta p}{\tfrac{1}{2}\rho V^2}\left(\frac{D}{L}\right) \;=\; f(\rho VD/\mu, \epsilon/D)$$

or

$$\frac{\Delta p}{\rho g} \;=\; H_L \;=\; \left(\frac{L}{D}\right)\frac{V^2}{2g}\, f \tag{5.23}$$

where f = friction factor. The friction factor has been determined experimentally and the results are shown in Fig. 5-17 below. Note that for Reynolds numbers below 2000 there is a single curve because the flow is laminar. The friction factor for laminar flow is determined analytically as (see Problem 5.6)

$$f \;=\; 64/N_R \tag{5.24}$$

Next we will consider minor losses. In accounting for losses in elbows, valves and expansions one must resort to experiment. It is customary to write such losses in the form

$$H_L \;=\; KV^2/2g \tag{5.25}$$

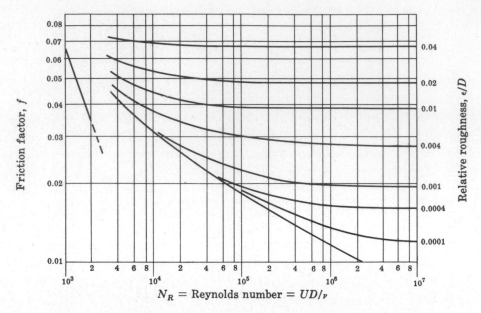

Fig. 5-17.   Friction factors for flow in pipes.

where K is a friction loss coefficient for various types of minor losses and is given for commercial pipe fittings in handbooks.   Table 5.2 lists some approximate K values.

Table 5.2.   **Head Loss Coefficients for Minor Losses, K**

Valves, Fittings and Piping	K
Globe valve (wide open)	10.0
Gate valve (wide open)	0.19
90° elbow	0.90
45° elbow	0.42
Sharp-edged entrance to circular pipe	0.50
Rounded entrance to circular pipe	0.25
Sudden expansion	$(1 - A_1/A_2)^{2}$*

*A_1 = upstream area, A_2 = downstream area

(iv) *Velocity Distributions for Turbulent Flow*

Typical velocity distributions for fully developed flow in a pipe are shown in Fig. 5-18 below.   The velocity is approximated by the power law velocity as was previously used for a flat plate.   We have

$$u/u_{max} = (y/R)^{1/n} \qquad (5.26)$$

where y is the distance from the pipe wall measured toward the center.

The exponent $1/n$ varies weakly with Reynolds number from $1/6$ to $1/10$ for Reynolds number ranging from 4×10^3 to 3×10^6.

The logarithmic form of the law of the wall may be used to approximate the velocity distribution except for the region not close to the centerline.   Here we have

$$u/u_\tau = 2.44 \ln (yu_\tau/\nu) + 4.9 \qquad (5.27)$$

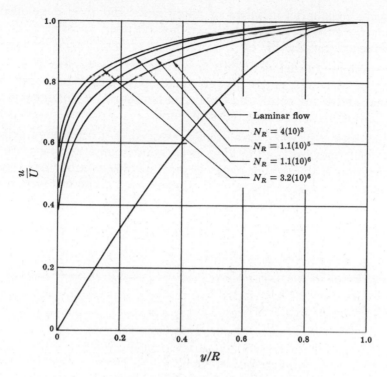

Fig. 5-18. Velocity distribution for fully developed flow in smooth pipes [ref. 8, page 92].

5.4 SUMMARY

In this chapter we have looked at flow with friction. It was convenient to divide the discussion into external flows and internal flows. The former was concerned with flow around objects and the latter with flow in pipes and ducts.

For external flows we obtained expressions for boundary layer growth on a flat plate, equation (5.5), and wall shear stress, equation (5.6). These were obtained from the control volume momentum integral equation where a velocity distribution was assumed.

The Blasius velocity distribution for laminar flow on a flat plate with zero pressure gradient was presented. Also the methods of describing turbulent velocity distributions were discussed. These were

$$u/U = (y/\delta)^{m/(2-m)} \qquad \text{(Power law)} \qquad (5.13)$$

$$u/u_\tau = 2.44 \ln (yu_\tau/v) + 4.9 \qquad \text{(Log form of law of wall)} \qquad (5.16)$$

$$(U-u)/u_\tau = -2.44 \ln (y/\delta) + 2.5 \qquad \text{(Log form of velocity defect law)} \qquad (5.17)$$

Methods of describing drag and lift were presented. There are two kinds of drag; one is skin friction drag which depends on the tangential stresses and the second is form drag which depends on the pressure distribution.

The pressure drag is strongly influenced by separation which may occur at some point on the rear portion on the body. The location of the point of separation is determined largely by the rate of growth of the boundary layer which in turn is determined by the external pressure gradient. Turbulence tends to delay separation and reduce the pressure drag.

Internal flows were considered in terms of entry flows and fully developed flows. The velocity distributions for fully developed laminar flow between parallel walls and in a circular pipe were derived.

Transition from laminar to turbulent flow in a circular tube occurs at a Reynolds number of 2300 nominally, although much higher values have been measured under special conditions. The shear stress for both fully developed laminar and turbulent flow was found to be a linear function of distance from the centerline.

The pressure changes for internal flow were presented in a highly empirical manner in terms of "head" or "friction loss". For flow in constant diameter pipes the results were given in terms of friction factor which depends on Reynolds number and wall roughness. For other types of losses (elbows, valves, etc.) the losses were given in terms of an empirical loss coefficient.

References

1. Bird, R. B., Stewart, W. E., and Lightfoot, E. N., *Transport Phenomena*, John Wiley, 1960.

2. Blasius, H., "Grenzchichten in Flussigkeiten mit kleiner Reibung", *Z. Math. u. Phys.*, 56, 1, 1908, English translation NACA TM, No. 1256.

3. Clauser, F. H., "The Turbulent Boundary Layer", *Advances in Applied Mechanics*, 4, pp. 1-51, Academic Press, 1956.

4. Goldstein, S., *Modern Developments in Fluid Dynamics*, Vols. I and II, Oxford University Press, 1938; also Dover Publications.

5. Hoerner, S. F., *Fluid Dynamic Drag*, published by author, Midland Park, New Jersey, 1958.

6. Klebanoff, P. S. and Diehl, F. W., "Some Features of Artificially Thickened Fully Developed Turbulent Boundary Layers with Zero Pressure Gradient", NACA Report 1110, 1952.

7. Li, W. H. and Lam, S. H., *Principles of Fluid Mechanics*, Addison-Wesley, 1964.

8. Nikuradse, J., "Gesetzmässigkeiten der turbulenten Strömung in glatten Rohren", *Forschungs — Arb. Ing.-Wesen*, 356, 1932.

9. Schlichting, H., *Boundary Layer Theory*, McGraw-Hill, 1955.

10. Shames, I. H., *Mechanics of Fluids*, McGraw-Hill, 1962.

11. Shapiro, A. H., *Shape and Flow*, Anchor Books, Doubleday, 1961.

12. Shepherd, D. G., *Elements of Fluid Mechanics*, Harcourt, Brace & World, 1965.

Solved Problems

5.1. Air at 70°F, 14.7 psi and 50 fps free stream velocity, flows over a flat plate. Determine the boundary layer thickness at a point 5 ft from the leading edge.

The kinematic viscosity for air at these conditions is $\nu = 1.8 \times 10^{-4}$ ft²/sec. The Reynolds number based on the plate length is

$$N_{R_x} = Ux/\nu = 50(5)/(1.8 \times 10^{-4}) = 1.39 \times 10^6$$

Now we will determine the boundary layer thickness assuming the boundary layer is laminar. Using equation (5.5),

$$\delta/x = 4.64/\sqrt{N_{R_x}}, \qquad \delta/5 = 4.64/(1.39 \times 10^6)^{1/2}, \qquad \delta = 0.0197 \text{ ft} = 0.236 \text{ in.}$$

If we assume the boundary layer is turbulent from the leading edge,

$$\delta/x = 0.376/(N_{R_x})^{1/5}, \qquad \delta/5 = 0.376/(13.9 \times 10^5)^{1/5}, \qquad \delta = 0.111 \text{ ft} = 1.33 \text{ in.}$$

We can see that there is a large difference in the answer depending on whether we assume laminar or turbulent flow. And neither answer is correct since the boundary layer is neither completely laminar or turbulent over the entire length. The length for transition to occur has been found experimentally and is given approximately when $N_{R_x} = 3.2 \times 10^5$. Thus the transition length X_T for this problem is

$$X_T = (\nu/U)N_{R_x} = [(1.8 \times 10^{-4})/50](3.2 \times 10^5) = 1.15 \text{ ft}$$

Thus the answer assuming a turbulent boundary layer would be closer to the correct value.

5.2. Work Problem 5.1 taking into account that part of the boundary layer is laminar and the rest is turbulent.

The boundary layer thickness at the point of transition is

$$\delta_{\text{transition}} = \frac{1.15(4.64)}{[3.2 \times 10^5]^{1/2}} = 0.00944 \text{ ft} = 0.113 \text{ in.}$$

At this point the turbulent boundary layer starts. If the boundary layer were turbulent from the leading edge to this point, the length X required would be given as

$$\frac{\delta}{X} = \frac{0.376}{(UX/\nu)^{1/5}} \qquad \text{or} \qquad X^{4/5} = \frac{\delta(U/\nu)^{1/5}}{0.376}$$

so that

$$X = \left(\frac{\delta}{0.376}\right)^{5/4}\left(\frac{U}{\nu}\right)^{1/4} = \left(\frac{0.944 \times 10^{-2}}{0.376}\right)^{5/4}\left(\frac{50}{1.8 \times 10^{-4}}\right)^{1/4} = 0.230 \text{ ft}$$

This means that the total length of the equivalent turbulent boundary layer would be

$$X = (5.0 - 1.15) + 0.23 = 4.08 \text{ ft}$$

and

$$\delta = \frac{4.08(0.376)}{[50(4.08)/(1.8 \times 10^{-4})]^{1/5}} = \frac{1.53}{[11.3 \times 10^5]^{1/5}} = 0.0942 \text{ ft} = 1.13 \text{ in.}$$

5.3. Determine the total drag force for Problem 5.1.

Assuming that the boundary layer is laminar, from equation (5.6) we have

$$\tau_0 = \frac{0.323\rho U^2}{(U/\nu)^{1/2}\,x^{1/2}} = \frac{0.323(0.00237)(50)^2\,x^{-1/2}}{[50/(1.8 \times 10^{-4})]^{1/2}} = (3.62 \times 10^{-3})x^{-1/2}$$

The drag is

$$D = \int_A \tau_0\,dA = W\int_0^5 \tau_0\,dx$$

so that

$$\frac{D}{W} = 3.62 \times 10^{-3}\int_0^5 x^{-1/2}\,dx = 0.0163 \text{ lb}_f/\text{ft}$$

Assuming that the flow is turbulent,

$$\tau_0 \;=\; \frac{0.0286\rho U^2}{(U/\nu)^{1/5}\,x^{1/5}} \;=\; \frac{0.0286(0.00237)(50)^2\,x^{-1/5}}{[50/(1.8\times 10^{-4})]^{1/5}} \;=\; 0.0139\,x^{-1/5}$$

and

$$\frac{D}{W} \;=\; 0.0139\int_0^5 x^{-1/5}\,dx \;=\; 0.0627 \text{ lb}_\text{f}/\text{ft}$$

5.4. How would the boundary layer thickness be affected in Problem 5.1 if the plate were curved as shown in Fig. 5-19?

Along the top surface there would be an adverse pressure gradient. This means that the boundary layer would grow more rapidly than for the flat plate case where the pressure gradient is zero. The opposite is true along the bottom surface; here we have a favorable pressure gradient and a more slowly growing boundary layer. Thus

$$\delta_\text{top} \;>\; \delta_\text{flat plate} \;=\; 1.13 \text{ in.}$$

$$\delta_\text{bottom} \;<\; \delta_\text{flat plate} \;=\; 1.13 \text{ in.}$$

Fig. 5-19

5.5. Determine the total force exerted by an 80 mph wind on a 10 ft × 40 ft billboard. The wind is blowing at right angles to the billboard.

Assume standard air with $\nu = 1.8 \times 10^{-4}$ ft^2/sec and $\rho = 0.00237$ slug/ft^3, so that

$$N_R \;=\; UW/\nu \;=\; 117(10)/(1.8\times 10^{-4}) \;=\; 6.50\times 10^6$$

where W is the width, 10 ft, and the velocity of the air is 80 mi/hr = 117 ft/sec. From Table 5.1, page 85, we find $C_D = 1.2$ and (5.18) gives

$$D \;=\; C_D(\tfrac{1}{2}\rho U^2)A \;=\; 1.2(\tfrac{1}{2})(0.00237)(117)^2(400) \;=\; 7850 \text{ lb}_\text{f}$$

5.6. Derive an expression for the friction factor for fully developed flow in a circular tube of length L where the Reynolds number is less than 2000.

The velocity distribution as given by equation (5.21), page 89, for laminar flow is

$$u \;=\; \frac{1}{4\mu}\frac{dp}{dx}\,(r^2 - R^2)$$

The volume flow rate, Q, is

$$Q \;=\; \int u\,dA \;=\; \int_0^R 2\pi u r\,dr$$

Integrating,

$$Q \;=\; -\frac{\pi R^4}{8\mu}\frac{dp}{dx}$$

and if V_av is the average velocity,

$$V_\text{av} \;=\; \frac{Q}{A} \;=\; \frac{Q}{\pi R^2} \;=\; -\frac{R^2}{8\mu}\frac{dp}{dx}$$

Then

$$\frac{dp}{dx} \;=\; -\frac{\Delta p}{L} \;=\; -\frac{8\mu\,V_\text{av}}{R^2}$$

From equation (5.23), page 89, we have

$$f \;=\; \frac{\Delta p}{L}\frac{4R}{\rho\,V_\text{av}^2}$$

and hence

$$f \;=\; \frac{8\mu\,V_\text{av}}{R^2}\frac{4R}{\rho\,V_\text{av}^2} \;=\; \frac{32\mu}{\rho R\,V_\text{av}} \;=\; \frac{64}{(\rho V_\text{av} D/\mu)} \;=\; \frac{64}{N_R}$$

5.7. Air at 70°F and 14.7 psi enters a 1.0 in. diameter pipe (Fig. 5-20) with a **uniform** velocity and a Reynolds number of 1000. Determine the decrease in pressure in going from the entrance to 100 in. downstream from the entrance. The entrance length L_e is given by $L_e/D = 0.0288 N_R$.

For air under the given conditions, $\nu = 1.8 \times 10^{-4}$ ft²/sec, $\rho = 0.00237$ slug/ft³.

Fig. 5-20

The entrance length L_e is

$$L_e = 0.030(1000)(1.0) = 30 \text{ in.}$$

The uniform velocity at the entrance is

$$U_0 = 1000\nu/D = 1000(1.8 \times 10^{-4})/(1.0/12) = 2.16 \text{ ft/sec}$$

From Problem 5.6 we see that the average velocity is

$$U_0 = V_{av} = -\frac{R^2}{8\mu}\frac{dp}{dx}$$

and the maximum velocity for fully developed flow is $(r = 0)$

$$U_{max} = -\frac{R^2}{4\mu}\frac{dp}{dx}$$

Thus

$$U_{max} = 2U_0 = 2(2.16) = 4.32 \text{ ft/sec}$$

We note that in going from section 1 to section 2 along the centerline the flow is **frictionless. Thus** we can apply Bernoulli's equation to determine the pressure difference between those two points.

$$p_1 - p_2 = \tfrac{1}{2}\rho(U_{max}^2 - U_1^2) = \tfrac{1}{2}(0.00237)[(4.32)^2 - (2.16)^2] = 0.0166 \text{ lb}_f/\text{ft}^2$$

From Problem 5.6 we have (between points 2 and 3)

$$p_2 - p_3 = \Delta p = \frac{8\mu U_1 L}{R^2} = \frac{8(1.8 \times 10^{-4})(0.00237)(2.16)(70/12)}{(0.5/12)^2} = 0.0250 \text{ lb}_f/\text{ft}^2$$

Then the total pressure drop is

$$p_1 - p_3 = (p_1 - p_2) + (p_2 - p_3) = 0.0166 + 0.0250 = 0.0416 \text{ lb}_f/\text{ft}^2$$

5.8. Determine the flow rate for the system shown in Fig. 5-21. The fluid is water and the pipe is hydrodynamically smooth. Neglect all losses except through the pipe.

First we write the energy equation (5.22), page 89, between points 1 and 2.

$$V_1^2/2g + p_1/\rho g + z_1 = V_2^2/2g + p_2/\rho g + z_2 + H_L$$

where

$$H_L = f(L/D)(V^2/2g)$$

Since $V_1 = V_2$ and $z_1 = z_2$, we have

$$(p_1 - p_2)/\rho g = f(L/D)(V^2/2g) = H_L$$

Next we write Bernoulli's equation between the free surface and point 1 along the dotted line as shown.

Fig. 5-21

$$p_S/\rho g + V_S^2/2g + z_S = p_1/\rho g + V_1^2/2g + z_1$$

We note also that $p_2 = p_{\text{atm}} = p_S$. Then we can combine the two equations to obtain

$$f(L/D)(V_1^2/2g) = H_L = (z_S - z_1) - V_1^2/2g$$

$$V_1^2 = \frac{2g(z_S - z_1)}{f(L/D) + 1} = \frac{64.4(20)}{f[15/(1/48)] + 1} = \frac{1290}{f(720) + 1}$$

The friction factor depends on the Reynolds number which depends on the velocity. Thus we must solve the problem by trial and error. The Reynolds number N_R is given by

$$N_R = V_1 D/\nu = V_1(1/48)/(1 \times 10^{-5}) = 2080 V_1$$

The table below shows the trial and error solution. We assume a value for V_1 and then calculate V_1.

V_1 (assumed)	N_R	f	V_1 (calculated)
10	$2.08(10)^4$	0.026	8.10
7	$1.46(10)^4$	0.028	7.70
7.9	$1.64(10)^4$	0.0272	7.92

Thus $V_1 = 7.92$ ft/sec and $Q = AV = AV_1 = \frac{1}{4}\pi D^2 V_1 = \frac{1}{4}\pi(1/48)^2(7.92) = 0.00270$ ft³/sec.

5.9. Determine the flow rate for the system shown in Fig. 5-22. The fluid is water and the pipe is hydrodynamically smooth. First find the flow rate neglecting minor losses, then find the flow rate with the minor losses included.

First we write Bernoulli's equation between points 1 and 2.

$$\frac{p_1}{\rho g} + \frac{V_1^2}{2g} + z_1 = \frac{p_2}{\rho g} + \frac{V_2^2}{\rho g} + z_2$$

or

$$\frac{p_2 - p_1}{\rho g} = (z_1 - z_2) - \frac{V_2^2}{2g} \qquad (a)$$

Bernoulli's equation between points 3 and 4 gives

$$\frac{p_3}{\rho g} + \frac{V_3^2}{2g} + z_3 = \frac{p_4}{\rho g} + \frac{V_4^2}{2g} + z_4$$

or

$$\frac{p_3 - p_4}{\rho g} = (z_4 - z_3) - \frac{V_3^2}{2g} \qquad (b)$$

Fig. 5-22

Next write the energy equation between 2 and 3 where head losses occur:

$$\frac{p_2}{\rho g} + \frac{V_2^2}{2g} + z_2 = \frac{p_3}{\rho g} + \frac{V_3^2}{2g} + z_3 + H_L$$

which becomes

$$\frac{p_2 - p_3}{\rho g} = (z_3 - z_2) + \frac{fL}{D}\frac{V^2}{2g} \qquad (c)$$

where $V_2 = V_3 = V$ and $p_1 = p_4 = p_{\text{atm}}$. Combining equations (a) and (b) gives

$$\frac{p_2 - p_3}{\rho g} = (z_1 - z_2) - (z_4 - z_3)$$

Now combining this equation with equation (c) yields

$$(z_3 - z_2) + \frac{fL}{D}\frac{V^2}{2g} = (z_1 - z_2) - (z_4 - z_3)$$

so that

$$V^2 = \frac{2g(z_1 - z_4)}{fL/D} = \frac{64.4(19)}{f(20/\frac{1}{3})} = \frac{20.4}{f}$$

Since both f and V are unknown we must work simultaneously with the friction factor diagram to obtain a solution. $N_R = VD/\nu = 3.33(10)^4 V$. We use the method of the previous problem:

V (assumed)	N_R	f	V (calculated)
10	$3.33(10)^5$	0.0143	37.9
40	$1.33(10)^6$	0.0114	42.3
43	$1.43(10)^6$	0.0112	43.0

and we arrive at $V = 43.0$ ft/sec and $Q = \frac{1}{4}\pi D^2 V = 3.75$ ft³/sec, where we have neglected minor losses. Minor losses would occur at the entrance and exit of the straight pipe. This would have the effect of altering the pressures as indicated by Bernoulli's equation in the previous calculations. We may account for these losses by modifying equation (c) as follows:

$$\frac{p_2 - p_3}{\rho g} = (z_3 - z_2) + \frac{fL}{D}\frac{V^2}{2g} + K_1\frac{V^2}{2g} + K_2\frac{V^2}{2g}$$

and we obtain by combining with equations (a) and (b) as before,

$$\frac{fL}{D}\frac{V^2}{2g} + K_1\frac{V^2}{2g} + K_2\frac{V^2}{2g} = z_1 - z_4$$

or

$$V^2 = \frac{2g(z_1 - z_4)}{fL/D + K_1 + K_2} = \frac{64.4(19)}{f(20/\frac{1}{3}) + 0.5 + 1.0} = \frac{1220}{f(60) + 1.5}$$

where K_1 = entrance loss coefficient = 0.50 and K_2 = exit loss coefficient = 1.0, obtained from Table 5.2, page 90. Then by trial and error we determine f and V as before.

V (assumed)	N_R	f	V (calculated)
10	$3.33(10)^5$	0.0143	22.8
24	$8.0(10)^5$	0.0122	23.4
23.3	$7.76(10)^5$	0.0122	23.4

We find $V = 23.4$ ft/sec and $Q = \frac{1}{4}\pi D^2 V = \frac{1}{4}\pi(4/12)^2(23.4) = 2.04$ ft³/sec.

5.10. Water flows from a large reservoir and discharges into the atmosphere as shown in Fig. 5-23. Determine the volume flow rate.

Fig. 5-23

First write Bernoulli's equation between the free surface and the entrance. By continuity, $V_1 = V_2 = V$.

$$\frac{p_1 - p_S}{\rho g} = (z_S - z_1) - \frac{V_1^2}{2g}$$

Next write the energy equation between sections 1 and 2:

$$\frac{p_1 - p_2}{\rho g} = (z_2 - z_1) + \frac{fL}{D}\frac{V^2}{2g} + K_1\frac{V^2}{2g} + 2K_2\frac{V^2}{2g}$$

where K_1 = loss coefficient for rounded entrance = 0.25, K_2 = loss coefficient for elbow = 0.90. Combining the two equations gives

$$(fL/D + K_1 + 2K_2 + 1)\frac{V^2}{2g} = (z_S - z_2)$$

or $$V^2 = \frac{2g(z_S - z_2)}{fL/D + K_1 + 2K_2 + 1} = \frac{64.4(100)}{f(450/\frac{1}{2}) + 0.25 + 2(0.90) + 1} = \frac{6440}{f(900) + 3.05}$$

Since both f and V are unknown, we must work simultaneously with the friction factor diagram to obtain a solution. N_R is given as

$$N_R = VD/\nu = V(\tfrac{1}{2})/(1 \times 10^{-5}) = (5 \times 10^4)V \quad\text{and}\quad \epsilon/D = 0.00015/\tfrac{1}{2} = 0.00030$$

V (assumed)	N_R	f	V (calculated)
10	$5(10)^5$	0.0165	361
370	$1.85(10)^7$	0.0150	390
390	$1.95(10)^7$	0.0150	390

We find $V = 390$ ft/sec and $Q = AV = \tfrac{1}{4}\pi D^2 V = \tfrac{1}{4}\pi(\tfrac{1}{2})^2(390) = 76.6$ ft³/sec.

5.11. Discuss the fully developed viscous laminar flow between two parallel plates, one of which is in motion as shown in Fig. 5-24. Such flow is known as Couette flow. The top plate has velocity U with respect to the bottom plate. The pressure at the inlet of the flow region is p_2 and the pressure at the outlet is p_1.

Fig. 5-24

We assume that the length L of the plate is much larger than the spacing h, so that the entrance or development effects may be neglected. The flow is essentially one dimensional then, with variations in velocity only in the y direction across the channel. A coordinate system is attached to the top plate which is moving. The plates are assumed to be very long in the z direction so that flow in that direction may be neglected. Assuming incompressible flow, the equations of motion may be obtained directly from the general equation of motion (the Navier-Stokes equation) or one may take a small element of fluid and write a momentum balance. The equations of motion become:

$$0 = -\frac{\partial p}{\partial x} + \mu\frac{\partial^2 u}{\partial y^2}, \qquad 0 = -\frac{\partial p}{\partial y}$$

where μ is the fluid viscosity, and u and v are respectively the x and y components of velocity measured relative to the top plate. The coordinate system is attached to and moves with the top plate, but the origin is made to coincide with the bottom plate for convenience. Then, relative to the top plate and coordinate system the bottom surface has velocity $-U$.

Since there is no variation in the x direction, the continuity equation $\partial u/\partial x + \partial v/\partial y = 0$ tells us that the y component of velocity, v, must be zero and hence $\partial p/\partial y$ must be zero and the pressure must be only a function of x. Integration of the equations of motion along with the boundary conditions that $u = -U$ at $y = 0$ and $u = 0$ at $y = h$ gives

$$u = \frac{1}{2\mu}\frac{dp}{dx}(y^2 - hy) + U[(y/h) - 1]$$

Since the pressure p is a function only of x, and u is only a function of y, the total flow rate $Q = \int_0^h u\,dy$ may be evaluated and the pressure drop found as

$$Q = -\frac{h^3}{12\mu}\frac{dp}{dx} - \frac{Uh}{2}$$

$$p_2 - p_1 = -\frac{12L\mu}{h^3}\left(\frac{Uh}{2} + Q\right)$$

The above equations tell us that the pressure gradient is a constant and relates the pressure drop to the flow rate Q, which is the flow rate relative to the top plate since our coordinate system is attached to that plate. A positive flow is a flow in the positive x direction. If the pressure gradient is zero, the velocity profile is linear and we have a simple shear flow.

We could just as well have taken the origin on the moving plate and let the y axis point downward. Then the differential equations would have been the same, but the boundary conditions would have been: $y = 0$, $U = 0$; $y = h$, $u = -U$. The velocities are again measured with respect to the top plate and again we find Q as above.

5.12. The lubrication of bearings is a problem in fluid mechanics. The oil or lubricant between the bearing and slider is a viscous fluid and the determination of the pressure distribution, load capacity, friction, etc., may be accomplished by studying the laminar viscous flow of the lubricant. Most bearings operate in the laminar range, with a very small Reynolds number. The spacing between the bearing and slider (the flow gap) is much smaller than the length of the slider so that the flow becomes fully developed throughout most of the gap. Because the Reynolds number is so small, the inertia of the fluid is negligible compared to the pressure and viscous forces. The treatment of a lubrication problem is similar to the Couette flow problem, Problem 5.11.

Consider a step bearing as shown in Fig. 5-25. The spacings h_1 and h_2 are much less than L_1 and L_2, and the width of the bearing in the z direction is assumed to be very large so that leakage in the z direction may be neglected. For a slider velocity U and a fluid of viscosity μ, find the pressure distribution in the bearing.

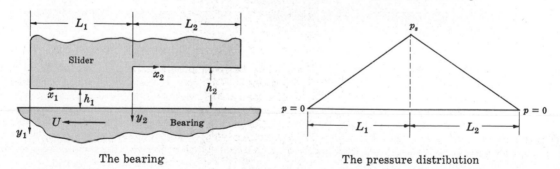

The bearing   The pressure distribution

Fig. 5-25

Each section, the L_1 and L_2 sections, may be treated just as the Couette problem. We attach a coordinate system to the slider as shown and let the stationary bearing move with velocity U in the negative x direction with respect to the slider. In each section then at $y = 0$, $u = 0$ and at $y = h$, $u = -U$. The pressure at the inlet, $x_2 = L_2$, and at the outlet, $x_1 = 0$, is zero gage. The pressure at the step, $x_1 = L_1$ or $x_2 = 0$, is unknown and must be found by using the continuity condition that $Q_1 = Q_2$. If we use the expressions developed in the previous problem we have

$$Q_1 = -\frac{h_1^3}{12\mu}\frac{p_s}{L_1} - \frac{Uh_1}{2} = Q_2 = \frac{h_2^3}{12\mu}\frac{p_s}{L_2} - \frac{Uh_2}{2}$$

The pressure in each section varies linearly with x and the pressure distribution forms a triangle as shown in the figure. The peak pressure p_s is found by equating Q_1 to Q_2, and the result is

$$p_s = \frac{6\mu U(h_2 - h_1)}{(h_1^3/L_1) + (h_2^3/L_2)}$$

which completely specifies the pressure as a function of x. The total load carrying capacity is simply the area under the pressure distribution curve. The load capacity W per unit z width is

$$W = (p_s/2)(L_1 + L_2)$$

Physically, if the load were changed the spacing h_1 and h_2 would change, the slider rising or sinking as the load is decreased or increased respectively.

Once the velocity is known throughout the flow film, the friction can be found by integrating the shear stress along either the slider or the bearing. Do this calculation as an exercise. You will find that the shear stresses along the top and bottom surfaces are not quite equal, but if the pressure force against the step is included in the calculation of the friction of the top plate or slider, the two calculations give the same result.

Supplementary Problems

5.13. Determine the boundary layer thickness 10 ft from the leading edge of a flat plate for the flow of air (70°F and 14.7 psi) where the free stream velocity is 60 fps. Assume laminar flow.

5.14. Determine the shear stress 10 ft from the leading edge for the conditions of Problem 5.13.

5.15. Determine the total drag force and drag coefficient for Problem 5.13 if the plate width is 3.0 ft.

5.16. Work Problem 5.13 assuming that the boundary layer is turbulent.

5.17. Work Problem 5.14 assuming that the boundary layer is turbulent.

5.18. Work Problem 5.15 assuming that the boundary layer is turbulent.

5.19. Derive an expression for the drag coefficient for flow over a flat plate. Express the results in terms of a Reynolds number based on the length of the plate.

5.20. A truck hauling 5 ft diameter 30 ft long thin wall tubing is traveling at 60 mph. Determine the power (hp), resulting from the drag, required for a single tube which is well above the cab of the truck.

5.21. What is the boundary layer thickness at the point where the air is leaving the tubing in Problem 5.20?

5.22. Air flows between two parallel walls as shown in Fig. 5-26. The velocity V_1 is uniform and equal to 100 fps at the entrance (section 1) and in the core region. Downstream a distance of 900 in. the velocity varies over the entire width. The velocity varies in the boundary layer region according to $V = V_c (y/\delta)^{1/7}$ where $\delta = 0.1\sqrt{x}$ and δ and x are measured in inches. Determine the acceleration on the axis of symmetry for $0 \leq x \leq 900$ in. Evaluate the acceleration at $x = 100$ in.

Fig. 5-26

5.23.   Assume a laminar flow over a flat plate given by

$$u = Uy/\delta \quad \text{for} \quad 0 \leqq y \leqq \delta$$
$$u = U \quad \text{for} \quad y > \delta$$

where $\delta = 0.1\sqrt{x}$ and $x =$ distance from the leading edge of the plate and y is the distance measured perpendicular to the plate. All dimensions are measured in feet. If the plate is 1 ft. wide and 25 ft. long, find the drag force.

5.24.   Air is flowing between the parallel flat plates as shown in Fig. 5-27. The velocity is uniform at the entrance, having a magnitude of 10 fps. The boundary layer thickness is $\delta = \frac{1}{10}\sqrt{x}$. The width of the plates, W, is much larger than the distance between the plates, h, and therefore end effects may be neglected. The velocity distribution in the boundary layer is given by $u/U = (y/\delta)^2$ where U is the core velocity and y is the coordinate measured from the wall of either plate. Determine the pressure at a point 25 ft from the entrance. δ and x are measured in feet.

Fig. 5-27

5.25.   In Problem 5.24 find the pressure at a position downstream located at twice the distance required for the flow to become fully developed.

5.26.   In Problem 5.24 determine the total force of the fluid on the walls between the entrance and the position where the flow becomes fully developed.

5.27.   Work Problem 5.24 for a pipe rather than parallel plates.

5.28.   Work Problem 5.26 for a pipe rather than parallel plates.

5.29.   It has been stated that a ball with a roughened surface will travel greater distances than a ball with a smooth surface, for the same initial velocity.   Explain.

5.30.   Determine an approximate value for the initial velocity of a golf ball which travels 250 yards on the fly. Assume that the ball has a velocity of 20 fps when it hits the ground.

5.31.   Determine the total force on a $\frac{1}{8}$ in. diameter 4 ft car radio antenna if the car is traveling at a speed of 60 mph.

5.32.   Determine the power required as a result of the force on the antenna in Problem 5.31.

5.33.   A cubical weight of 5 lb falls between two parallel walls, as shown in Fig. 5-28, at a velocity of $\frac{1}{2}$ fps. Determine the viscosity of the oil.

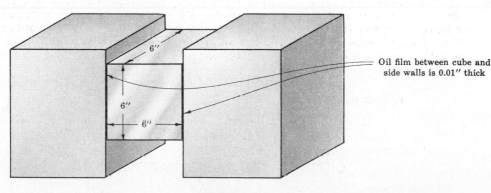

Fig. 5-28

5.34. A rotating sleeve bearing, between the shaft and the bearing housing, is used in a turbosupercharger in order to minimize the relative velocity between moving parts.

The dimensions of the turbosupercharger bearing are shown in inches on the sketch, Fig. 5-29. The shaft rotates at a speed of 60,000 revolutions per minute. The oil used in this bearing has a viscosity of $\mu = 1 \times 10^{-4}$ lb-sec/ft². Calculate the angular speed of the sleeve bearing. The various clearances C_1, C_2, C_3 between the sleeve bearing and the housing and the shaft are indicated in the figure.

Fig. 5-29   Fig. 5-30

5.35. In Fig. 5-30 is shown a fan drive designed such that there is relative motion between the drive shaft and disk assembly "A", and the housing and fan assembly "B". The angular velocities are ω_1 and ω_2 respectively ($\omega_1 > \omega_2$). Torque T is transmitted between the two parts by means of a fluid having viscosity μ. Determine the clearance a required for the given conditions. Express a in terms of $\omega_1, \omega_2, \mu, r_1, r_2$ and T.

5.36. Water that is at 60°F ($\nu = 1.217 \times 10^{-5}$ ft²/sec) is flowing through a $\frac{1}{8}$ inch inside diameter smooth tube as shown in Fig. 5-31. Considering friction losses between sections 1 and 2 only, find the velocity at the outlet (section 2).

Fig. 5-31

5.37. Air is flowing in a galvanized iron pipe ($\epsilon = .0005$ ft) having a 3.5 ft diameter at a rate of 12,000 ft³/min. The length of the pipe is 800 ft. The air temperature is 60°F. What is the difference in elevation between inlet and outlet if the static pressure change is zero?

5.38. Calculate the average velocity of water at 70°F for the pipe as shown in Fig. 5-32.

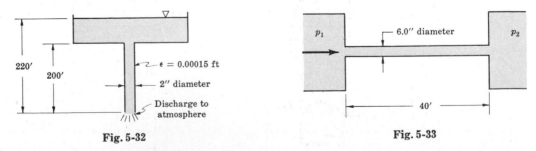

Fig. 5-32   Fig. 5-33

5.39. Determine the length of pipe which will produce the maximum flow rate in Problem 5.38.

5.40. Two water reservoirs are connected by 100 ft of 2 in. diameter smooth pipe. What is the flow rate when the difference in elevation is 25 ft?

5.41. Consider air flowing at an average velocity of 100 fps in a 6 in. smooth pipe between the two plenum chambers as shown in Fig. 5-33. Determine the difference in pressure, $p_1 - p_2$, assuming no minor losses. The air temperature is 70°F.

5.42.   Determine the pressure difference in Problem 5.41 if the minor losses are included.

5.43.   A straight-sided open glass tank for washing photographic prints has a siphon tube in one side which drains off the water. The operation is as follows. Referring to Fig. 5-34 a stream of water flows into the tank until the water reaches the top of the siphon tube, then it is cut off. The water that has filled the tank runs through the siphon until the end of the siphon is uncovered, then the cycle begins again with more fresh water flowing into the tank. How long does the drainage part of the cycle take?

Fig. 5-34

Fig. 5-35

5.44.   Water is flowing in the piping system shown in Fig. 5-35. For a flow rate in the 8 in. pipe of 4.0 ft³/sec up to the reservoir, calculate the flow rates in the other pipes and the necessary pump horsepower. The friction factors f, pipe lengths and reservoir elevations are given.

5.45.   The 200 inch Mt. Palomar telescope is mounted on a yoke mechanism which allows the lens to be focused on a desired star or nebula. The yoke can be preset so that it will track a star if its path is known.

Due to the exceptionally heavy construction of the supporting frame and yoke, the bearing design was extremely important. The total weight of the telescope is in excess of 1,000,000 pounds. This weight is supported by two sets of bearings at the north and south ends of the main rotating frame. The semicircular horseshoe shaped yoke is supported by four pad type hydrostatic bearings. Each pad must sustain a load of 164,000 lb under conditions of zero velocity. Hence the oil must be forced into the pads under pressure.

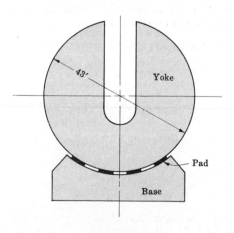

Fig. 5-36

Fig. 5-37

Fig. 5-36 and Fig. 5-37 show the yoke and pad detail. Each pad is 28 in. square and has four deep recessed regions 7 in. square. The oil is forced up through small tubes into the center of these recessed regions, the pressure over each recess being constant at the inlet value. The oil then flows slowly through the thin gap between the pad surface and the yoke surface, out to a reservoir at atmospheric pressure where it is recirculated through the pump. Assume that the oil film in the flow gap is 0.005 in. Find the following quantities:

1. Necessary oil flow rate

2. Oil inlet pressure

3. Capacity of the oil pump

4. Coefficient of friction between the yoke and bearing

5. The necessary motor capacity to rotate the yoke at a rate of one revolution per 24 hours for tracking purposes.

For the purpose of this calculation assume the oil to be SAE 20 which has a specific gravity of about 0.8 and a viscosity of about 3.85×10^{-6} lb-sec/in².

5.46.   A hydraulic dashpot or damper shown in Fig. 5-38 consists of an outer cylinder of inside diameter D_c into which is placed a solid cylinder of diameter D which is nearly equal to D_c. The ends of the outer casing cylinder are closed except for a small hole which allows the shaft to be attached to the solid inner cylinder or plunger. The casing is filled with oil and the shaft is sealed so that oil cannot leak out around it. The outer casing may be fastened rigidly to a mounting and the shaft fastened to a machine member which is to be damped. Automobile shock absorbers work on this principle.

The small clearance between the two cylinders impedes the flow of oil from the front of the plunger to the rear, or vice versa, so that the plunger can only move very slowly. As the plunger moves, the oil must flow around it through the small passage·created by the clearance.

Find the resisting force of the dashpot as a function of the relevant parameters and the velocity V at which the plunger is moved.

Hint. Neglect the inertia of the fluid in the clearance space. Treat the flow in this region as a lubrication type film. The pressure difference between the front and rear of the plunger determines the flow rate between the two regions. The force on the plunger is the sum of the pressure forces and the viscous shear.

Fig. 5-38

NOMENCLATURE FOR CHAPTER 5

A = area

C_D = drag coefficient

C_f = skin friction coefficient

C_L = lift coefficient

D = drag force and diameter

f = friction factor, functional notation

F_s = surface force

F_{s_x} = surface force in the x direction

h = distance or half distance between parallel plates

H_L = head loss

K = loss coefficient for minor losses

L = length

m = exponent for power law velocity distribution, mass

$\dot{m}$ = mass flux

$\dot{M}$ = momentum flux

n = exponent for power law velocity distribution

N_R = Reynolds number

N_{R_x} = length Reynolds number = Ux/ν

p = pressure

q = heat transfer per unit mass of flowing fluid

Q = volume flow rate

r = radial coordinate

R = radius of pipe

u = velocity in x direction, internal energy per unit mass

u_τ = wall friction velocity, $\sqrt{\tau_0/\rho}$

U = free stream or maximum velocity

v = velocity in r direction or y direction

V = velocity

$\mathbf{V}$ = velocity vector

V_x = velocity in x direction

W = width

x = coordinate

X_L = entrance length for the flow to become fully developed

y = coordinate

z = elevation

δ = boundary layer thickness

ϵ = average roughness height

η = similarity parameter

μ = viscosity

ν = kinematic viscosity

ρ = density

τ = shear stress

τ_0 = shear stress at the wall

ψ = stream function

Chapter 6

Incompressible Potential Flow

6.1 POTENTIAL FLOW THEORY

In Chapter 1 we mentioned that outside the boundary layer the flow is frictionless and irrotational and hence is known as potential flow. By potential flow we mean that the velocity is derivable from a scalar velocity potential ϕ as

$$\mathbf{V} = -\nabla\phi \tag{6.1}$$

In this chapter we will be concerned with incompressible two-dimensional potential flow theory which is valid for subsonic flow where the Mach number M is less than about 0.3. In Chapter 8 we will discuss potential compressible flow where M approaches unity or exceeds unity for supersonic flow. If the flow is incompressible, simplifications are possible which allow the use of complex variable theory to "map" the flow by means of conformal transformations.

Remember, from Chapter 3, that the rotation ω (or vorticity as it is often called) in a fluid is defined as

$$\omega = \nabla \times \mathbf{V} \tag{6.2}$$

and the angular velocity of an infinitesimal element of fluid Ω is related to the vorticity as

$$\omega = 2\Omega \tag{6.3}$$

We can illustrate this concept geometrically by examining Fig. 6-1. Restricting the analysis to one cartesian component for simplicity, the z component of $\nabla \times \mathbf{V}$ is

$$\omega_z = (\nabla \times V)_z = \frac{\partial v}{\partial x} - \frac{\partial u}{\partial y}$$

and from Fig. 6-1 we see that ω_z is twice the average value of the z component of the angular velocity of the element $\Delta x\,\Delta y$. The Δx line has angular velocity $(v|_{x+\Delta x} - v|_x)/\Delta x$ and the Δy line has angular velocity $-(u|_{y+\Delta y} - u|_y)/\Delta y$ which when averaged gives $\frac{1}{2}(\partial v/\partial x - \partial u/\partial y)$, the average angular velocity of the square $\Delta x\,\Delta y$.

Fig. 6-1. Rotation of a fluid element.

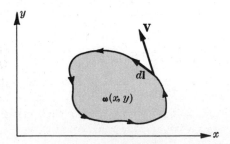

Fig. 6-2. Rotation and circulation. $\omega(x, y)$ may exist throughout the area and is related to the line integral $\oint \mathbf{V} \cdot d\mathbf{l}$.

If we now consider any two-dimensional flow (in the xy plane so that only ω_z exists), we can use Stokes' theorem to relate the rotation to a line integral as follows (see Fig. 6-2).

$$\int_A \boldsymbol{\omega} \cdot d\mathbf{A} \;=\; \int \nabla \times \mathbf{V} \cdot d\mathbf{A} \;=\; \oint \mathbf{V} \cdot d\mathbf{l} \tag{6.4}$$

which states that the area sum of the rotation over a given area is equal to the integral of the velocity (along the curve) integrated around the curve bounding the area. This line integral is called circulation, which is denoted as Γ. For any closed curve, then, the circulation is given by

$$\Gamma \;=\; \oint \mathbf{V} \cdot d\mathbf{l} \;=\; \int \boldsymbol{\omega} \cdot d\mathbf{A} \tag{6.5}$$

We can obtain a physical picture of rotation in a fluid as follows. Imagine a tiny straw floating on a fluid surface (see Fig. 6-3). If the fluid is truly irrotational, the straw moves along always parallel to itself since the fluid nowhere has any angular velocity. In actuality, of course, the straw has finite length and so may actually begin to rotate even though the fluid is irrotational. However, in the limit as the length of the test straw becomes infinitesimal it would not rotate in an irrotational flow. In contrast to this behavior, imagine a straw floating in a viscous shear flow which has rotation. Obviously the straw rotates as it moves along with the fluid, since the shearing behavior of the fluid tends to move the ends of the straw with different velocities.

Fig. 6-3. The potential vortex.

A simple example of irrotational flow is the potential vortex, of which the common whirlpool or tornado is a close approximation. In the potential vortex the velocity (which has only an angular component v_θ) is given by

$$v_\theta \;=\; C/r \tag{6.6}$$

and hence the velocity potential ϕ is

$$\phi \;=\; -C\theta \tag{6.7}$$

so that $-\nabla\phi$ is $(C/r)\,\hat{\theta}$ where C is a constant and $\hat{\theta}$ is a unit vector in the θ direction. The flow is irrotational since

$$\nabla \times \mathbf{V} \;=\; \frac{1}{r}\frac{\partial}{\partial r}\left(r \cdot \frac{C}{r} \right) \;=\; 0$$

However, at $r = 0$ there is a singularity. The circulation Γ about any contour not enclosing the origin is zero, but if the contour encloses the origin there is a finite value of Γ which is due to the rotation at the origin. Referring to Fig. 6-4, let us form Γ_1 about contour C_1.

$$\Gamma_1 \;=\; \int_0^{2\pi} v_\theta|_{r=b}\, b\, d\theta \;=\; 2\pi C$$

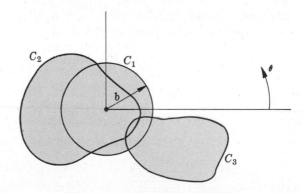

Fig. 6-4. Contours of integration about the potential vortex.

Any other contour such as C_2 enclosing the origin also gives $2\pi C$ for the circulation. The velocity potential can be written then as $\phi = -\Gamma\theta/2\pi$. Any contour such as C_3 will give zero circulation. The constant $C = \Gamma/2\pi$ is known as the strength of the vortex. In reality a vortex cannot have infinite velocity at its center and the central core of the vortex rotates as a rigid body of diameter a and angular velocity Ω. From Stokes' theorem then, $\frac{1}{2}a\Omega^2 = 2\pi C$. In nature, the tropical hurricane or typhoon is an example of a vortex. The eye of the hurricane is a central core of comparative calm where the fluid rotates approximately as a rigid body.

6.2 THE BERNOULLI THEOREM

In Chapter 3 we derived the Bernoulli equation by integrating the inviscid equation of motion along a streamline. We also obtained the same relationship by integrating the energy equation for frictionless flow. Since we are now concerned only with incompressible flow, the energy equation is unnecessary, complete information being obtainable from the equation of motion and the continuity equation.

In irrotational flow with conservative body forces (derivable from a potential as $\mathbf{B} = -\nabla\psi$), the Bernoulli equation holds between any two points in the flow (not necessarily on the same streamline). Let $d\mathbf{r}$ be an element of distance in the flow field. Then for steady incompressible irrotational flow,

$$\rho \int \nabla(V^2/2)\cdot d\mathbf{r} \;=\; -\int \nabla p \cdot d\mathbf{r} \;-\; \rho \int \nabla\psi \cdot d\mathbf{r} \tag{6.8}$$

so that
$$V^2/2 + p/\rho + \psi \;=\; \text{constant} \tag{6.9}$$

throughout the flow. We can further show that if a fluid is frictionless and the body forces are irrotational (conservative), then the flow is necessarily irrotational (except perhaps at singular points as in the potential vortex). By forming the scalar product of $\mathbf{V}$ and the equation of motion, we obtain

$$\rho \frac{D}{Dt}(V^2/2) \;+\; \mathbf{V}\cdot(\nabla p + \rho\,\nabla\psi) \;=\; 0$$

which in steady state is
$$(\mathbf{V}\cdot\nabla)(V^2/2 + p/\rho + \psi) \;=\; 0 \tag{6.10}$$

which means physically that $(V^2/2 + p/\rho + \psi)$ is a constant throughout the flow field. However, by comparing (6.10) and (6.8) we see that $\nabla\times\mathbf{V} = \boldsymbol{\omega} = 0$ is a necessary condition for (6.8) to yield (6.9) which must be valid for inviscid flow.

We conclude that inviscid steady flow must be irrotational (except at singular points) under the action of irrotational body forces.

6.3 THE KELVIN VORTEX THEOREM AND VORTEX MOTION

The circulation Γ about any contour always composed of the same fluid particles (a fluid line) is constant in an inviscid fluid with only conservative body forces. Although the vorticity under such conditions is generally zero, circulation can exist because of local regions of vorticity or singular points of vorticity.

By multiplying the equation of motion by $d\mathbf{l}$ and integrating around a contour, we obtain
$$\left(\text{remembering that } \frac{D}{Dt}(\mathbf{V}\cdot d\mathbf{l}) \;=\; \mathbf{V}\cdot\frac{D}{Dt}(d\mathbf{l}) + d\mathbf{l}\cdot\frac{D\mathbf{V}}{Dt} \right)$$

$$\frac{D\Gamma}{Dt} \;=\; \oint \frac{D}{Dt}(\mathbf{V}\cdot d\mathbf{l}) \;=\; -\oint\left(\frac{\nabla p}{\rho} + \nabla\psi\right)\cdot d\mathbf{l} \;+\; \oint \mathbf{V}\cdot\frac{D}{Dt}(d\mathbf{l})$$

But since $d\mathbf{l} = d\mathbf{r}$ and $\mathbf{V}\cdot\frac{D}{Dt}(d\mathbf{r}) = \mathbf{V}\cdot d\mathbf{V} = d(V^2/2)$,

$$\frac{D\Gamma}{Dt} \;=\; \oint \left[-dp/\rho - d\psi - d(V^2/2)\right] \;=\; 0$$

since the terms in the integrand are single valued.　Hence

$$\frac{D\Gamma}{Dt} = 0 \qquad\qquad (6.11)$$

which means physically that Γ about any fluid line contour remains constant in time as we move along with the fluid, a very important result.　Note that (6.11) is valid for both incompressible or compressible fluids.

Consider a three-dimensional vortex, such as a tornado, whose core forms a line of perhaps irregular configuration.　This line, which is the continuous locus of the centers of the two-dimensional vortices, is called a *vortex line*.　More precisely, a *vortex line* is a line in the fluid such that the tangent to it at each point is in the direction of the vorticity vector at that point.　In a rotational fluid an infinite set of vortex lines exist, but only a single line exists along the centers of the potential vortices if the vorticity is due to potential vortex motion.

A *vortex tube* is a tube which is the locus of vortex lines drawn through every point of a closed curve.

A *vortex filament* is a vortex tube of infinitesimal cross sectional area.　We can think of the solid core of a tornado as being a vortex tube, and as the core becomes smaller the tube becomes infinitesimal in cross sectional area and becomes a vortex line.　See Fig. 6-5.

A *vortex filament* and a *vortex line* are identical except that we associate strength with the filament.　The vortex tube or filament can be associated with strength defined as the integral $\int \boldsymbol{\omega} \cdot d\mathbf{A}$ over the cross section. This strength must be constant along the vortex tube. For a filament, $\boldsymbol{\omega} \cdot d\mathbf{A}$ is an intensity, vorticity per unit area, and must be constant along the filament.　Hence filaments must form closed rings (vortex rings), like a smoke ring, or end at the fluid boundaries.　A vortex filament cannot just end in the fluid unless viscosity is present to dissipate the vorticity.

Our discussion has not been confined to steady state and we must remember that all these lines and filaments move along with the fluid.

Fig. 6-5.　A vortex filament associated with a potential vortex in a fluid.　In a tornado, the core is of finite dimensions, enclosed in a vortex tube.

6.4　THE VELOCITY POTENTIAL AND STREAM FUNCTION

The condition of irrotationality is a necessary and sufficient one for the velocity to be derivable from a scalar velocity potential ϕ as

$$\mathbf{V} = -\nabla\phi \qquad\qquad (6.12)$$

which in cartesian coordinates is

$$u = -\partial\phi/\partial x, \quad v = -\partial\phi/\partial y, \quad w = -\partial\phi/\partial z$$

A velocity potential may be defined for general three-dimensional flow of a compressible fluid.　However, we will reserve such a general discussion for Chapter 8 and confine our study here to two-dimensional steady incompressible flow.　The assumption of incompressible flow is valid for subsonic aerodynamics (Mach number $M < 0.3$, approximately) and the restriction to two dimensions allows a tractable mathematical analysis, although we can discuss, at least qualitatively here, three-dimensional effects. Although the velocity potential can be defined for any irrotational flow, the term "potential flow" is often taken to mean two-dimensional incompressible flow unless otherwise indicated.

Under the conditions of incompressibility, the velocity in terms of the potential ϕ may be substituted into the continuity equation $\nabla \cdot \mathbf{V} = 0$ to yield the condition that ϕ is harmonic (satisfies Laplace's equation):

$$\nabla^2 \phi = 0 \qquad (6.13)$$

which in cartesian coordinates is

$$\frac{\partial^2 \phi}{\partial x^2} + \frac{\partial^2 \phi}{\partial y^2} + \frac{\partial^2 \phi}{\partial z^2} = 0$$

Another important function, the stream function ψ, may be defined for any two-dimensional flow field regardless of whether the flow is irrotational or not, and incompressible or compressible, although we will restrict ourselves here to steady incompressible flow. In a two-dimensional flow, the lines of constant ψ are the streamlines, and the difference between the numerical values of two streamlines is equal to the flow rate between the streamlines. The physical significance of the stream function may be seen by referring to Fig. 6-6. Going along a path from ψ_1 to ψ_2, the flow is considered positive from right to left. ψ is defined in terms of $\mathbf{V}$ in cartesian coordinates as

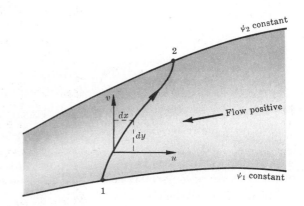

Fig. 6-6. The streamlines and stream function ψ.

$$u = -\partial\psi/\partial y, \quad v = \partial\psi/\partial x \qquad (6.14)$$

The flow rate between ψ_1 and ψ_2 (positive from right to left) is

$$Q_{12} = \int_1^2 (v\,dx - u\,dy) = \int_1^2 \left(\frac{\partial\psi}{\partial x}dx + \frac{\partial\psi}{\partial y}dy \right) = \int_1^2 d\psi = \psi_2 - \psi_1 \quad (6.15)$$

The integral is independent of the path so long as it connects the two streamlines. Physically, we insist that ψ be single-valued so that $\oint d\psi = 0$ about any closed contour unless the contour encloses a singularity such as a source or sink, in which case ψ may not be single-valued unless we restrict its domain to, say, $0 < \theta < 2\pi$.

For two-dimensional flow, then, we have from the condition of irrotationality, $\nabla \times \mathbf{V} = 0$ or $\partial v/\partial x - \partial u/\partial y = 0$, which combined with the definition of ψ gives for any steady two-dimensional incompressible potential flow,

$$\frac{\partial^2 \psi}{\partial x^2} + \frac{\partial^2 \psi}{\partial y^2} = 0$$

so that ψ is harmonic and in any coordinate system

$$\nabla^2 \psi = 0 \qquad (6.16)$$

Further, $$u = -\frac{\partial\phi}{\partial x} = -\frac{\partial\psi}{\partial y}, \quad v = -\frac{\partial\phi}{\partial y} = \frac{\partial\psi}{\partial x} \qquad (6.17)$$

which are known as the Cauchy-Riemann conditions.

In polar coordinates r and θ, we can write the fundamental relationships as

$$v_r = -\frac{\partial \phi}{\partial r} = -\frac{1}{r}\frac{\partial \psi}{\partial \theta}, \qquad v_\theta = -\frac{1}{r}\frac{\partial \phi}{\partial \theta} = \frac{\partial \psi}{\partial r} \qquad (6.18)$$

and of course we obtain $\nabla^2\phi = \nabla^2\psi = 0$.

An important consequence of the fact that ϕ and ψ are harmonic and satisfy the Cauchy-Riemann conditions is that lines of constant ϕ and ψ are orthogonal. We can easily demonstrate this fact by proving that

$$\frac{dy}{dx}\bigg|_{\phi = \text{constant}} = -\frac{dx}{dy}\bigg|_{\psi = \text{constant}}$$

Along a constant ϕ line,

$$\begin{aligned}
d\phi &= \frac{\partial \phi}{\partial x}dx + \frac{\partial \phi}{\partial y}dy = 0 \\
&= -u\,dx - v\,dy
\end{aligned}$$

and along a constant ψ line,

$$\begin{aligned}
d\psi &= \frac{\partial \psi}{\partial x}dx + \frac{\partial \psi}{\partial y}dy = 0 \\
&= v\,dx - u\,dy
\end{aligned}$$

so that from $d\phi = 0$ we obtain $dy/dx = -u/v$ and from $d\psi = 0$ we have $dy/dx = v/u$, and thus

$$\frac{dy}{dx}\bigg|_{\phi = \text{constant}} = -\frac{dx}{dy}\bigg|_{\psi = \text{constant}}$$

which is the mathematical statement that constant ϕ lines and constant ψ lines form an orthogonal network. Since these lines are perpendicular and satisfy the same differential equations, the role of ϕ and ψ may be interchanged to represent different flows.

The lines of constant ϕ and constant ψ form a mesh or network of so-called curvilinear squares. In a uniform flow the lines are all straight, but in general the streamlines and potential lines are curved. Since no fluid crosses constant ψ lines, they may be taken as solid boundaries. That is, a solid boundary may replace a streamline (ψ line) without changing the flow pattern.

Since the equations $\nabla^2\phi = \nabla^2\psi = 0$ are linear, we may superpose solutions for different flows and add directly the values of ϕ and ψ at every point in space to obtain the new values of ϕ and ψ, which represent physically the direct superposition of the various flows.

For example, we may superpose the flows created by a source, or sink, or potential vortex onto a uniform flow. In the next section we will discuss some simple two-dimensional flow patterns and some of the methods of superposing these simple flows to create more complex flow fields.

After the ϕ and ψ lines are determined for a given flow, the velocity components are then known and the pressure may be found from Bernoulli's equation.

6.5 SOME SIMPLE FLOW PATTERNS

In this section we will discuss some simple flows and their ϕ and ψ functions. In the next section we will outline some methods of solutions. However, once the simple flows are understood, many more complicated flows can be synthesized merely by superposing these simple solutions.

(a) Uniform Flow.

Assume the flow fills all space and is uniform; the velocity is $U_0\hat{\mathbf{x}}$ parallel to the x axis, where $\hat{\mathbf{x}}$ is a unit vector in the x direction. The only velocity component is u, so that $-\partial\phi/\partial x = U_0 = $ constant. Hence $\phi = -\int U_0\,dx + f(y) = -U_0 x + C_1$ since v is zero and ϕ must be independent of y. The constant C_1 is arbitrary and we take it as zero. The stream function is found from $U_0 = -\partial\psi/\partial y$ so that by similar reasoning,

$$\psi = -U_0 y + C_2 = -U_0 y$$

The flow rate between any two lines of constant ψ $(y = $ constant$)$ is given then by

$$\psi_2 - \psi_1 = \psi\big|_{y=y_2} - \psi\big|_{y=y_1} = Q_{12} = -U_0(y_2 - y_1)$$

a negative number for positive flow from right to left, since the flow here is of course from left to right. Hence for uniform flow $U_0\hat{x}$ parallel to the x axis,

$$\phi = -U_0 x, \quad \psi = -U_0 y \tag{6.19}$$

The ϕ and ψ lines are shown in Fig. 6-7.

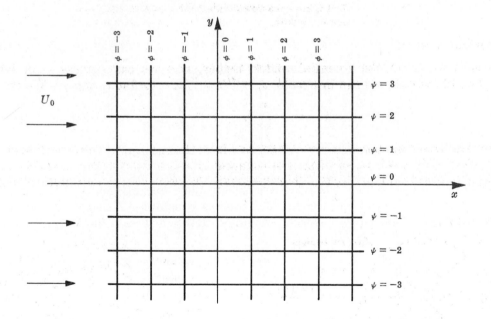

Fig. 6-7. Uniform flow parallel to the x axis.

(b) Sources and Sinks.

A point source or sink is a singularity from which the ψ lines radiate and about which the ϕ lines form concentric circles. For a source of flow rate Q, the radial velocity v_r is $Q/2\pi r$ and the angular velocity v_θ is zero. Q is the source strength and is physically the total flow rate per unit depth of fluid. Hence since $v_r = -\dfrac{\partial\phi}{\partial r} = -\dfrac{1}{r}\dfrac{\partial\psi}{\partial\theta}$,

$$\psi = -\frac{Q}{2\pi}\theta, \quad \phi = -\frac{Q}{2\pi}\ln r \tag{6.20}$$

For a sink (6.20) is still valid but Q is negative, so that v_r is negative and the flow is inward. Of course any arbitrary constant may be added to ϕ or ψ without changing the velocities.

The flow pattern is shown in Fig. 6-8. At the origin, of course, $\phi \to \infty$ as $r \to 0$, which is no surprise since, in reality, we must always have a finite area, not a point, into which the fluid flows.

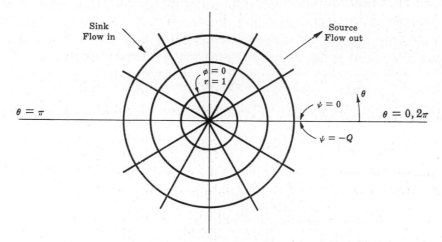

Fig. 6-8. The source and sink. If at $\theta = 2\pi$ we say $\psi = -Q$, then Q is a positive number for a source and negative for a sink.

(c) Potential Vortex.

We have discussed the potential vortex earlier; now we can discuss it in terms of ϕ and ψ. For the vortex, we can integrate $v_\theta = C/r = \Gamma/2\pi r$ to find ϕ and ψ. We obtain

$$\phi = -\frac{\Gamma}{2\pi}\theta, \quad \psi = \frac{\Gamma}{2\pi}\ln r \qquad (6.21)$$

We may note that the role of ϕ and ψ here are interchanged from the source and the sink. And, indeed, in Fig. 6-9 we see that the constant ϕ and ψ lines form a similar pattern of radial lines and concentric circles. The term $\Gamma/2\pi$ is known as the strength of the vortex.

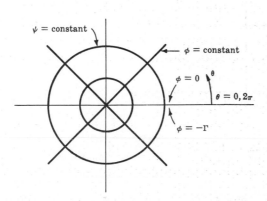

Fig. 6-9. The potential vortex and its ϕ and ψ lines.

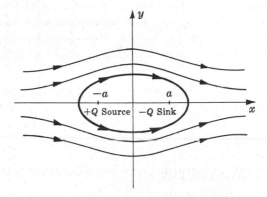

Fig. 6-10. The flow over a Rankine oval. The oval is the dividing streamline between the fluid flowing between the source and sink and the fluid in the free stream.

(d) Superposition.

As an example of the superposition of two or more potential flows let us examine the flow shown in Fig. 6-10, the Rankine oval. A source and sink of equal strength are spaced equidistant from the origin on the x axis in a uniform flow $U_0\hat{\mathbf{x}}$. All of the fluid from the source is absorbed by the sink, and there is a definite dividing streamline between the fluid of the uniform stream and the fluid transferring from the source to the sink. This dividing streamline may be considered as the surface of the cross section of an oval-shaped cylinder. The superposition of these flows, then, will give us the external flow around an oval cylinder. By combining many sources and sinks we could obtain the approximate flow about an arbitrarily-shaped cylinder, symmetrical about the x axis. And, by using a distributed source along the x axis we can find the exact flow about such a body; however, the strength distribution function may be difficult to calculate in general, and involves the solution to an integral equation. Such methods are useful in aerodynamics.

Returning to the Rankine oval, we have

$$
\begin{aligned}
\phi &= -U_0 x - Q/2\pi \ln r_1 + Q/2\pi \ln r_2 \\
\psi &= -U_0 y - (Q/2\pi)\theta_1 + (Q/2\pi)\theta_2
\end{aligned}
\tag{6.22}
$$

which may be written as

$$
\begin{aligned}
\phi &= -U_0 x - \frac{Q}{4\pi} \ln \frac{(x+a)^2 + y^2}{(x-a)^2 + y^2} \\
\psi &= -U_0 y - \frac{Q}{2\pi}\left(\tan^{-1}\frac{y}{x+a} - \tan^{-1}\frac{y}{x-a} \right)
\end{aligned}
\tag{6.23}
$$

(e) The Method of Images.

As we have stated, a streamline may be considered as a solid boundary. If we can find a flow such that a constant ψ line coincides with a boundary, we can specify the flow along that boundary. For flow over an object, the surface of the object is a line of constant ψ.

Often it is possible by superposing flow patterns to create a constant ψ line coincident with a wall or boundary. One useful example of this method is the method of images. Consider two identical flows separated by a midplane; the midplane must have no flow across it and hence can be thought of as a solid boundary.

By the method of images we superpose flows by reflecting about a solid boundary across which there is no flow. Many rather complex flows can be synthesized by this method.

For example, consider the flow from a source (or sink) near a wall (the x axis) as shown in Fig. 6-11. We construct the flow due to a source at $y = a$ and an image source at

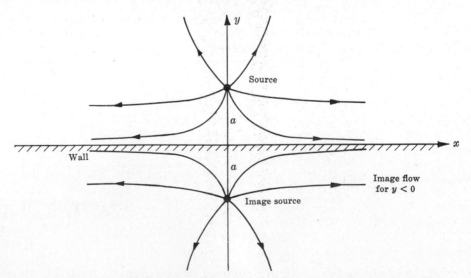

Fig. 6-11. The method of images used to create the flow from a source near a wall.

$y = -a$. The two flows buck each other along the x axis which is a dividing streamline or wall. The functions ϕ and ψ are, obviously,

$$\phi = -\frac{Q}{4\pi} \ln \{[(y-a)^2 + x^2][(y+a)^2 + x^2]\}$$

$$\psi = -\frac{Q}{2\pi}\left(\tan^{-1}\frac{y-a}{x} + \tan^{-1}\frac{y+a}{x}\right) \tag{6.24}$$

such that at $y = 0$ the component of velocity normal to the wall, $v(y = 0)$, is zero.

6.6 THE COMPLEX POTENTIAL

In general, problems in potential flow involve the solution of the Laplace equations $\nabla^2\phi = 0$ and $\nabla^2\psi = 0$ subject to the appropriate boundary conditions, which are usually that at infinity the flow is uniform or zero and that the fluid does not cross solid bodies over which the fluid flows. However, except for certain simple geometries for which ϕ and ψ may be easily found either by solving the harmonic equation or by direct integration of $\mathbf{V} = -\nabla\phi$ if the velocity is known such as in the simple examples of the preceding section, the determination of ϕ and ψ is best accomplished by the use of complex variable theory and conformal transformations.

(a) The Complex Function $F(z)$.

In two dimensions, the fact that ϕ and ψ are harmonic and satisfy the Cauchy-Riemann equations is necessary and sufficient for the definition of a complex function F (called the complex potential) as

$$F = \phi + i\psi = F(z) \tag{6.25}$$

where $i = \sqrt{-1}$ and $z = x + iy$. In the complex $(\phi + i\psi)$ plane, ϕ and ψ form a rectangular co-ordinate grid. We consider ϕ and ψ to be functions of z, the complex variable, instead of x and y. The xy plane represents the physical flow plane.

In general,

$$z = x + iy = re^{i\theta} = r(\cos\theta + i\sin\theta)$$

See Fig. 6-12. z is a complex number with real part x and imaginary part y. F may be written as a function of z; then the real part of F is $\phi(x, y)$ and the imaginary part of F is $\psi(x, y)$.

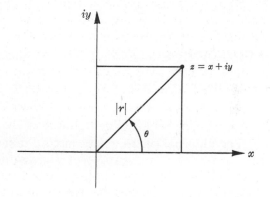

Fig. 6-12. The complex z plane.

Together, the Cauchy-Reimann conditions with the conditions that ϕ and ψ be single-valued and all partial derivatives of ϕ and ψ be continuous, imply that F is analytic (or holomorphic). An analytic function $F(z)$ is one which (1) is finite and single-valued within a closed contour C and (2) all derivatives exist and are single-valued. The real and imaginary parts of an analytic function of z are called conjugate functions and are harmonic. ϕ and ψ are conjugate functions and we know that $\nabla^2\phi = \nabla^2\psi = 0$.

Referring to Fig. 6-12, dF/dz may be evaluated for an arbitrary Δz. If we take Δz parallel to the x axis, we have $\Delta z = \Delta x$ and

$$\frac{dF}{dz} = \frac{\partial\phi}{\partial x} + i\frac{\partial\psi}{\partial x}$$

and if we take Δz parallel to the y axis we have $\Delta z = i\,\Delta y$ and

$$\frac{dF}{dz} = -i\frac{\partial\phi}{\partial y} + \frac{\partial\psi}{\partial y}$$

Hence either expression is appropriate and both must be equal, so that we obtain the Cauchy-Riemann conditions by equating real and imaginary parts:

$$\frac{\partial \phi}{\partial x} = \frac{\partial \psi}{\partial y} \quad \text{and} \quad \frac{\partial \psi}{\partial x} = -\frac{\partial \phi}{\partial y}$$

(b) The Complex Velocity.

By differentiating the complex potential F, we get

$$\frac{dF}{dz} = \frac{\partial \phi}{\partial x} + i\frac{\partial \psi}{\partial x}$$

or
$$-\frac{dF}{dz} = u - iv \tag{6.26}$$

and $-dF/dz = u - iv$ is called the complex velocity. The conjugate potential $\bar{F} = (\phi - i\psi)$ may also be differentiated with respect to $\bar{z}$, $(x - iy)$ the complex conjugate variable, to give $-d\bar{F}/d\bar{z} = u + iv$. Then

$$\frac{dF}{dz} \cdot \frac{d\bar{F}}{d\bar{z}} = u^2 + v^2 = V^2 \tag{6.27a}$$

which is the square of the velocity in the fluid. It is often useful to find V^2 once $F(z)$ is known, without further calculation. To illustrate the meaning of $\bar{F}$, suppose $F = z + iz^2$, then $\bar{F} = \bar{z} - i\bar{z}^2$. If $F = z + a^2/z$, $\bar{F} = \bar{z} + a^2/\bar{z}$. $\bar{F}(\bar{z})$ means that all explicit i are changed in sign and all z are changed to $\bar{z}$. Alternatively,

$$V^2 = \left|\frac{dF}{dz}\right|^2 \tag{6.27b}$$

since $|V|$ is the modulus of $(u - iv)$.

Once V^2 is known, the Bernoulli equation may be used to find the pressure in the flow.

A stagnation point where $u = v = 0$ is found by setting $dF/dz = 0$.

(c) Conformal Mapping.

The physical plane where motion takes place is the z or (x, y) plane where $\psi = $ constant lines are curved and represent streamlines. In the F plane ϕ and ψ form a rectangular network. Now it is possible to pass from the z plane to another plane, say the $\zeta = \eta + i\xi$ plane by a transformation which preserves the orthogonal nature of ϕ and ψ. Such a transformation is known as a mapping function of the form

$$\zeta = f(z) \tag{6.28}$$

It can be shown that an infinitesimal triangle in the z plane maps into a similar infinitesimal triangle in the ζ plane with preservation of the angles and similarity. Such transformations are used in map making; the Mercator projection is a conformal mapping of the Earth onto a flat surface. By choosing appropriate functions of the form (6.28), we can construct flow patterns about complex shapes if we know the flow pattern $F(z)$ for a simple shape. Then by (6.28) we can arrive at $F(\zeta)$ which allows description in the ζ plane of a more complex flow.

For example, consider the mapping shown in Fig. 6-13 below. The upper half of the ζ plane may be mapped into the sector shown in the z plane by the transformation

$$\zeta = z^\alpha \tag{6.29}$$

where the origin $0 \rightarrow 0'$ is excluded.

Fig. 6-13. Conformal mapping of the upper half of the ζ plane into the sector π/α in the z plane.

If we were to consider a uniform flow from left to right in the ζ plane,

$$F = -U_0\zeta = -U_0\eta - iU_0\xi = \phi + i\psi \tag{6.30}$$

then this flow would be $\qquad F = -U_0\zeta = -U_0 z^\alpha \tag{6.31}$

in the z plane and be as shown in Fig. 6-13(b), representing flow in a corner.

6.7 THE COMPLEX POTENTIAL FOR SOME SIMPLE FLOWS

The method of complex variables is one of the most powerful tools in potential flow theory and forms the basis of subsonic aerodynamics. By successive transformations from a simple flow pattern into a more complex one it is often possible to construct the flow around objects such as cylinders, airfoils, etc. In this section we list a few important complex potentials and describe their flow patterns. Furthermore, complex potentials can be superposed, just as ϕ and ψ were, to generate various patterns.

(a) The Uniform Flow Field.

As we have previously stated,

$$F = -U_0 z = -U_0(x + iy) = \phi + i\psi \tag{6.32}$$

is the complex potential for a uniform flow U_0 parallel to the x axis. Equating real and imaginary parts, $\phi = -U_0 x$ and $\psi = -U_0 y$, which we have already learned previously and which has been shown in Fig. 6-7.

(b) Sources and Sinks.

For a source of strength Q, the complex potential is

$$F = -(Q/2\pi) \ln z = -(Q/2\pi) \ln re^{i\theta} \tag{6.33}$$

It is convenient to represent z as $re^{i\theta}$ here so that we can separate F into real and imaginary parts: $F = -(Q/2\pi)(\ln r + i\theta)$. Hence we obtain $\phi = -(Q/2\pi) \ln r$ and $\psi = -(Q/2\pi)\theta$ as shown in Fig. 6-8. A sink is identical except that Q is negative, or if we define Q as the strength of the sink,

$$F = (Q/2\pi) \ln z \tag{6.34}$$

(c) Potential Vortex.

For a potential vortex, as shown in Fig. 6-9,

$$F = i\frac{\Gamma}{2\pi} \ln z = i\frac{\Gamma}{2\pi} \ln re^{i\theta} \tag{6.35}$$

so that $\phi = -(\Gamma/2\pi)\theta$ and $\psi = \Gamma/2\pi \ln r$, where $\Gamma/2\pi$ is the strength of the vortex and Γ is the circulation.

(d) The Dipole or Doublet.

Consider a source of strength Q at point A and a sink of strength $-Q$ at point B. Let point A be located at $z = ae^{i\alpha}$ and B at $-ae^{i\alpha}$ as shown in Fig. 6-14. The complex potential for the superposed flow is then

$$F = -\frac{Q}{2\pi} \ln (z - ae^{i\alpha}) + \frac{Q}{2\pi} \ln (z + ae^{i\alpha}) \qquad (6.36)$$

The streamlines are circles passing through A and B.

Now as the points A and B approach each other, the limiting flow as $A \to B$ $(a \to 0)$ is known as a doublet or dipole. The complex potential for this flow (as $a \to 0$ and A and B coincide) is

$$F = \frac{me^{i\alpha}}{z} \qquad (6.37)$$

where $m = Qa/\pi = $ constant, even as $a \to 0$. As $a \to 0$, $Q \to \infty$ and $\lim\limits_{a \to 0} Qa/\pi = m$, the strength of the dipole. The flow patterns are nested circles for streamlines and velocity potential as shown in Fig. 6-15. These patterns are similar to the electrostatic dipole field configuration of a positive and a negative charge, and to the radiation pattern from a dipole radio antenna.

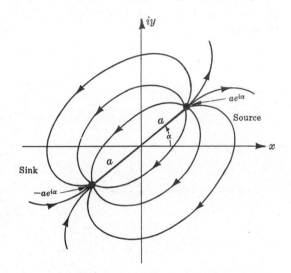

Fig. 6-14. A source and sink.

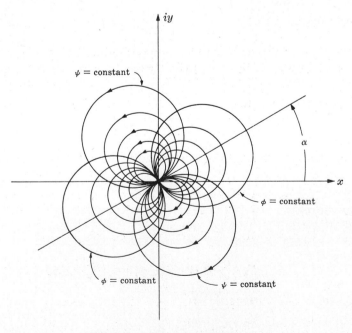

Fig. 6-15. The dipole flow.

Separating (6.37) into ϕ and ψ, we get

$$\phi = \frac{m(x\cos\alpha + y\sin\alpha)}{(x^2 + y^2)}, \qquad \psi = \frac{m(x\sin\alpha - y\cos\alpha)}{(x^2 + y^2)} \qquad (6.38a)$$

which represent circles tangent to the origin. If $\alpha = 0$ we get

$$\phi = \frac{mx}{x^2 + y^2}, \qquad \psi = -\frac{my}{x^2 + y^2} \qquad (6.38b)$$

(e) Streaming Motion Past A Circular Cylinder.

Referring to Fig. 6-16, a uniform flow U_0 flows in the positive x direction. A cylinder of radius a is located at the origin. The complex potential for flow about the cylinder is given by

$$F = -U_0(z + a^2/z) \qquad (6.39)$$

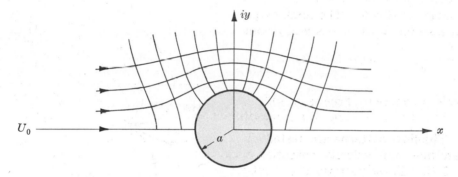

Fig. 6-16. Flow around a circular cylinder. The figure is symmetric about the x axis.

The stream function is obtained from (6.39) as

$$\psi = -U_0\left(r\sin\theta - \frac{a^2}{r}\sin\theta\right) = -U_0 y(1 - a^2/r^2) = -U_0 y + \frac{a^2 U_0 y}{x^2 + y^2} \qquad (6.40)$$

which shows that the flow over a cylinder is represented as the superposition of a uniform flow over a dipole of strength $-a^2 U_0$. (The negative sign merely interchanges the role of source and sink in Fig. 6-15.)

The velocity potential ϕ is given by

$$\phi = -U_0 x(1 + a^2/r^2) \qquad (6.41)$$

At $r = a$, the contour of the cylinder must coincide with a streamline. And indeed, at $r = a$, $\psi = 0$.

The velocity field may be found from $-dF/dz = u - iv$ which may be put into polar coordinate form,

$$\frac{dF}{dz} = -U_0 + \frac{U_0 a^2}{z^2} = -U_0 + \frac{U_0 a^2 e^{-2i\theta}}{r^2}$$

$$= U_0\left(\frac{a^2}{r^2}\cos 2\theta - 1\right) + iU_0\frac{a^2}{r^2}\sin 2\theta$$

so that the cartesian velocity components are

$$u = -U_0\left(\frac{a^2}{r^2}\cos 2\theta - 1\right), \qquad v = -U_0\frac{a^2}{r^2}\sin 2\theta \qquad (6.42)$$

and the polar coordinate velocity components v_r and v_θ are then

$$v_r = U_0(1 - a^2/r^2)\cos\theta, \qquad v_\theta = -v_0(1 + a^2/r^2)\sin\theta \qquad (6.43)$$

and hence

$$V^2 = u^2 + v^2 = v_r^2 + v_\theta^2 = \frac{dF}{dz}\cdot\frac{d\bar{F}}{d\bar{z}} = U_0^2\left[1 + \frac{a^4}{r^4} + \frac{2a^2}{r^2}(\sin^2\theta - \cos^2\theta)\right]$$

The pressure around the cylinder can now be found from Bernoulli's equation

$$\frac{p}{\rho} + \frac{V^2}{2} = \text{constant} = \frac{p_\infty}{\rho} + \frac{U_0^2}{2} = \frac{p_0}{\rho}$$

where p_0 is the stagnation pressure at any point in the flow where V is zero and p_∞ is the free stream pressure where the velocity is U_0. On the surface of the cylinder, at $r = a$,

$$p|_{r=a} = p_0/\rho - 2U_0^2(1 + \sin^2\theta - \cos^2\theta)$$

The maximum velocity is $2U_0$ and occurs on the top and bottom of the cylinder ($\theta = \pi/2, 3\pi/2$), and there the pressure is a minimum. Since the pressure is symmetrical about the x and y axes, there is no net force on the cylinder. In actuality, of course, separation would occur on the rear of the cylinder and drag would be present. However, if the cylinder is deformed so that the rear is drawn out to a point, separation may be prevented and the potential flow solution is quite good except for the boundary layer which gives rise to skin friction. In the next section we will discuss airfoil theory where potential flow theory gives good results for the velocity and pressure distribution over a streamlined body.

6.8 CIRCULATION AND THE JOUKOWSKI THEOREM

In this section we will discuss the superposition of a potential vortex flow (of finite circulation) on the uniform flow over a cylinder. The resultant pressure distribution gives rise to a lift on the cylinder, and forms the basis for aerodynamic theory.

(a) The Circulation about a Circular Cylinder.

Consider the uniform flow over a circular cylinder with circulation. The circulation could be brought about by rotation of the cylinder such that if there were no uniform flow, the peripheral velocity of the cylinder of radius a would be the corresponding tangential velocity of the potential vortex at radius a. The total complex potential is then

$$F = -U_0(z + a^2/z) + i\frac{\Gamma}{2\pi}\ln z/a \qquad (6.44)$$

so that the cylinder is part of the line $\psi = 0$. To determine the form of the streamlines ($\psi = \text{constant}$) we find the complex velocity $-dF/dz$.

$$\frac{dF}{dz} = U_0(a^2/z - 1) + i\frac{\Gamma}{2\pi z}$$

and the stagnation points are given by solving for z the equation

$$U_0(a^2/z - 1) + i\frac{\Gamma}{2\pi z} = 0$$

so that

$$z|_{V=0} = a\left(i\frac{\Gamma}{4\pi a U_0} \pm \sqrt{1 - \frac{\Gamma^2}{16\pi^2 a^2 U_0^2}}\right) \qquad (6.45)$$

There are three cases: $\Gamma^2 < (4\pi a U_0)^2$, $\Gamma^2 = (4\pi a U_0)^2$, $\Gamma^2 > (4\pi a U_0)^2$. In Fig. 6-17 below we plot the flow for each case.

There is a lift L on the cylinder, and we develop below a general formula for this lift and show that it is $L = -i\rho U_0\Gamma$; that is, it is a force in the y direction of $-\rho U_0\Gamma$.

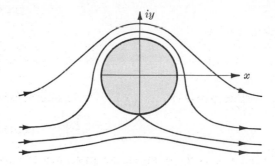

(a) $\Gamma^2 < (4\pi a U_0)^2$. The two stagnation points lie on bottom of the cylinder.

(b) $\Gamma^2 = (4\pi a U_0)^2$. One stagnation point lies on the bottom center.

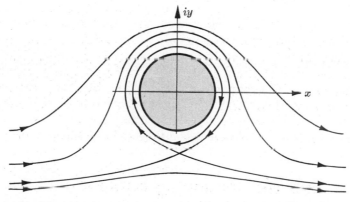

(c) $\Gamma^2 > (4\pi a U_0)^2$. The single stagnation point moves down.

Fig. 6-17.   The streamlines for flow with circulation over a circular cylinder.

The value of Γ here depends on the rotary speed of the cylinder, and that is why a baseball, golf ball, or ping-pong ball curves when it has spin. For the flow shown in Fig. 6-17 the value of Γ is negative and the lift is in the $+y$ direction.

(b) The Blasius Theorem and the Theorem of Kutta and Joukowski.

We will derive now the general forces and moments acting on a cylinder in potential flow and will apply the results to the calculation of lift on an airfoil. Referring to Fig. 6-18, we integrate the pressure around the cylinder to find the total complex force $X + iY$ and moment M acting on the cylinder (per unit length). From Bernoulli's equation, $p = p_0 - \tfrac{1}{2}\rho V^2$ where p_0 is a constant. Then,

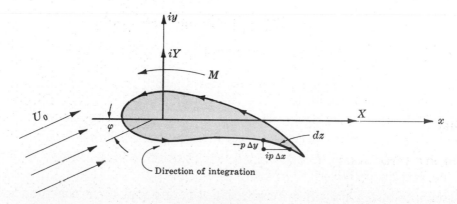

Fig. 6-18.   Flow over a cylinder with lift and drag indicated.

$$p = p_0 - \tfrac{1}{2}\rho V^2 = p_0 - \tfrac{1}{2}\rho \frac{dF}{dz} \cdot \frac{d\bar{F}}{d\bar{z}}$$

and the integral of p_0 around the cylinder makes no contribution. On the cylinder, $\psi = $ constant, so that $d\bar{F} = dF$. We have, referring to Fig. 6-18,

$$
\begin{aligned}
X - iY &= -\oint_C (p\,dy + ip\,dx) = -\oint_C ip\,d\bar{z} \\
&= \oint_C -\tfrac{1}{2}\rho \frac{dF}{dz} \cdot \frac{d\bar{F}}{d\bar{z}} \cdot d\bar{z} = -\tfrac{1}{2}\rho \oint_C \left(\frac{dF}{dz}\right)^2 dz
\end{aligned}
\tag{6.46}
$$

The moment M is given by

$$
\begin{aligned}
M &= \oint_C p(x\,dx + y\,dy) = \mathrm{Re} \oint_C pz\,d\bar{z} \\
&= \mathrm{Re} \oint_C -\tfrac{1}{2}\rho \frac{dF}{dz} \cdot \frac{d\bar{F}}{d\bar{z}} \cdot z\,d\bar{z} = \mathrm{Re} \left\{-\tfrac{1}{2}\rho \oint_C z\left(\frac{dF}{dz}\right)^2 dz\right\}
\end{aligned}
\tag{6.47}
$$

where Re indicates the real part.

Once we know $F(z)$, then the lift and moment can be found immediately. Further, by expanding $F(z)$, explicit expressions for X, Y and M may be found. These are given by the theorem of Kutta and Joukowski for flow of a uniform stream over a cylinder of arbitrary shape.

The complex function dF/dz may be expanded (for $|z|$ sufficiently large) as

$$-\frac{dF}{dz} = U_0 e^{-i\varphi} + A/z + B/z^2 + \cdots \tag{6.48}$$

because clearly as $z \to \infty$, $-dF/dz$, the complex velocity, becomes U_0 which is the free stream value of the velocity which in general makes an angle φ with the x axis as shown in Fig. 6-18. Then F may be determined as

$$F = -U_0 e^{-i\varphi} z - A \ln z + B/z + \cdots \tag{6.49}$$

We see that the second term is exactly the complex potential due to circulation. Hence $A = -i\Gamma/2\pi$. Thus

$$\left(\frac{dF}{dz}\right)^2 = U_0^2 e^{-2i\varphi} - i\frac{\Gamma U_0 e^{-i\varphi}}{\pi z} - \frac{\Gamma^2 - 8\pi^2 B U_0 e^{-i\varphi}}{4\pi^2 z^2} + \cdots$$

and from the Blasius theorem and the theory of complex integration we obtain

$$X - iY = \tfrac{1}{2}i\rho \left[2\pi i \left(-i\frac{\Gamma U_0 e^{-i\varphi}}{\pi z}\right)\right] = i\rho\Gamma U_0 e^{-i\varphi} \tag{6.50}$$

which is the Kutta-Joukowski theorem. It states that the net force (lift) on the cylinder is directed perpendicular to the free stream velocity and equal to $-\rho U_0 \Gamma$. In general we can conclude:

1. The force is always perpendicular to the free stream velocity (and is hence designated as a lift force).

2. The lift is positive if Γ is negative (for a positive U_0 in the x direction). There is no lift without circulation. The lift depends only on Γ (which may depend on the profile).

3. There is no force parallel to the direction of U_0 (drag force). Drag can only be produced by skin friction in the boundary layer if the flow is potential around the body and there is no separation.

4. In real flows the above results are accurate and form the foundation of subsonic aerodynamics, so long as the cylinder is streamlined. If separation occurs, a drag

force due to a pressure decrease in the wake occurs but is not predicted by potential flow.   Flow over a circular cylinder always separates (except in very slow viscous flow) and the potential flow is not very accurate there.

In summary, then, lift is $-\rho U_0 \Gamma$, and the task that remains is to determine Γ for a given cylinder such as an airfoil, Fig. 6-19.   The angle of attack α is the angle between the free stream velocity and a fixed chord line on the profile.   It is defined so that L and hence Γ are zero for $\alpha = 0$.   The value of Γ tends to increase for certain shapes as α is increased until stall occurs and separation occurs.   Then a drastic reduction in lift suddenly occurs as Γ drops.

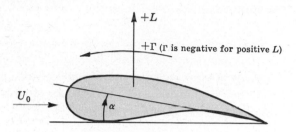

Fig. 6-19.   Lift L on a cylinder.   The angle of attack is α.   When $\alpha = 0$, $L = 0$, by definition of α.

6.9   AIRFOIL THEORY

We will now apply the results of the previous section to the calculation of lift for some simple shapes.   In particular, we are interested in the airfoil shape and the physical cause of circulation.   As we pointed out, a rotating circular cylinder generates circulation; but what about an airfoil which certainly isn't rotating?   The cause of circulation there is explained by the Joukowski hypothesis which very simply states that infinite velocities are inadmissible in real flows.

(a)   The Airfoil.

As we have seen, lift is due to circulation; and there is, indeed, circulation about an airfoil.   Referring to Fig. 6-20, the Kutta-Joukowski hypothesis states that the singular point at the trailing edge, where the velocity must be infinite by potential flow theory, is impossible in a real flow and the flow will adjust itself so that the stagnation point moves to the trailing edge and hence removes the singular point.   The value of circulation, Γ, about the airfoil is just that amount necessary to shift the stagnation point to the trailing edge.   Clearly Γ must be negative to effect this transfer, and hence the lift $L = -\rho U_0 \Gamma$ is positive as shown.

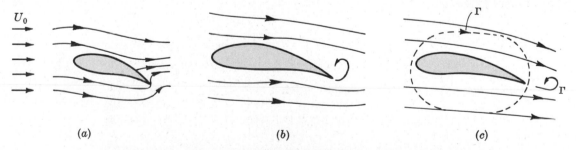

Fig. 6-20.   Circulation and its formation about an airfoil.   The stagnation point moves to the rear as the flow progresses and this transfer determines Γ.   Fig. (a), (b) and (c) show successive stages in the startup of the airfoil.

As the flow starts up, the potential flow is as shown in Fig. 6-20(a).   The stagnation point moves to the rear and a small vortex is formed which sheds off and is lost downstream. By Kelvin's theorem the total circulation in the fluid must be constant in time and hence a Γ equal but of opposite sign to the shed vortex is created about the airfoil.   The total circulation in the fluid remains zero but the value about the airfoil is a negative number. The shed vortex falls far behind and gets left on the airfield. (A large control contour including the airfoil and the airfield gives zero circulation.)

The formation of this trailing vortex can easily be seen by dragging a spoon through a cup of coffee. Draw the spoon, inclined at an angle of attack through the coffee and you will see the trailing vortex form and shed off. (See Fig. 6-21.)

Fig. 6-21. A spoon in a coffee cup generating a trailing vortex. The curved spoon approximates a cambered airfoil.

(b) Calculation of the Potential Flow and Lift.

The flow around any given airfoil may be described by the appropriate complex potential F. The simplest airfoil is the Joukowski airfoil which may be obtained from the flow about a circular cylinder by a single conformal transformation. Referring to Fig. 6-22, flow about the cylinder in the ζ plane maps into the flow in the z plane by the Joukowski transformation. The transformation from ζ to z here is

$$z = \zeta + l^2/\zeta \qquad (6.51)$$

and the flow about the displaced cylinder (center at C) for flow at an apparent angle of attack φ is

$$F = -U_0\left[(\zeta - be^{i\theta})e^{-i\varphi} + \frac{a^2}{(\zeta - be^{i\theta})e^{-i\varphi}}\right] \qquad (6.52)$$

If $b = 0$ (C at the origin) the Joukowski transformation maps the cylinder into an ellipse centered at the origin with major axis along the x axis. The point $\zeta = l$ transforms into $z = 2l$ and is the trailing edge where dF/dz has a singularity which must be removed by circulation.

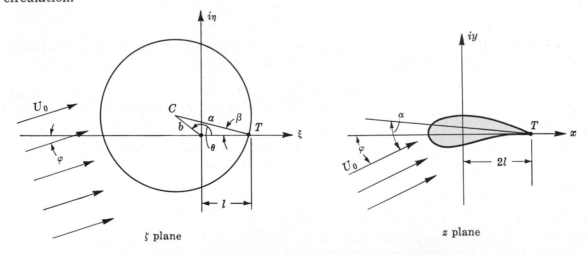

Fig. 6-22. The Joukowski transformation. The apparent angle of attack is φ. L is $\perp$ to U_0. The absolute angle of attack is α (to be determined). When $\alpha = 0$, $L = 0$ by definition of α.

To equation (6.52) we must add the complex potential due to circulation, so that the velocity at the trailing edge can be made finite. The total $F(\zeta)$ about the cylinder must then be

$$F(\zeta) = -U_0\left[e^{-i\varphi}(\zeta - be^{i\theta}) + \frac{a^2 e^{i\varphi}}{(\zeta - be^{i\theta})} + i\frac{\Gamma}{2\pi}\ln\left(\frac{\zeta - be^{i\theta}}{a}\right)\right] \qquad (6.53)$$

The complex velocity in the z plane at point T, the trailing edge, is

$$\frac{dF}{dz}\bigg|_T = \frac{dF}{d\zeta} \cdot \frac{d\zeta}{dz}\bigg|_{\text{point } T}$$

and $dz/d\zeta = 1 - l^2/\zeta^2 = 0$ at the trailing edge. Hence the value of $dF/d\zeta$ must be zero at $z = -2l$ for dF/dz to be finite there, and this condition determines the value of Γ and hence the lift on the airfoil.

From (6.53) we find $dF/d\zeta = 0$ as

$$\frac{dF}{d\zeta} = -U_0\left(e^{-i\varphi} - \frac{a^2 e^{i\varphi}}{(\zeta - be^{i\theta})^2}\right) + i\frac{\Gamma}{2\pi}\frac{1}{(\zeta - be^{i\theta})} = 0 \tag{6.54}$$

and from Fig. 6-22, $(\zeta - be^{i\theta}) = [\zeta - l + ae^{i(\pi-\beta)}]$ so that at $\zeta = l$, (6.54) gives

$$-U_0(1 - e^{-2i(\pi-\beta)+2i\varphi}) + i\frac{\Gamma}{2\pi a}e^{-i(\pi-\beta)+i\varphi} = 0 \tag{6.55}$$

which may be solved for Γ. We can equate either the real or imaginary parts of (6.55) and get the same answer for Γ.

$$\Gamma = 4\pi a U_0 \sin(\pi - \beta - \varphi) = -4\pi a U_0 \sin(\beta + \varphi) \tag{6.56}$$

and we see that Γ is a negative number which depends on the free stream velocity, apparent angle of attack φ, and the parameters a and β which determine the size and camber of the airfoil. Since $L = -\rho U_0 \Gamma$ is perpendicular to the free stream, L is a positive number for values of $(\beta + \varphi)$ positive. We call the angle $(\beta + \varphi)$ the absolute angle of attack α. By definition, when $\alpha = 0$, the lift L is zero.

In aerodynamics, the term angle of attack usually refers to the angle α, not φ.

The lift coefficient C_L is defined by

$$C_L = \frac{L}{c\rho U_0^2/2} \tag{6.57}$$

where L is the lift per unit length of the airfoil and c is the chord length or width of the airfoil. For a Joukowski airfoil $c \approx 4a$ and we get for C_L,

$$C_L = \frac{\rho U_0(4\pi a U_0)\sin\alpha}{4a\rho U_0^2/2} \cong 2\pi\alpha \tag{6.58}$$

In practice C_L increases with α linearly as (6.58) shows for small α, then drops off rapidly when the stall angle α_S is reached as separation occurs and the circulation is lost. The stall angle and exact C_L versus α curves are best determined experimentally.

(c) Three-dimensional Effects.

The lift on an airfoil is due to the line vortex which moves with the airfoil (the *bound vortices*). As we showed earlier, these line vortices cannot just end at the tip of the wing, but must continue into the free fluid (until dissipated by viscosity). If the circulation were uniform along the wing the vortices would be shed off the tips and pass downstream in the *trailing vortices*, as shown in Fig. 6-23. This simple "horseshoe" vortex system is not quite correct, however, because the value of Γ generally varies along the wing. As a consequence, vorticity is shed off the trailing

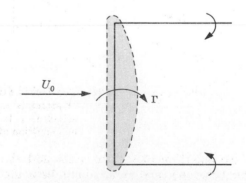

Fig. 6-23. A simple horseshoe vortex pattern over a three-dimensional wing. The top view of the wing is shown.

edge all along the wing, generating a vortex sheet made of a superposition of "horseshoe" vortex systems of various strength, as shown in Fig. 6-24. Alternatively, a physical picture of the vortex sheet can be obtained by imagining a plane of ball bearings extending downstream behind the wing; the air on top tends to flow inward, and the air on the bottom tends to flow outward. This difference in flow direction of the wind coming off the trailing edge generates the vortex layer or sheet. The reason for the skewing of the flow is readily understood by remembering that there is pressure differential between the top and bottom of the wing and from the center to the tips.

(a)   (b)

Fig. 6-24.   The vortex sheet behind a wing.

Ultimately, a few wing lengths or less behind the wing, the vortex sheet forms two distinct vortex lines as shown in Fig. 6-25. This phenomenon may be observed in multi-jet aircraft (where the nacelles are wing suspended). The jet vapor trails may be seen to coalesce to form two distinct trails, one from the left wing and one from the right wing.

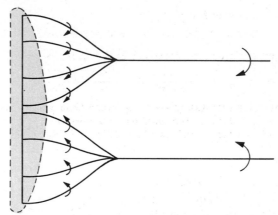

Fig. 6-25.   The vortex sheet rolls up into two distinct vortices,
spaced at somewhat less than the wing span.

One last point to mention is the induced drag. Because of the vortex sheet, there is an induced "downwash" which, in effect, changes the angle of attack of the wing and causes the lift vector to point at a slight angle (to the rear) to the free stream velocity. Hence the lift vector has a component parallel to the flight direction. This component is a drag force, called the "induced" drag. The remainder of the drag, the "profile" drag, is made of the skin friction drag of the boundary layer and a "form" drag due to the shedding of the Karman vortices in the vortex sheet (i.e. the wake).

We cannot pursue the subject here, but potential flow theory and boundary layer theory together constitute the foundation of subsonic aerodynamics.

References

1. Glauert, H., *The Elements of Aerofoil and Airscrew Theory*, 2nd ed., Cambridge University Press, 1948.

2. Lamb, Sir Horace, *Hydrodynamics*, 6th ed., Cambridge University Press, 1932, (also Dover).

3. Milne-Thompson, L. M., *Theoretical Hydrodynamics*, 3rd ed., Macmillan, 1957.

4. Prandtl, L., and Tietjens, O. G., *Applied Hydro- and Aeromechanics*, Dover, 1957.

5. Robertson, J. M., *Hydrodynamics in Theory and Application*, Prentice-Hall, 1965.

6. Streeter, V. L., *Fluid Dynamics*, McGraw-Hill, 1948.

Solved Problems

6.1. A tornado may be idealized as a potential vortex with a rotational "eye" or core which behaves approximately as a solid body. A rough rule of thumb is that the radius of the eye is of the order of 100 ft. How does the pressure vary along the ground around the "eye"? For a tornado with a maximum wind velocity of 100 mi/hr, what is the maximum drop in pressure? This underpressure is partly responsible for the lifting of roofs and much of the damage inflicted by tornados.

The velocity v_θ is $\Gamma/2\pi r$ and hence

$$\Gamma = 2\pi r v_\theta = 2\pi(100 \text{ ft})(100 \times 5280/3600 \text{ ft/sec}) = 9.2 \times 10^4 \text{ ft}^2/\text{sec}$$

From Bernoulli's equation (assuming standard air at pressure p_0),

$$p - p_0 = \tfrac{1}{2}V^2\rho = -\frac{\Gamma^2\rho}{8\pi^2r^2} = -\frac{(9.2\times 10^4)^2(0.0023)}{8\pi^2r^2} = -\frac{2.4\times 10^5}{r^2} \text{ psf}$$

The negative sign indicates that the pressure is lower than the atmospheric pressure far from the tornado. At $r = 100$ ft (which is the smallest r where we can apply potential flow theory) the pressure is reduced by 24.6 psf (which is about 1.7 psi) below atmospheric.

6.2. In Fig. 6-26 a source is located at a distance a from a wall. What is the total pressure force on the wall? Behind the wall $(x > 0)$ the pressure is p_0, the stagnation pressure.

The flow is given by assuming an image source at $x = a$ when we place the real source at $x = -a$ as shown in the figure. The complex potential for the total flow is

$$F = -\frac{Q}{2\pi}[\ln(z+a) + \ln(z-a)]$$

and

$$\bar{F} = -\frac{Q}{2\pi}[\ln(\bar{z}+a) + \ln(\bar{z}-a)]$$

and we find

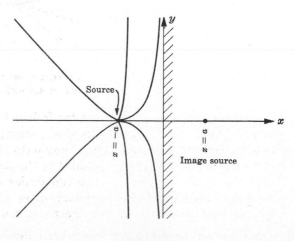

Fig. 6-26

$$V^2 = \frac{dF}{dz} \cdot \frac{d\bar{F}}{d\bar{z}} = \frac{Q^2}{4\pi^2}\left[\frac{1}{(z+a)} + \frac{1}{(z-a)}\right]\left[\frac{1}{(\bar{z}+a)} + \frac{1}{(\bar{z}-a)}\right]$$

which may be simplified to the following (since $z = x + iy$ and $\bar{z} = x - iy$):

$$V^2 = \frac{Q^2(x^2 + y^2)}{\pi^2[(x^2 + y^2)^2 - 2a^2(x^2 - y^2) + a^4]}$$

and from Bernoulli's equation $p^2/\rho + \frac{1}{2}V^2 = p_0/\rho$ we find the pressure difference across the wall as $p - p_0 = -\frac{1}{2}V^2\rho$, and the total force per unit length of the wall (out of the paper) on the wall (positive to the right) is

$$\text{Force} = \int_{-\infty}^{+\infty} (p - p_0)|_{x=0}\, dy = -\frac{1}{2}\rho \int_{-\infty}^{+\infty} V^2|_{x=0}\, dy = -\rho Q^2 \frac{\rho Q^2}{2\pi^2}\int_{-\infty}^{+\infty} \frac{y^2\, dy}{(y^2 + a^2)^2} = -\frac{\rho Q^2}{4\pi a}$$

The negative result indicates that the net force is to the left and the wall is sucked towards the source.

6.3. Rework Problem 6.2 except that the source is replaced by a sink.

The complex potential is identical except that Q is now a negative number. However, in the solution for the force on the wall, Q appears squared so that the sign is irrelevant. Hence we conclude that the net force on the wall is the same for a source or a sink. The wall tends to be sucked towards the source or sink.

The result might seem surprising, but in each case the velocity increase near the wall causes a pressure defect and the result is the same.

6.4. Wind flows down a hill and over a rise, in the shape of a sector of a circle of radius b, and out onto the plains. Map the flow. Find ϕ and ψ explicitly. This flow is shown in Fig. 6-27.

We begin with flow over a circular cylinder, then map it into an angle with the transformation of equation (6.29).

In the ζ plane, referring to Fig. 6-28,

$$F(\zeta) = -U_0(\zeta + a^2/\zeta)$$

so that from $\zeta = z^\alpha$ we have

$$F(z) = -U_0(z^\alpha + a^2/z^\alpha)$$

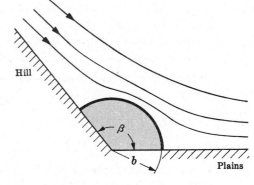

Fig. 6-27

as the complex potential in the physical z plane. α is given by $\pi/\alpha = \beta$. It is important to note that the free stream velocity V_0 in the z plane is not uniform but varies with r and θ. U_0 does not map directly from the ζ to the z plane as it did for the Joukowsky airfoil transformation. Furthermore, the radius a of the circle in the ζ plane is not the same as the radius b of the sector in the z plane.

ζ plane z plane

Fig. 6-28

We have
$$z^\alpha = r^\alpha e^{\alpha i\theta} = r^\alpha(\cos\alpha\theta + i\sin\alpha\theta)$$

and
$$F = -U_0[r^\alpha(\cos\alpha\theta + i\sin\alpha\theta) + (a^2/r^\alpha)(\cos\alpha\theta - i\sin\alpha\theta)]$$

so that
$$\phi = \operatorname{Re} F = -U_0 r^\alpha[\cos\alpha\theta + a^2 r^{-2\alpha}\cos\alpha\theta]$$

$$\psi = \operatorname{Im} F = -U_0 r^\alpha[\sin\alpha\theta - a^2 r^{-2\alpha}\sin\alpha\theta]$$

The behavior of the free stream velocity may be seen by finding the radial velocity v_r, given by $-\partial\phi/\partial r$.

$$v_r = \alpha U_0 r^{\alpha-1}[\cos\alpha\theta - a^2 r^{-2\alpha}\cos\alpha\theta]$$

so that for $\theta = \pi/\alpha$ (along the wall), we have

$$v_r|_{\theta=\pi/2} = -\alpha U_0[r^{\alpha-1} - a^2 r^{-(1+\alpha)}]$$

For large r, and $\alpha > 1$, $v_r|_{\theta=\pi/2}$ becomes large and is approximately $-\alpha U_0 r^{(\alpha-1)}$. The negative sign indicates flow inward from infinity.

The radius b can be related to the radius a. The radius b is given by setting $v_r = 0$. Thus

$$1 - a^2 r^{-2\alpha}|_{r=b} = 0 \qquad \text{from which} \qquad b = a^{1/\alpha}$$

0.5.   The transformation

$$z = C(\zeta + \lambda\zeta^{-1}), \qquad 0 \le \lambda \le 1, \ 0 \le C$$

transforms a circle with unit radius in the ζ plane to an ellipse in the z plane which is shown in Fig. 6-29.

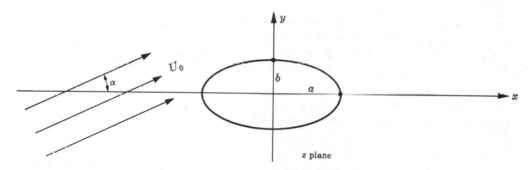

Fig. 6-29

(a) Making use of this transformation, find the complex potential $F(z)$ for the steady flow past an elliptic cylinder with semi-axes a and b as shown in Fig. 6-29. The undisturbed velocity at the infinity has magnitude U_0 and makes an angle α with respect to the x axis.

(b) Let $z = k\cosh\gamma$ where k is a real constant and $\gamma = \xi + i\eta$. Then constant ξ lines are a family of ellipses in the z plane and constant η lines are a family of confocal hyperbolas orthogonal to the ellipses. The resulting grid of constant ξ and η lines in the z plane are referred to as elliptic coordinates. Using these elliptic coordinates and denoting the magnitude of the velocity of the fluid on the surface of the elliptic cylinder described in part (a) by V, express V in terms of η when $\alpha = 0$.

(a) Let us first examine the $\zeta-z$ transformation, $z = C(\zeta + \lambda\zeta^{-1})$. Let $\zeta = e^{i\theta}$ for a circle of unit radius and $z = x + iy$. Then

$$z = C(e^{i\theta} + \lambda e^{-i\theta}) = C(1+\lambda)\cos\theta + iC(1-\lambda)\sin\theta$$

and $x = C(1+\lambda)\cos\theta$, $y = C(1-\lambda)\sin\theta$ so that $\dfrac{x^2}{C^2(1+\lambda)^2} + \dfrac{y^2}{C^2(1+\lambda)^2} = 1$. Hence

$$a = C(1+\lambda), \ b = C(1-\lambda); \quad C = (a+b)/2, \ 4c^2\lambda = a^2 - b^2 \tag{1}$$

γ plane $\qquad\qquad\qquad\qquad\qquad$ ζ plane

Fig. 6-30

Now for flow over a unit circle in a γ plane shown in Fig. 6-30,

$$F(\gamma) \;=\; A(\gamma + \gamma^{-1})$$

Then $\zeta = \gamma e^{i\alpha}$ so that $\qquad\qquad F(\zeta) \;=\; A(\zeta e^{-i\alpha} + \zeta^{-1} e^{i\alpha})$

From the given transformation $z = C(\zeta + \lambda\zeta^{-1})$ we obtain

$$\zeta \;=\; \frac{1}{2C}(z \pm \sqrt{z^2 - 4C^2\lambda})$$

We take $(+)$ here so that the domain outside of the circle in the ζ plane, Fig. 6-30, is transformed to the domain outside of the ellipse in the z plane. Then

$$F(z) \;=\; A\left[\frac{e^{-i\alpha}}{2C}(z + \sqrt{z^2 - 4C^2\lambda}) + \frac{2Ce^{i\alpha}}{(z + \sqrt{z^2 - 4C^2\lambda})}\right] \qquad (2)$$

Now $\left.\dfrac{dF}{dz}\right|_{z \to \infty} = \dfrac{A}{C}e^{-i\alpha}$ but $-\left.\dfrac{dF}{dz}\right|_{z \to \infty} = (u - iv)\Big|_{z \to \infty} = U_0 e^{-i\alpha}$; hence

$$A/C \;=\; -U_0 \qquad (3)$$

Using values of C, λ and A obtained by equations (1) and (3), equation (2) becomes

$$F(z) \;=\; -\tfrac{1}{2}U_0(a+b)\left\{\frac{[z + \sqrt{z^2 - (a^2 - b^2)}]e^{-i\alpha}}{a + b} + \frac{[z - \sqrt{z^2 - (a^2 - b^2)}]e^{i\alpha}}{a - b}\right\} \qquad (4)$$

(b) We are given $z = k\cosh\gamma$, $\gamma = \xi + i\eta$ and we can write

$$x + iy \;=\; k\cosh(\xi + i\eta) \;=\; k(\cosh\xi\cos\eta + i\sinh\xi\sin\eta)$$

Hence $\qquad\qquad \dfrac{x^2}{k^2\cosh^2\xi} + \dfrac{y^2}{k^2\sinh^2\xi} = 1, \qquad \dfrac{x^2}{k^2\cos^2\eta} - \dfrac{y^2}{k^2\sin^2\eta} = 1$

Let $\xi = \xi_0$ represent the ellipse with semi-axes a and b in the z plane; then $k\cosh\xi_0 = a$ and $k\sinh\xi_0 = b$, or

$$\left.\begin{aligned} k^2 = a^2 - b^2, \qquad \tanh\xi_0 = b/a \\[2mm] \frac{e^{2\xi_0}}{(a+b)^2} = \frac{e^{-2\xi_0}}{(a-b)^2} = \frac{1}{k^2} \end{aligned}\right\} \qquad (5)$$

Equation (4) becomes (with $\alpha = 0$)

$$F(\gamma) \;=\; -\tfrac{1}{2}U_0(a+b)\sqrt{a^2 - b^2}\left(\frac{e^\gamma}{a+b} + \frac{e^{-\gamma}}{a-b}\right)$$

$$\bar{F}(\bar{\gamma}) \;=\; -\tfrac{1}{2}U_0(a+b)\sqrt{a^2 - b^2}\left(\frac{e^{\bar{\gamma}}}{a+b} + \frac{e^{-\bar{\gamma}}}{a-b}\right)$$

$$(V_\gamma^2)_{\xi=\xi_0} = \frac{dF}{d\gamma} \cdot \frac{d\bar{F}}{d\bar{\gamma}} = \frac{U_0^2}{4}(a+b)^2(a^2-b^2)\left\{ \frac{e^{2\xi}}{(a+b)^2} + \frac{e^{-2\xi}}{(a-b)^2} - \frac{e^{2i\eta}}{(a^2-b^2)} - \frac{e^{-2i\eta}}{(a^2-b^2)} \right\}$$

Equation (5) gives

$$V_\gamma^2\big|_{\xi=\xi_0} = \tfrac{1}{4}U_0^2(a+b)^2\{2 - 2\cos 2\eta\} = U^2(a+b)^2\sin^2\eta$$

$$V^2 = V_z^2\big|_{\xi=\xi_0} = \frac{V_\gamma^2\big|_{\xi-\xi_0}}{|dz/d\gamma|_{\xi=\xi_0}^2} = U_0^2\left(\frac{a+b}{a-b}\right)\left(\frac{\sin^2\eta}{\sin^2\eta + \sinh^2\xi_0}\right)$$

where $\xi_0 = \tanh^{-1} b/a$.

6.6. Find the complex potential for a source located in the midplane of a two-dimensional channel as shown in Fig. 6-31.

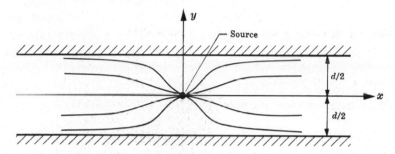

Fig. 6-31

By the method of images we set up an infinite array as shown in Fig. 6-32.

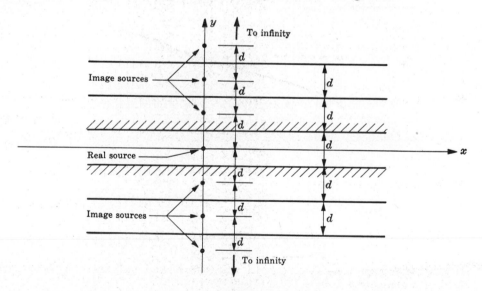

Fig. 6-32

The complex potential then is found by summing over all the images:

$$F = \sum_{n=0}^{\infty} -\frac{Q}{2\pi}\ln(z+ind) + \sum_{n=1}^{\infty} -\frac{Q}{2\pi}\ln(z-ind) = \sum_{n=-\infty}^{+\infty} -\frac{Q}{2\pi}\ln(z+ind) = -\frac{Q}{2\pi}\ln\left(\sinh\frac{\pi z}{d}\right)$$

By evaluating F for $-d/2 < y < d/2$, we have the flow between the walls at $\pm d/2$.

We can find ϕ and ψ as

$$\phi = -\frac{Q}{2\pi}\ln\left(\sinh\frac{\pi x}{d}\cos\frac{\pi y}{d}\right), \qquad \psi = -\frac{Q}{2\pi}\ln\left(\cosh\frac{\pi x}{d}\sin\frac{\pi y}{d}\right)$$

6.7.   A cylinder of 1 in. diameter, shown in Fig. 6-33, rotates
as indicated at 3600 rpm in standard air which is flowing over the cylinder at 100 ft/sec. Estimate the lift
on the cylinder (per unit length).

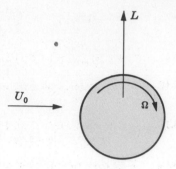

Fig. 6-33

Use $L = -\rho U_0 \Gamma$, where Γ here may be estimated by assuming

$$\Gamma = \oint \mathbf{V} \cdot d\mathbf{l} = \int_0^{2\pi} -(r\Omega)(r\,d\theta) = -2\pi r^2 \Omega$$
$$= -2\pi(1/24 \text{ ft})^2 (3600 \times 2\pi/60 \text{ rad/sec}) = -4.1 \text{ ft}^2/\text{sec}$$

Thus $L = -\rho U_0 \Gamma = -(0.0023 \text{ slug/ft}^3)(100 \text{ ft/sec})(-4.1 \text{ ft}^2/\text{sec}) =$
0.94 lb/ft.

6.8.   The flow over a two-dimensional cylinder (symmetrical about the x axis) may be determined for any arbitrary shape $f(x)$ by the appropriate distribution, $q(x)$, of sources
along the x axis as indicated in Fig. 6-34. For a given shape $y = f(x)$, determine
$q(x)$. We assume the nose of the body to be at the origin.

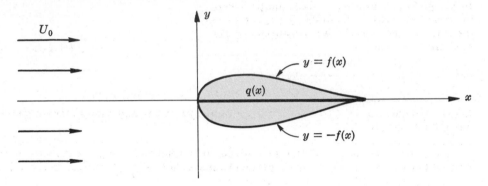

Fig. 6-34

The body surface $\pm f(x)$ is a streamline, and clearly the distribution $q(x)$ must change sign
along the x axis and no fluid crosses the body boundary, $\pm f(x)$.

For any elemental source $q(x)\,dx$ the complex potential is

$$dF = -\frac{q(x')\,dx'}{2\pi} \ln(z - x')$$

where we use the primes on x to indicate a variable of integration as opposed to x in $z = x + iy$,
the position where F is evaluated. Then

$$F = \int_0^L -\frac{q(x')}{2\pi} \ln(z - x')\,dx'$$

But the imaginary part of F is ψ, and $\psi(x, y) = $ arbitrary constant $= 0$ is the same as $y = f(x)$.
Taking the imaginary part of F, we have

$$\text{Im } F = \psi = \int_0^L -\frac{q(x')}{2\pi} \tan^{-1}\frac{y}{x - x'}\,dx'$$

and on the surface, $y = f(x)$ and $\psi = 0$ so that

$$0 = \int_0^L -\frac{q(x')}{2\pi} \tan^{-1}\frac{f(x)}{x - x'}\,dx'$$

which is an integral equation to be solved for $q(x)$. In general, the solution is not simple. The flow
over the Rankine oval (Fig. 6-10) was a special, simple example of this method.

This technique is useful for flow calculations over airships and ship hulls.

Supplementary Problems

6.9. Can a vortex tube terminate in the fluid or must it form a ring?

6.10. In a tornado, can you define a vortex filament or only a tube? Suppose the core is of uniform cross section.

6.11. In a viscous shear flow, can a vortex filament be defined? Can a vortex tube be defined? In Poiseuille flow, what do the vortex lines look like?

6.12. Why does the air over the top of a wing flow inward towards the center of the wing and outward towards the wing tips on the bottom of the wing?

6.13. An arctic quonset hut experiences a lift due to wind blowing over it. Its shape is approximately semicircular. For a wind of 80 mph and air temperature of 0°F, what is the lift per unit length on a 10 ft diameter hut shown in Fig. 6-35?

Fig. 6-35

6.14. In the preceding problem, does it matter where the door is located in determining the lift when the door is left open? What determines the pressure inside the hut?

6.15. Discuss the flow $z = C \cosh F$. Show that

$$x = C \cosh\phi \cos\psi, \qquad y = C \sinh\phi \sin\psi$$

and the streamlines ($\psi = $ constant) are confocal hyperbolas and this pattern might represent flow through an aperture.

6.16. Calculate the force on a wall due to a dipole of strength m located a distance a from the wall. Assume the wall is parallel to the x axis and the dipole is aligned parallel to the x axis.

6.17. In the preceding problem, what is the force if the dipole is inclined at an angle α to the wall?

6.18. What happens in Problems 6.16 and 6.17 if we take the dipole strength as $-m$? Does the force on the wall have a different sign?

6.19. Discuss the motion $F = z^2 - 1$.

6.20. Find F, ϕ, and ψ and plot the streamlines for flow due to a source in the wall of a channel of width d shown in Fig. 6-36. (*Hint.* Set up an infinite array of images and sum up.)

6.21. Discuss the flow $F = Az^2$.

6.22. Discuss the flow $z^2 = F^3$.

Fig. 6-36

6.23. Find F and draw the streamlines for flow through a channel with two sources located opposite each other as shown in Fig. 6-37.

Fig. 6-37

Fig. 6-38

6.24. A potential vortex is located a distance d from a wall. Discuss the flow. See Fig. 6-38.

6.25. Discuss the flow about a circular cylinder near a wall, Fig. 6-39, assuming $d \gg D$.

6.26. In Problem 6.25 the cylinder rotates about its axis with angular speed Ω. Discuss the flow.

6.27. Discuss the force on the cylinder in Problem 6.26.

Fig. 6-39

6.28. A light piece of cardboard with a pin stuck through it and inserted up through a spool, is shown in Fig. 6-40. If one blows air lightly down through the spool the cardboard disk is held up and does not fall. Why? Actually the air is deflected radially and the flow between the cardboard and spool is similar to a potential source flow. What would the pressure distribution be along the surface of the disk. Does this explain the lift?

If one blows very hard, the disk falls. Why? What about the momentum of the air rushing down through the spool? The air must change its direction if it begins to flow radially. Does this help you explain it?

Fig. 6-40

6.29. A source is located at position z_1 and a sink at position z_2. For general strengths, what is F, ϕ and ψ?

6.30. For a source and sink of equal strength lying along a line $z = e^{i\alpha}$ and equidistant, a, from the origin, and submerged in a uniform flow along the x axis, plot the streamlines.

6.31. A source is located as shown in Fig. 6-41 between a right angle. What is the complex potential? Find the complex velocity.

Fig. 6-41

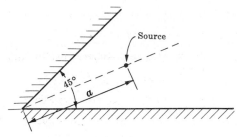

Fig. 6-42

6.32. A source is located midway between a $45°$ angle wall, at a distance a from the origin. Find F and describe the flow. See Fig. 6-42.

6.33. A tornado of circulation Γ has a solid core of diameter a. Calculate the pressure distribution in the tornado. Do you think this low pressure might contribute to the devastating effect of a tornado?

6.34. An ocean whirlpool is shown in Fig. 6-43. The pressure along any line A-A decreases from the hydrostatic value $\rho g h$ at large radii to zero (gage) at point P. From potential vortex theory estimate the equation of the free surface of the whirlpool. What happens in the center at sufficient depths? Can the whirlpool just stop, or must it go all the way to the ocean floor? Can you explain why objects caught in a whirlpool tend to get sucked down?

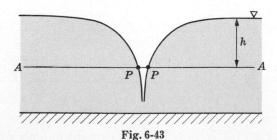

Fig. 6-43

NOMENCLATURE FOR CHAPTER 6

F = complex potential

Im = denotes imaginary part

L = lift

M = moment

p = pressure

p_0 = stagnation pressure

p_∞ = free stream pressure, where $V = U_0$

Q = volumetric flow rate

Re = denotes real part

U_0 = free stream velocity

u = x component of velocity

$\mathbf{V}$ = velocity vector

v = y component of velocity

v_r = r component of velocity

v_θ = θ component of velocity

w = z component of velocity

X = x component of force

Y = y component of force

z = $(x + iy)$ = complex variable

Γ = circulation

ρ = density

ϕ = velocity potential

ψ = stream function, gravitational potential

$\boldsymbol{\Omega}$ = angular velocity vector

$\boldsymbol{\omega}$ = vorticity or rotation vector

$(^-)$ = denotes complex conjugate

Chapter 7

One-Dimensional Compressible Flow

7.1 INTRODUCTION

For many physical flows the assumptions of "frictionless" and "incompressible" lead to a reasonably accurate model representation (Chapter 6). In other flows the viscosity was seen to be important (Chapter 5). In this chapter we consider one-dimensional flows where the density variations are of major importance in determining the character of the flow. Although the restriction of one-dimensional flow may seem rather severe, this physical model is found to be a good approximation to many actual flows.

This chapter is restricted exclusively to internal flows. In applying the one-dimensional assumption, it is assumed that the quantities (pressure, temperature, velocity, etc.) are uniform over any cross section of the channel.[1]

Internal flows (flow in pipes, channels, and ducts) may involve property changes along the channel resulting from area change, heating and friction. And, indeed, all of these do take place in real flows. However, we will investigate these effects by looking at them one at a time. This is done for two reasons: first, there are many flows where only one effect is actually important; second, this leads to a better understanding of the role of these effects in more general flows.

(a) Ideal Gas Approximation.

The ideal gas approximation is valid for low and moderate density gases. This approximation yields property relations which are convenient in making up the total mathematical model. For example, if we assume the fluid is an ideal gas, we have

$$p v = R T \qquad (7.1)$$

where p is absolute pressure, v is specific volume, R is the gas constant, and T the absolute temperature. In addition, if it is assumed that the specific heats at constant volume and constant pressure do not vary with temperature, we have between two states 1 and 2 the following additional property relationships

$$u_2 - u_1 = c_v(T_2 - T_1) \qquad (7.2)$$

$$h_2 - h_1 = c_p(T_2 - T_1) \qquad (7.3)$$

where u is the specific internal energy, h is specific enthalpy, and c_v and c_p are the specific heats at constant volume and constant pressure respectively. Further, if the flow is assumed to be frictionless and adiabatic (and thus isentropic) and follows the ideal gas equation of state, then we have the following equation describing the process

$$p v^k = \text{constant} \qquad (7.4)$$

where k is the ratio of specific heats, c_p/c_v.

---

[1]Strictly speaking, one-dimensional flow is defined as a flow where only one spatial coordinate is required for description. This could be realized by fully developed pipe flow. However, we are concerned only with the flows of uniform conditions at each cross section.

(b) Propagation of an Infinitesimal Disturbance.

A disturbance in a fluid will propagate through the fluid at a well-defined velocity which depends on the properties of the fluid. The velocity of propagation depends on the magnitude of the disturbance. If the disturbance is very small, then the velocity of propagation of the disturbance is called the velocity of sound or acoustic velocity. This velocity is itself a property of the fluid — a very important property in compressible flow.

The velocity of sound may be determined by considering a fluid in a long tube as shown in Fig. 7-1. An infinitesimal disturbance has occurred and the wave front is moving at velocity a. We will fix our coordinate system to the wave so that the undisturbed fluid is moving relative to the wave with velocity a.

Fig. 7-1.   Propagation of a sound wave.

The momentum equation for the control volume of cross sectional area A shown is

$$A[p - (p + dp)] = \rho A a[(a + dV) - a]$$

which gives

$$dp = \rho a\, dV$$

where ρ is the density and a is the speed of the sound wave and is known as the sonic speed. The continuity equation for the control volume is

$$\rho A a = (\rho + d\rho)(a + dV)A$$

Simplifying and neglecting higher order terms we have

$$\frac{d\rho}{\rho} = -\frac{dV}{a}$$

Combining the momentum and continuity equations,

$$dp/d\rho = a^2$$

This equation is often written

$$(\partial p/\partial \rho)_s = a^2 \qquad (7.5)$$

since the disturbance is infinitesimal and thus the process is reversible and adiabatic and hence isentropic as the subscript s on the derivative indicates.

For an ideal gas we may use equation (7.4) to show that

$$a^2 = kRT \qquad (7.6)$$

(c) The Mach Cone.

A small disturbance at a point in a stationary fluid will be propagated radially in all directions, with the wave fronts for different times forming concentric spheres as shown in Fig. 7-2. Next, if we allow the disturbance source to move at velocity V, which is less than a, we have again spheres depicting the wave fronts for different times, but these are no longer concentric. This is shown in Fig. 7-3 below. For the case where $V > a$, i.e. the velocity of the disturbance is greater than the acoustic velocity, a conical surface is formed where the flow is undisturbed on one side and

Fig. 7-2. Stationary infinitesimal disturbance.

has felt the effect of the wave on the other. The half angle of the cone is $\alpha = \sin^{-1}(a/V) = \sin^{-1}(1/M)$ as shown in Fig. 7-4. Here M is the Mach number V/a.

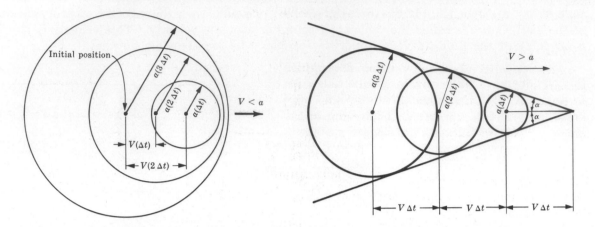

Fig. 7-3. Infinitesimal disturbance having $V < a$.

Fig. 7-4. Infinitesimal disturbance having $V > a$. $\alpha = \sin^{-1}(1/M)$.

We can imagine the disturbances of Fig. 7-3 and Fig. 7-4 as being stationary and the fluid having velocity V from right to left and obtain the same pictures. These figures demonstrate the basic difference in subsonic and supersonic flow. In subsonic flow, $M < 1$, an infinitesimal disturbance will be felt throughout the entire flow. In supersonic flow, $M > 1$, a disturbance is felt only over a portion of the flow. This leads to some interesting and important differences in the behavior of subsonic and supersonic flows.

7.2 ISENTROPIC FLOW

Many flows may be described with reasonable accuracy by assuming that they are isentropic. This assumption implies they are frictionless and adiabatic with no discontinuities in the flow properties. Examples of such flows are (1) external flows in regions of small velocity and temperature gradients and (2) internal flows such as in nozzles and diffusers where the area change is the predominant cause of change of flow conditions.

(a) Effect of Area Change.

The energy equation for steady, one-dimensional, adiabatic flow of an ideal gas with no shaft work is

$$V^2/2 + c_p T = \text{constant}$$

Using equation (7.6) for the acoustic velocity, we have

$$V^2/2 + \frac{k}{k-1}\frac{p}{\rho} = \text{constant}$$

Differentiation gives

$$V\,dV + a^2\frac{d\rho}{\rho} = 0 \tag{7.7}$$

The one-dimensional steady flow continuity equation may be differentiated to give

$$\frac{d\rho}{\rho} + \frac{dA}{A} + \frac{dV}{V} = 0 \tag{7.8}$$

Equations (7.7) and (7.8) are combined to give

$$\frac{dA}{A} = \frac{dV}{V}(M^2 - 1) \tag{7.9}$$

Equation (7.9) yields some surprising results. We see that for $M < 1$ an increase in area produces a decrease in velocity. However, for $M > 1$ just the opposite is true and an increase in area produces an increase in velocity. Now we see once again the importance of the Mach number as a parameter in describing the flow.

(b) Converging Nozzle Flow.

Let us investigate the flow in a converging passage such as shown in Fig. 7-5. We will assume that the fluid is an ideal gas, the flow is one-dimensional, steady, adiabatic and frictionless. The continuity equation is

$$\dot{m} = A_2 V_2 / v_2 \qquad (7.10)$$

where $\dot{m}$ is the mass rate of flow and v is the specific volume, $1/\rho$. The energy equation in terms of enthalpy h is

$$\tfrac{1}{2}(V_2^2 - V_1^2) = h_1 - h_2 \qquad (7.11)$$

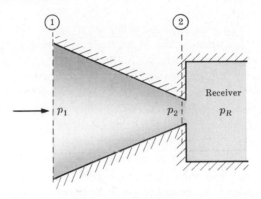

Fig. 7-5. Converging nozzle.

If we assume that $V_1 \ll V_2$, the equation (7.11) may be written as (using isentropic and property relationships)

$$V_2 = \left\{ \frac{2k}{k-1} p_1 v_1 [1 - (p_2/p_1)^{(k-1)/k}] \right\}^{1/2} \qquad (7.12)$$

Equations (7.10) and (7.12), along with the isentropic relationship $p_1 v_1^k = p_2 v_2^k$, are combined to give

$$\dot{m}/A_2 = \left\{ \frac{2k}{k-1} \frac{p_1}{v_1} [(p_2/p_1)^{2/k} - (p_2/p_1)^{(k+1)/k}] \right\}^{1/2} \qquad (7.13)$$

If we take the inlet conditions as fixed, then the mass flow change takes place as a result of a change in p_2 only. This result is shown in Fig. 7-6 as plotted from equation (7.13). Also, the actual mass flow results are shown in a plot of $\dot{m}$ versus p_R/p_1 where p_R is the receiver pressure.

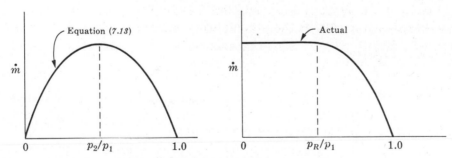

Fig. 7-6. Mass flow in a converging nozzle.

There is obviously some discrepancy between the actual and predicted results. The actual results and those predicted by the equation are in good agreement from the point where $p_R/p_1 = 1.0$ down to the value of receiver pressure where the mass flow reaches a maximum. We see that a further reduction in receiver pressure yields no change in the mass flow rate. We also observe that experimentally the throat pressure p_2 is never less than the value for maximum mass flow. This minimum throat pressure is called the critical pressure p_c and is found by differentiating equation (7.13) and setting the result equal to zero. For this we obtain

$$(p_2/p_1)_{\text{max flow}} = p_c/p_1 = [2/(k+1)]^{k/(k-1)} \qquad (7.14)$$

By combining equations (*7.12*) and (*7.14*), the Mach number is found to be equal to unity where the pressure is critical. These results are not surprising, then, in light of the results of the previous section. We see that in order to increase the Mach number above unity, a diverging section extension would need to be added.

(c) Converging-diverging Nozzle.

We saw that in a converging nozzle the maximum Mach number was unity. And from equation (*7.9*) we saw that in order to increase the Mach number above unity, the area must increase. Thus in order to make supersonic flow possible, the flow passage must be a section of decreasing area followed by a section of increasing area as shown in Fig. 7-7.

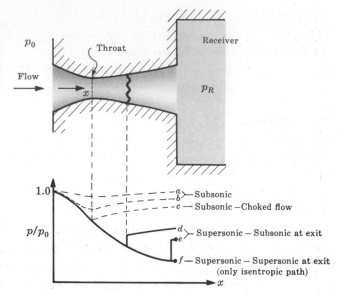

If the receiver pressure is slightly reduced (a, b), there is flow from left to right. The flow is subsonic throughout, with the converging portion functioning as a nozzle and the diverging portion as a diffuser. If the receiver pressure is further reduced (c) the pressure at the throat reaches a minimum (critical) and the velocity there will equal the sonic velocity. The flow in the diverging section is subsonic.

Fig. 7-7. Flow regimes of a converging-diverging nozzle.

If the receiver pressure is further reduced (d, e), then the flow following the throat for a short distance will be supersonic. This is followed by a discontinuity in pressure (normal shock) and the flow will be subsonic for the remaining distance to the exit. Condition (e) is just that where the shock has moved to the nozzle exit.

There is only one receiver pressure (f) where the flow can be isentropic for supersonic flow. If the pressure of the receiver is between e and f, then the nozzle is said to be overexpanded. Here shock patterns occur outside the nozzle where the pressure adjusts from a lower to a higher value. If the receiver pressure is below f, then the nozzle is said to be underexpanded. For this case a series of expansion waves and oblique shock waves occur outside the nozzle, with the pressure going from a higher to a lower value.

The important assumptions of this section are one-dimensional, steady adiabatic flow of an ideal gas. Now, in most real flows these assumptions are not fully satisfied. However, this model gives predicted results (say, of exit velocity or thrust) which are within a few percent of the experimental results for many flows.

In some problems the designer would like not to be even a few percent off in the predictions. Then the fact that the flow is not actually one-dimensional, that there is a boundary layer, that there is some heat transfer, and that the gas is not an ideal gas must be taken into account.

(d) Isentropic Equations.

If the flow is one-dimensional, steady, adiabatic and the fluid is an ideal gas, the energy equation is

$$c_p T_1 + V_1^2/2 = c_p T_2 + V_2^2/2$$

Writing the velocity in terms of Mach number and using $c_p - c_v = R$, the energy equation becomes

$$\frac{T_2}{T_1} = \frac{1 + \frac{1}{2}(k-1)M_1^2}{1 + \frac{1}{2}(k-1)M_2^2} \tag{7.15}$$

If the isentropic relationship between pressure and temperature for an ideal gas is used, we have

$$\frac{p_2}{p_1} = \left[\frac{1 + \frac{1}{2}(k-1)M_1^2}{1 + \frac{1}{2}(k-1)M_2^2}\right]^{k/(k-1)} \qquad (7.16)$$

The mass flow can be determined from

$$\dot{m} = \rho A V$$

or in terms of Mach number, we have

$$\dot{m}/A = \sqrt{k/RT}\, pM \qquad (7.17)$$

7.3 NORMAL SHOCKS

We saw that there was a discontinuity in pressure (density and temperature) in a converging-diverging nozzle when the exit pressure was within a certain range of values. This discontinuity is called a normal shock. In this section we are going to (1) show that such a discontinuity may occur and (2) develop equations describing the change in conditions across a shock.

Let us assume that the normal shock illustrated in Fig. 7-8 can be represented by the following model:

1. Area is constant through the shock. (The channel area may vary but not appreciably through the shock thickness.)

2. Ideal gas

3. Steady flow

4. One-dimensional flow

5. Adiabatic

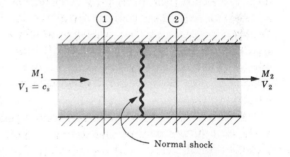

Fig. 7-8. Flow model for normal shock.

It is important to realize that the flow through a shock is irreversible and hence the isentropic equations cannot be used. The control volume forms of energy, momentum and continuity become (see previous section)

Energy:
$$\frac{T_2}{T_1} = \frac{1 + \frac{1}{2}(k-1)M_1^2}{1 + \frac{1}{2}(k-1)M_2^2} \qquad (7.15)$$

Continuity:
$$p_2/p_1 = \sqrt{\frac{T_2}{T_1}}\,\frac{M_1}{M_2} \qquad (7.18)$$

Momentum:
$$(p_1 - p_2)A = \dot{m}(V_2 - V_1)$$

which becomes
$$\frac{p_2}{p_1} = \frac{1 + kM_1^2}{1 + kM_2^2} \qquad (7.19)$$

The equation of state combined with the thermodynamic expression for entropy change gives

$$s_2 - s_1 = c_p \ln(T_2/T_1) - R \ln(p_2/p_1) \qquad (7.20)$$

Equations (7.15), (7.18) and (7.19) involve three unknowns (T_2, p_2, M_2) and may be combined to give

$$M_2 = \left[\frac{M_1^2(k-1) + 2}{2kM_1^2 - k + 1}\right]^{1/2} \qquad (7.21)$$

Equations (7.15), (7.19) and (7.21) completely describe the conditions behind a shock in terms of the upstream conditions.*

The question we have not answered is: when can a normal shock occur? Let us assume that all of the conditions of the model are satisfied except the momentum equation. Then equations (7.15), (7.18) and (7.20) (i.e. energy, continuity and equation of state) define a curve on the enthalpy-entropy diagram which passes through the initial state 1, as shown in Fig. 7-9. This curve is called the Fanno line.

Now if all of the conditions of the model are satisfied except the energy equation, we have another curve on the enthalpy-entropy diagram. This curve is called the Rayleigh line.

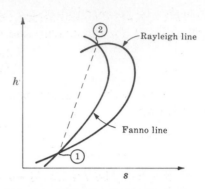

Fig. 7-9.   Fanno and Rayleigh lines.

In order that all the conditions of the model be satisfied, the equilibrium states of the Fanno and Rayleigh lines must be satisfied simultaneously. Since there are two intersections of the curves, two states will satisfy the conditions and all other states are not allowed. We note also that the allowed states have finite differences in properties.

Thus if the flow has conditions of state 1, it would be possible for a discontinuity to occur and the flow to take on conditions of state 2. Would it be possible for the flow conditions to go from state 2 to state 1? The answer is no because this would involve an entropy decrease and would be a violation of the second law of thermodynamics. The flow for the intersection on the lower portion of the curves is supersonic, while the intersection on the upper portion is subsonic flow. Thus we have shown that a discontinuity may occur if the flow is supersonic and cannot occur if the flow is subsonic.

7.4   ADIABATIC CONSTANT AREA FLOW (FANNO LINE)

Consider adiabatic, one-dimensional, steady flow of an ideal gas in a constant area duct. The equations describing this flow are (where the subscript 1 denotes a reference upstream state):

Energy: $$h_1 + V_1^2/2 \; = \; h + V^2/2 \; = \; h_0$$

where h_0 is the stagnation enthalpy defined by the above equation.

Momentum: $$(p_1 - p)A - \tau_0 LC \; = \; A(\rho V^2 - \rho_1 V_1^2)$$

where τ_0 = wall shear stress, L = length and C = circumferential distance.

Continuity: $$V_1/v_1 \; = \; V/v \quad \text{or} \quad V_1\rho_1 \; = \; V\rho$$

Equation of state: $$p_1 v_1/T_1 \; = \; pv/T$$

Property relation: $$s - s_1 \; = \; c_v \ln(h/h_1) + R \ln(v/v_1)$$

Combining the energy and continuity equations gives

$$h \; = \; h_0 - \tfrac{1}{2}(V_1/v_1)^2 v^2$$

Further, by combining this equation with the property relation, we obtain the Fanno line curve of Fig. 7-9. This curve represents the possible conditions for the fixed upstream con-

---

*The property variations across a normal shock have been numerically tabulated in convenient form and their use eliminates the necessity of making calculations using the above equations. Shock tables may be found in references 1, 2, and 4, page 148.

ditions as designated by 1. We observe that there is a maximum entropy for this curve. This has important significance. For example, if the upstream conditions 1 are on the lower portion of the curve as shown in Fig. 7-9, then there will be an increasing value of enthalpy as shown. Note that the entropy must increase according to the second law of thermodynamics. This means that if the flow conditions reach those corresponding to the maximum entropy, then the flow conditions cannot change further. The condition of maximum entropy represents the flow at the exit of the constant area channel for "choked" flow.

Combining the $T\,ds$ equation (i.e. $T\,ds = dh - v\,dp$, a properties relationship) with the differential form of the energy and continuity equations gives

$$\frac{ds}{dh} = \frac{1}{T}\left(1 - \frac{1}{V^2}\frac{dp}{d\rho}\right)$$

If we set this equation equal to zero, we get the conditions at the exit of the pipe for choked flow, obtaining

$$V^2 = dp/d\rho = (\partial p/\partial\rho)_s = a^2$$

or

$$M = 1.0$$

Thus we see that the frictional effects cause the fluid to tend toward a Mach number of unity for both initially subsonic (upper curve) and supersonic (lower curve) conditions.

We can determine the property changes for one-dimensional adiabatic flow of a gas in a constant area duct from the equations. Summarizing the results, we have

Property	Subsonic Flow	Supersonic Flow
s	increases	increases
h	decreases	increases
T	decreases	increases
M	increases	decreases
V	increases	decreases
p	decreases	increases

7.5 FRICTIONLESS CONSTANT AREA FLOW WITH HEATING AND COOLING

The equations for frictionless, one-dimensional, steady flow in a constant area duct with heating and cooling are (where q is the heat transferred to unit mass of fluid flowing):

Energy: $h_1 + V_1^2/2 + q = h + V^2/2$

Momentum: $p_1 - p = \rho V^2 - \rho_1 V_1^2$

Continuity: $\rho_1 V_1 = \rho V$

Equation of state: $p_1/\rho_1 T_1 = p/\rho T$

Combining the momentum and continuity equations and writing in differential form gives

$$(\partial p/\partial\rho)_s = a^2 = V^2$$

for maximum entropy. Thus, for this flow too, the Mach number at the exit for choked conditions is unity. Heating of the flowing gas causes an increase in entropy. Therefore for both subsonic and supersonic flow, the effect of heating is to cause the Mach number to tend toward unity.

An interesting observation for Rayleigh line flow is that there is a portion of the curve which shows that when heat is added to the gas there will be a decrease in temperature.

7.6 ISOTHERMAL FLOW WITH FRICTION

There are some flows which are approximately isothermal, e.g. flow of natural gas in a long pipeline. We will develop an expression describing pressure drop for this flow.

Consider volume of gas for this flow as shown in Fig. 7-10. The one-dimensional steady flow momentum equation for this volume is

$$\sum F_x = \dot{m}(V + dV - V)$$

$$[p - (p + dp)](\tfrac{1}{4}\pi D^2) - \tau_0\pi D \, dx = (\tfrac{1}{4}\pi D^2)\rho V \, dV$$

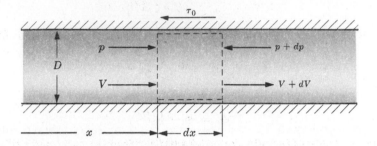

Fig. 7-10.   Volume element for isothermal flow in a constant area duct.

Then combining the expression for friction factor

$$f \equiv \tau_0/(\tfrac{1}{2}\rho V^2)$$

with the momentum equation and simplifying, we have

$$\frac{v}{V^2}dp + \frac{2f}{D}dx + \frac{dV}{V} = 0$$

If the continuity equation is combined with the ideal gas equation of state for constant temperature, we have

$$\frac{v}{V^2} = \frac{v_1}{V_1^2 p_1}p$$

This can be combined with the momentum equation to give

$$\frac{v_1}{V_1^2 p_1}p \, dp + \frac{2f}{D}dx + \frac{dV}{V} = 0$$

We will assume that the friction factor depends only on the Reynolds number (for a given pipe). Then the Reynolds number is a constant for isothermal flow and the friction factor is also constant. (Note $\rho V = $ constant and $\mu = f(T) = $ constant.)

Now the momentum equation can be integrated, giving

$$(p/p_1)^2 = 1 - kM_1^2(2 \ln V/V_1 + 4fL/D) \tag{7.22}$$

where L is the length between stations as designated by the subscript 1 and those quantities having no subscript. We can rewrite equation (7.22) as

$$fL/D = \frac{1}{4kM_1^2}[1 - (p/p_1)^2] + \tfrac{1}{2}\ln p/p_1 \tag{7.23}$$

Thus the pressure is a nonlinear function of length, whereas in incompressible flow it is a linear function of distance.

We can combine the momentum and continuity equations to show that the pipe exit Mach number for choked flow is $M^* = 1/\sqrt{k}$. The corresponding pressure is $p^*/p_1 = M_1\sqrt{k}$.

7.7 INCOMPRESSIBLE FLOW FOR LOW MACH NUMBERS

Starting with the energy equation

$$\tfrac{1}{2}(V_1^2 - V^2) = h - h_1$$

and writing in terms of an ideal gas for an isentropic process, we have

$$\tfrac{1}{2}(V_1^2 - V^2) = \frac{kRT}{k-1}[1 - (p_1/p)^{(k-1)/k}]$$

Letting $V_1 \to 0$ we obtain the expression for the stagnation pressure,

$$p_0/p = [1 + \tfrac{1}{2}(k-1)M^2]^{k/(k-1)}$$

If this equation is written in terms of a binomial expansion for the Mach number, we have

$$p_0 = p + \tfrac{1}{2}\rho V^2[1 + \tfrac{1}{4}M^2 + \tfrac{1}{24}(2-k)M^4 + \cdots] \qquad (7.24)$$

For small values of Mach numbers the equation becomes

$$p_0 = p + \tfrac{1}{2}\rho V^2 \qquad (7.25)$$

which is the same as the expression for stagnation pressure for incompressible flow.

The importance of this result is that adiabatic flow of gases around objects and in ducts may be considered as incompressible as long as the Mach number is small (say, for $M < 0.3$), and as we have seen there is a substantial simplification in the model for constant density.

7.8 THE SHOCK TUBE

The shock tube is a device used to produce a high velocity, high temperature gas over a short interval of time. The tube is sealed, with a diaphragm separating two portions of the tube, one of which is at a high pressure, the other at a low pressure. The diaphragm is suddenly burst and a shock wave propagates into the still gas on the low pressure side, and an expansion wave propagates into the still gas on the high pressure side. The disturbed gas (between the shock and expansion waves) travels at a high velocity which may be supersonic (relative to the undisturbed gas and tube). Shock tubes are used for short duration wind tunnels much like blow-down tunnels.

(a) The Piston Generated Shock.

Before looking at the shock tube itself, let us examine the types of waves generated in the tube. Consider a shock wave generated in a tube by a moving piston as shown in Fig. 7-11. The shock is a normal shock for which we have already calculated the jump conditions. The gas between the piston and the shock has the same velocity as the shocks.

The x-t plot shows the development or motion of the piston and shock wave. The slopes of the lines are the reciprocals of the speeds.

(b) Centered Expansion Waves.

If the piston in part (a) above is withdrawn from the tube instead of driven in, an expan-

Fig. 7-11. A shock wave generated by a moving piston. (a) The x-t plot, (b) the tube at time t_1. V is the gas absolute velocity.

sion wave develops and propagates away from the piston. This expansion wave is isentropic.

The sudden withdrawal of the piston creates a step function change in particle velocity (the particles immediately adjacent to the piston move with it) and pressure. This step function flattens as the wave begins to propagate; and locally, within the wave, the disturbances travel at the local sonic speed. Since the pressure (and temperature) vary through the wave (which began as a step in these variables) the local speed of disturbance propagation varies through the wave. On the edge of the wave adjacent to the undisturbed gas (region 4) the temperature and sonic speed are greatest. On the opposite side (region 3) the temperature is the smallest and hence the sonic speed is also. As a consequence, the expansion wave expands or "fans" out as it propagates as shown in Fig. 7-12. The x-t plot is a fan of constant sonic speed lines which show the development of the wave. These lines are called "characteristics" and follow the path of local isentropic disturbances. Clearly the absolute speed of the disturbances is the sum of the local sonic speed and the local absolute gas speed. The terminating characteristic on the right (condition 4) has slope $dx/dt = a_4$, and the one on the left has slope $dx/dt = a_3 + V_3$. V_3 is defined positive to the right and is negative here (since V_3 must be equal to $-V_P$). Hence dx/dt may be positive or negative depending on whether $a_3 > V_3$ or $a_3 < V_3$ respectively.

Fig. 7-12.   The centered expansion fan generated by a piston being withdrawn from a tube.

We may explicitly evaluate a_3 and the structure of the fan as follows. In terms of a_4 the local sonic speed in the fan may be written (using the isentropic relationships)

$$a = a_4 (\rho/\rho_4)^{(k-1)/2}$$

and the particle velocity in the wave may be written locally (see reference 1, page 148)

$$dV = a\frac{d\rho}{\rho}$$

and may be integrated by using the previous expression to yield

$$a = a_4 + \tfrac{1}{2}(k-1)V$$

The absolute wave speed c (of the portion of the wave behind the front) then is the sum of the local sonic speed and fluid velocity,

$$c = a + V = a_4 + \tfrac{1}{2}(k+1)V$$

Now, V is negative, so c decreases through the wave as we go from region 4 to 3. The terminating characteristic on the left has slope

$$c_3 = a_4 + \tfrac{1}{2}(k+1)V_3 = a_4 - \tfrac{1}{2}(k+1)V_P \tag{7.26}$$

(which may be positive or negative and may slope to the right or left). From the isentropic relationships the density and pressure change across the fan are given by

$$\rho_3/\rho_4 = [1 - \tfrac{1}{2}(k-1)(V_P/a_4)]^{2/(k-1)} \qquad (7.27)$$

$$p_3/p_4 = [1 - \tfrac{1}{2}(k-1)(V_P/a_4)]^{2k/(k-1)} \qquad (7.28)$$

where V_P is a positive number.

(c) The Shock Tube Flow.

Now we can combine the piston driven shock and centered expansion fan to describe the shock tube. Referring to Fig. 7-13 we see that when the diaphragm is burst, a shock and expansion wave are generated. A contact surface is formed across which the pressure and velocity are constant, but the temperature and density and hence Mach number are different. The two conditions

$$p_2 = p_3, \quad V_2 = V_3$$

are sufficient to determine the conditions in regions 2 and 3 and hence the jumps across the shock and fan. ($V_2 = V_3$ is a negative number since the gas flows to the left.) In terms of known conditions in regions 1 and 4, we solve for V_3 in terms of p_3 and p_4 from (7.28) and V_2 in terms of p_1 and p_2 from the normal shock relations. Then we set $V_2 = V_3$ (and since $p_2 = p_3$) we can obtain a relationship for p_2. The result is

$$\frac{p_4}{p_1} = \frac{p_2}{p_1}\left[1 - \frac{(k-1)(a_1/a_4)(p_2/p_1 - 1)}{\sqrt{2k}\sqrt{2k + (k+1)(p_2/p_1 - 1)}}\right]^{-2k/(k-1)} \qquad (7.29)$$

which gives p_2/p_1 implicitly. Once p_2 is known, all the other parameters of the problem can easily be found.

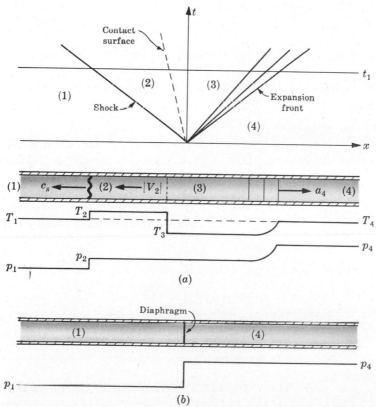

Fig. 7-13. The shock tube. (a) Time $t = t_1$, (b) time $t = 0$.

References

1. Liepmann, H. W., and Roshko, A., *Elements of Gasdynamics*, John Wiley, 1957.

2. Owczarek, J. A., *Fundamentals of Gas Dynamics*, International Textbook, 1964.

3. Shames, I. H., *Mechanics of Fluids*, McGraw-Hill, 1962.

4. Shapiro, A. H., *The Dynamics and Thermodynamics of Compressible Fluid Flow*, Ronald Press, 1953.

Solved Problems

7.1. An airplane is flying at 10,000 ft where the air temperature is 20°F and the pressure is 21.0 in. of mercury. At a certain point on the wing (Fig. 7-14) the static pressure is 980 lb/ft² and the local Mach number is 0.95. Assuming frictionless adiabatic flow, what is the velocity of the airplane relative to the undisturbed air?

$p_1 = 21$ in. Hg
$T_1 = 20°$F
$V_1 = ?$

$p_2 = 980$ lb/ft²
$M_2 = 0.95$

Fig. 7-14

Consider the airplane as stationary and the air moving as shown. For isentropic flow of an ideal gas, we have

$$T_2 = T_1(p_2/p_1)^{(k-1)/k} = (460+20)\left[\frac{980}{21(0.491)(144)}\right]^{0.286} = 427°R$$

and

$$V_2 = M_2 a_2 = M_2\sqrt{kRT_2} = 0.95\sqrt{1.4(32.2)(53.3)(427)} = 955 \text{ ft/sec}$$

Then from the energy equation,

$$V_1^2/2 + h_1 = V_2^2/2 + h_2$$

and

$$V_1^2 = V_2^2 + 2c_p(T_2 - T_1) = (955)^2 + 2(32.2)(778)(0.24)(427 - 480)$$

$$= 275,000 \text{ ft}^2/\text{sec}^2$$

so that $V_1 = 524$ ft/sec.

7.2. Air is flowing in a converging channel shown in Fig. 7-15 with conditions as indicated. Determine the pressure, temperature, velocity and Mach number at the throat 2.

Assume frictionless adiabatic flow. Next, determine the conditions upstream where the velocity is negligible. From the energy equation we have

$V_1 = 800$ ft/sec
$T_1 = 140°$F
$p_1 = 10$ lb/in²
$p_R = 5.40$ lb/in²

Fig. 7-15

$$T_0 \;=\; T_1 + \frac{V_1^2}{2c_p} \;=\; (140+460) + \frac{(800)^2}{2(32.2)(778)(0.24)} \;=\; 653°\text{R}$$

and

$$p_0 \;=\; p_1(T_0/T_1)^{k/(k-1)} \;=\; 10[653/(140+460)]^{3.5} \;=\; 13.52 \text{ lb/in}^2$$

so that

$$p_R/p_0 \;=\; 5.40/13.52 \;=\; 0.407$$

where T_0 and p_0 are the stagnation temperature and pressure respectively.

The critical pressure ratio is $p_c/p_0 = [2/(k+1)]^{k/(k-1)} = 0.528$. Therefore the receiver pressure is below critical pressure and the nozzle is operating under choked conditions. Thus $p_2 = p_c$ where p_c is the critical pressure, $0.528\,p_0$.

Hence we find

$$p_2 \;=\; 0.528(13.52) \;=\; 7.14 \text{ lb/in}^2$$

$$T_2 \;=\; T_1(p_2/p_1)^{(k-1)/k} \;=\; (140+460)(7.14/10)^{0.286} \;=\; 546°\text{R}$$

$$M_2 \;=\; 1.0 \text{ (choked flow)}$$

$$V_2 \;=\; a_2 \;=\; \sqrt{kRT_2} \;=\; \sqrt{1.4(32.2)(53.3)(546)} \;=\; 1140 \text{ ft/sec}$$

7.3. For air flowing in a converging-diverging nozzle, the pressure and temperature at the inlet are 14.7 psi and 70°F. At some location in the diverging portion of the nozzle the pressure is 1.37 psi. Determine the area at this location. The area at the throat is 1.0 in².

Assume frictionless adiabatic flow. We note that the pressure in the diverging portion of the nozzle is below critical pressure. Thus the nozzle is operating under choked conditions and the pressure at the throat, p_t, is

$$p_t \;=\; p_c \;=\; 14.7[2/(k+1)]^{k/(k-1)} \;=\; 14.7(0.528) \;=\; 7.79 \text{ lb/in}^2$$

so that

$$T_t \;=\; T_0(p_t/p_0)^{(k-1)/k} \;=\; (460+70)(1.37/14.7)^{0.286} \;=\; 269°\text{R}$$

and

$$V_t \;=\; \sqrt{kRT_t} \;=\; \sqrt{1.4(32.2)(53.3)(269)} \;=\; 1030 \text{ ft/sec}$$

The energy equation gives

$$V_3^2/2 + h_3 \;=\; h_0$$

so that

$$V_3 \;=\; \sqrt{2c_p(T_0-T_3)} \;=\; \sqrt{2(32.2)(778)(0.24)(530-269)} \;=\; 1770 \text{ ft/sec}$$

The continuity equation is

$$\rho_t A_t V_t \;=\; \rho_3 A_3 V_3$$

and hence

$$A_3 \;=\; A_t \frac{\rho_t}{\rho_3} \frac{V_t}{V_3} \;=\; A_t \frac{p_t}{p_3} \frac{T_3}{T_t} \frac{V_t}{V_3} \;=\; 1.0 \frac{7.79}{1.37} \frac{269}{442} \frac{1030}{1770} \;=\; 2.00 \text{ in}^2$$

7.4. Air is flowing in an insulated constant diameter horizontal duct shown in Fig. 7-16. The inlet conditions are $p_1 = 100 \text{ lb/in}^2$, $T_1 = 100°\text{F}$ and $V_1 = 500 \text{ ft/sec}$. The diameter of the pipe is 6.0 in. and the flow is "choked". Determine the net force of the fluid on the pipe.

The control volume momentum equation can be applied to the control volume enclosing the fluid between the entrance and exit as shown.

Fig. 7-16

$$\sum F_x = \dot{m}(V_2 - V_1)$$

which is
$$(p_1 - p_2)(\pi D^2/4) - F_{\text{shear}} = \rho_1 A_1 V_1 (V_2 - V_1)$$

Now we need to determine the conditions at the exit. We have

$$M_2 = M^* = 1.0 \text{ (choked flow)}$$

so that
$$V_2 = \sqrt{kRT_2}$$

From the energy equation,

$$V_2^2 = V_1^2 + 2c_p(T_1 - T_2) = V_1^2 + 2c_p(T_1 - V_2^2/kR)$$

Then
$$V_2^2 = \frac{V_1^2 + 2c_p T_1}{1 + 2c_p/kR} = \frac{V_1^2 + 2c_p T_1}{1 + 2/(k-1)}$$

$$V_2 = \left[\frac{(500)^2 + 2(32.2)(778)(0.24)(460 + 100)}{1 + 2/(1.4 - 1)}\right]^{1/2} = 1030 \text{ ft/sec}$$

The temperature at the exit is

$$T_2 = \frac{V_2^2}{kR} = \frac{(1030)^2}{1.4(32.2)(53.3)} = 442°\text{R}$$

From the continuity equation we have
$$\rho_2 V_2 = \rho_1 V_1$$

Hence
$$(p_2/T_2)V_2 = (p_1/T_1)V_1$$

and
$$p_2 = p_1 \frac{T_2 V_1}{T_1 V_2} = 100\left(\frac{442}{460 + 100}\right)\left(\frac{500}{1030}\right) = 38.2 \text{ lb/in}^2$$

Then
$$(p_1 - p_2)(\pi D^2/4) = (100 - 38.2)(36\pi/4) = 1750 \text{ lb}_f$$

and
$$\rho_1 A_1 V_1 (V_2 - V_1) = \frac{100}{53.3(32.2)(460 + 100)}(36\pi/4)(500)(1030 - 500) = 780 \text{ lb}_f$$

so that finally the force of the pipe on the fluid is

$$F_{\text{shear}} = 1750 - 780 = 970 \text{ lb}_f$$

and the direction is as shown in Fig. 7-16

7.5. Show that for a compressible fluid in isothermal flow with no external work,

$$\frac{dM^2}{M^2} = 2\frac{dV}{V}$$

From the definition of Mach number we have $M^2 = V^2/a^2$. If we assume that the fluid follows the ideal gas equation of state, we have $a = \sqrt{kRT}$. Thus for isothermal flow a is a constant. By taking the logarithm of both sides of the equation defining Mach number, we have

$$\ln M^2 = \ln V^2 - \ln a^2$$

or
$$\ln M^2 = 2\ln V - \ln a^2$$

Then differentiation gives
$$\frac{dM^2}{M^2} = 2\frac{dV}{V}$$

7.6. Show that for a perfect gas flowing through a constant area duct at constant temperature conditions,

$$\frac{dp}{p} = -\frac{dV}{V} = -\frac{1}{2}\frac{dM^2}{M^2}$$

Assuming one-dimensional and steady flow, the continuity equation is $\rho V A = $ constant; and since the area is constant, we have $\rho V = $ constant. Using the ideal gas equation of state the density may be eliminated from the above equation to give $pV = $ constant. Differentiating this equation gives

$$p\,dV + V\,dp = 0$$

and dividing by pV gives

$$\frac{dp}{p} = -\frac{dV}{V}$$

Then using the results of Problem 7.5 we have

$$\frac{dp}{p} = -\frac{dM^2}{M^2}$$

7.7. Show that for adiabatic flow of a perfect gas,

$$T/T_0 = 1 - \tfrac{1}{2}(k-1)(V/a_0)^2$$

where T_0 is the stagnation temperature and a_0 is the velocity of sound for stagnation conditions $(a_0 = \sqrt{kRT_0}\,)$.

From the one-dimensional steady flow energy equation for zero work and adiabatic flow we have

$$h - h_0 = -V^2/2$$

For a perfect gas and constant c_p we have

$$c_p(T - T_0) = -V^2/2$$

Dividing by T_0 and c_p gives

$$T/T_0 = 1 - V^2/2c_p T_0$$

But $c_p = Rk/(k-1)$ and $T_0 = a_0^2/Rk$, which substituted into the above equation gives

$$T/T_0 = 1 - \tfrac{1}{2}(k-1)(V/a_0)^2$$

Supplementary Problems

Distinguish between the true and false statements of Problems 7.8-7.25.

7.8. Sound waves and shock waves
   (a) have no similarities.
   (b) are the same except for the magnitude of the property changes across the waves.
   (c) are both irreversible processes.
   (d) are both reversible processes.
   (e) travel through still air at different velocities.

7.9. For isentropic flow of an ideal gas
   (a) the stagnation temperature is constant.
   (b) the stagnation pressure is constant.
   (c) the entropy is constant.
   (d) the maximum Mach number is one.
   (e) the temperature decreases as the pressure increases.

7.10. In case of flow of an ideal gas in a converging channel
       (a) the temperature decreases in the direction of flow.
       (b) there is a maximum possible flow for fixed inlet conditions and throat diameter.
       (c) it may be possible for a normal shock to occur.
       (d) the velocity will always increase in the direction of flow.
       (e) the Mach number may be greater than one.

7.11. For an ideal gas flowing in a converging channel
       (a) there is a maximum rate of flow for fixed exit area and inlet conditions.
       (b) the Mach number at the throat is always one.
       (c) the maximum temperature will be at the throat.
       (d) the velocity of the gas at the throat is equal to the velocity of sound at the entrance for choked
            conditions.
       (e) a normal shock will occur at the throat for critical conditions.

7.12. A supersonic nozzle with isentropic flow
       (a) may have a normal shock occurring in the converging section.
       (b) may have a normal shock occurring in the diverging section.
       (c) will be "shockless".

7.13. For a converging-diverging flow channel
       (a) when the Mach number at the exit is greater than unity no shock has occurred.
       (b) when the critical pressure ratio is exceeded, the Mach number at the throat is greater than
            unity.
       (c) for sonic velocity at the throat only one value of pressure is possible at a given downstream
            position.
       (d) the Mach number at the throat is always unity.

7.14. For flow of a compressible fluid in a converging-diverging flow channel operating under choked
       conditions,
       (a) the flow is supersonic in all of the diverging section.
       (b) a normal shock may occur in the converging section.
       (c) a normal shock may occur in the diverging section.
       (d) the Mach number is always equal to one at the throat.
       (e) the ratio of the throat pressure to the inlet pressure does not depend upon the flow geometry.

7.15. In a normal shock in one-dimensional flow
       (a) velocity, pressure, and density increase.
       (b) pressure, density, and temperature increase.
       (c) velocity, temperature, and density increase.
       (d) the stagnation enthalpy is unchanged.

7.16. A normal shock
       (a) may occur only when the flow is supersonic.
       (b) always involves a temperature increase.
       (c) always involves a pressure decrease.
       (d) always moves (relative to the fluid) with a velocity equal to the velocity of sound.
       (e) may occur for subsonic flow.

7.17. A normal shock
       (a) will form ahead of a blunt object moving at supersonic velocity through a compressible fluid.
       (b) will occur only when the flow is supersonic.
       (c) will cause the entropy of the fluid to increase.
       (d) involves a frictionless adiabatic process.
       (e) is impossible.

7.18. For adiabatic subsonic flow with friction in a constant area duct
  (*a*) the temperature will increase in the direction of flow.
  (*b*) the stagnation temperature decreases.
  (*c*) the stagnation pressure decreases.
  (*d*) the velocity increases.
  (*e*) the limiting Mach number is one.

7.19. The Fanno Line
  (*a*) represents a series of equilibrium states on the *h-s* diagram for adiabatic flow.
  (*b*) represents a series of equilibrium states on the *h-s* diagram for flow with friction.
  (*c*) was developed from energy, continuity and equations of state.
  (*d*) represents only subsonic flow.
  (*e*) represents isothermal flow in a constant area duct.

7.20. For adiabatic supersonic flow with friction in a constant area duct
  (*a*) the temperature will increase in the direction of flow.
  (*b*) the stagnation temperature decreases.
  (*c*) the stagnation pressure decreases.
  (*d*) the velocity increases.
  (*e*) the limiting Mach number is one.

7.21. For isothermal flow of an ideal gas in a constant area duct
  (*a*) the pressure decreases in the direction of flow.
  (*b*) heat is removed from the fluid.
  (*c*) the fluid particles are accelerated.
  (*d*) the fluid density is decreased.
  (*e*) the maximum Mach number is one.

7.22. For flow of an ideal gas in an insulated constant area duct having an initial Mach number less than one
  (*a*) the velocity decreases in the direction of flow.
  (*b*) the temperature decreases in the direction of flow.
  (*c*) the Mach number can increase to a value greater than one.
  (*d*) the entropy will always increase in the direction of flow.
  (*e*) the pressure is constant.

7.23. Some of the results of heating and cooling of an ideal fluid flowing in a constant area frictionless duct are
  (*a*) heating will always cause an increase in entropy.
  (*b*) heating will always cause an increase in velocity.
  (*c*) heating will always cause an increase in temperature.
  (*d*) heating will always cause an increase in velocity.
  (*e*) the limiting Mach number is one for subsonic flow.

7.24. For adiabatic flow of an ideal gas in a frictionless constant area duct
  (*a*) the stagnation temperature increases as the entropy increases.
  (*b*) the maximum temperature occurs at $M = 1$.
  (*c*) the plot of equilibrium states on the *h-s* diagram is called the Rayleigh line.
  (*d*) the isentropic equations apply.
  (*e*) the limiting Mach number is one for supersonic flow.

7.25. For adiabatic flow of an ideal gas in a frictionless constant area duct
  (*a*) the pressure must decrease in the direction of flow.
  (*b*) the temperature will remain constant.
  (*c*) the velocity will remain constant.
  (*d*) the entropy will increase.
  (*e*) the Mach number will remain constant.

7.26. What is the velocity of sound in carbon dioxide at 300°F? What is the acoustic velocity in water at 60°F?

7.27. At point A in the undisturbed region of an airstream which flows past a body, the density is 0.002378 slugs per cubic foot, the pressure is 14.7 psi and the velocity is 350 fps. The pressure at a point B on the body is 7.35 psi. What is the Mach number at each point for frictionless adiabatic flow?

7.28. An airplane is flying through standard air at 600 fps. Calculate the local Mach number at a point on the plane where the air velocity relative to the plane is 200 fps.

7.29. A body moves through standard air at 400 fps. What is the pressure at a point on the body where the velocity of the air relative to the body is zero?

7.30. A blunt projectile moves through stationary air at 14.7 psia and 60°F at 1900 fps. Find the stagnation pressure, the stagnation enthalpy and the stagnation temperature.

7.31. A nozzle is to be designed to expand air isentropically from 50 psia and 200°F to 18 psia at a rate of 0.30 lb/sec. Calculate (a) the Mach number at the nozzle exit and (b) the exit area (in ft²).

7.32. Air flows isentropically through a converging nozzle having a throat area of 0.1 ft². Air which enters with negligible velocity is at 60 psia, 200°F. The receiver pressure is 15 psia. Calculate the mass rate of flow in lb/sec.

7.33. Air is to be expanded through a converging-diverging nozzle by a frictionless adiabatic process from a pressure of 160 psia and a temperature of 24°F to a pressure of 20 psia. Determine (a) the throat and exit areas for a well designed shockless nozzle if the rate of flow is 4.5 lb/sec and (b) the Mach number at the nozzle outlet.

7.34. Air, initially at 50 psia and 250°F, flows isentropically through a converging-diverging nozzle with a throat area of 0.4 in². The downstream pressure is 14.7 psia and the temperature is 40°F. Calculate (a) the rate of flow in lb/sec and (b) the velocity at the nozzle outlet.

7.35. Air at 100 psia and 140°F flows through a converging tube into a receiver in which the pressure is 20 psia. Assuming frictionless adiabatic flow and negligible upstream velocity, calculate the velocity at the throat.

7.36. Air at 100 psia and 140°F flows through a converging tube into a receiver in which the pressure is 20 psia. Assuming frictionless adiabatic flow and negligible upstream velocity, calculate the velocity at the throat.

7.37. Sketch the h-s and T-s diagrams for an ideal gas flowing adiabatically through a (1) long pipe line, (2) nozzle, (3) diffuser.

7.38. A gas (molecular weight 18, $k = 1.3$) is to be pumped through a 36 inch I.D. pipe connecting two compressor stations 40 miles apart. At the upstream station the pressure is not to exceed 90 psig and the downstream station is to be at least 10 psig. Calculate the maximum allowable rate of flow (cubic feet per day at 70°F and 1 atm), assuming that there is sufficient heat transfer through the pipe to maintain the gas at 70°F. The kinematic viscosity is 4×10^{-4} ft²/sec.

7.39. Air enters a 6 inch diameter pipe at 200 psia and 60°F with a velocity of 190 fps. The friction coefficient f is 0.016. What is the Mach number and distance from entrance at the section where the pressure is 75 psia for isothermal flow?

7.40. Air enters a horizontal pipe at 600 psia, temperature of 200°F, and a velocity of 300 fps. What is the limiting pressure for isothermal flow? What is the limiting pressure for adiabatic flow?

7.41. Air at a pressure of 120 psia and a temperature of 80°F enters a clean steel pipe 950 ft long and 5 inches in diameter. The inlet velocity is 80 fps. Assuming isothermal flow, find (a) the pressure drop (psi) if the fluid is considered compressible, (b) the pressure drop (psi) if the fluid is considered incompressible.

7.42. Hydrogen at an initial pressure of 60 psia and a temperature of 140°F flows through a horizontal insulated pipe 900 feet long and 0.2 feet in diameter. The friction factor is 0.015. What is the maximum possible rate of flow and what pressure drop would be required to maintain this flow?

7.43. A large tank in the laboratory can be filled with air at 200 psia and at room temperature. Design a supersonic nozzle which can be screwed into the wall of this tank and discharge air to the atmosphere at supersonic velocities. (If a small airfoil or test body is placed in the stream of this nozzle, we have in effect a blowdown supersonic windtunnel.) Assume that the air in the tank remains at 200 psia for the short period of time that we are interested in the performance. The throat should have an area of 0.5 in^2.

NOMENCLATURE FOR CHAPTER 7

A = area

a = velocity of sound

c_p = specific heat at constant pressure

c_s = shock speed

c_v = specific heat at constant volume

f = friction factor

h = enthalpy per unit mass

k = specific heat ratio, c_p/c_v

L = length of duct

M = Mach number, V/a

$\dot{m}$ = mass flow rate

p = static pressure

R = gas constant

s = entropy per unit mass

T = absolute temperature

t = time

u = internal energy per unit mass

V = velocity

v = specific volume = $1/\rho$

x = axial coordinate

ρ = density

τ_0 = wall shear stress

$(\ )_c$ = denotes critical condition

$(\ )_0$ = denotes stagnation condition

$(\ )^*$ = denotes condition where flow is choked

Chapter 8

Two-Dimensional Compressible Flow Gasdynamics

8.1 EQUATIONS OF FRICTIONLESS COMPRESSIBLE FLOW

In Chapter 6 we discussed two-dimensional incompressible potential flow and in Chapter 7 we considered one-dimensional compressible flow. We can now extend both these approaches to develop the more general treatment of compressible frictionless (ideal) flow. Since the flow is ideal we can again show that it is irrotational throughout (if the free stream flow is irrotational) and hence potential. We are concerned then with general three-dimensional compressible potential flow, although for explicit calculations we will usually restrict ourselves to two dimensions.

As before, we will discuss the flow outside the boundary layer (where the flow is irrotational) and will be concerned mainly with aerodynamic problems — flow over wings and aircraft shapes.

At low speeds (Mach number M less than about 0.3) the fluid behaves nearly incompressibly and the analysis of incompressible potential flow (Chapter 6) is adequate. As the flow speed increases, the compressibility effects become more and more important; and as the Mach number passes unity, shock waves can form on the body about which we are studying the flow. If the Mach number of the free stream is greater than unity ($M > 1$), the flow is supersonic and is very different from flow which is subsonic ($M < 1$). Transonic flow over a body occurs when the flow over one part of the body is subsonic and over another part is supersonic. In steady transonic flow over a body one can find regions over the body where $M > 1$, where $M = 1$, and where $M < 1$. Mathematically, transonic flow is rather more complicated than either purely subsonic or supersonic flow. When an aircraft accelerates from subsonic to supersonic flow it must pass through a transonic condition.

In this chapter we will study the full range of Mach numbers, beginning in the subsonic region and extending to very large Mach numbers. For M greater than about 6 the flow is considered hypersonic and many assumptions made for ordinary supersonic flow are not valid and the analysis becomes more complicated. As M increases into the hypersonic region the boundary layer friction increases and the stagnation temperature becomes so great (for M greater than about 6) that the temperature in the boundary layer rises and the aircraft surface may become so hot that special refractory or ablative material must be used to prevent structural damage. Re-entry vehicles pass through a range of such high Mach numbers. In Chapter 10 we will discuss the structure of the hypersonic boundary layer. Now, let us concentrate on the potential flow solution outside the boundary layer. The laws governing the flow are basically the same for subsonic through hypersonic flow, but various terms in the fundamental equations become more or less important as M changes and, indeed, the entire character of the differential equations changes as M is greater or less than unity. As a result the flow pattern is drastically different for subsonic and supersonic flow.

In most compressible aerodynamic flow problems it is accurate to assume that the flow is frictionless and irrotational and isentropic throughout. However, in supersonic flow, whenever shock waves may occur, the flow is *not isentropic* through the shock waves.

Let us now briefly review the basic equations of frictionless, isentropic flow which may be used except in shock wave calculations. These equations, in general, will be nonlinear and various approximate solutions must be developed. In some instances exact solutions may be constructed even when shock waves occur.

The basic equations are the same as those developed in Chapter 5 except that compressibility effects must be taken into account and consequently the energy equation or an equivalent must be also considered. The basic equations are continuity, motion and energy. If the energy equation is written in terms of temperature, an equation of state is also necessary. If the flow is isentropic throughout, the isentropic relationship between the pressure and density may be used, obviating the necessity of using the energy equation.

As we showed in Chapter 5, adiabatic frictionless flow is isentropic along a streamline if it is irrotational. Further if the flow has a uniform value of total (or stagnation) enthalpy, $h_0 = h + V^2/2$ throughout, in addition to being irrotational, then the flow is isentropic throughout. Such a flow is sometimes called *homentropic*.*

For homentropic flow (in which body forces are negligible) for a perfect gas in two dimensions, the basic relationships are

Continuity:
$$\frac{\partial \rho}{\partial t} + \frac{\partial}{\partial x}(\rho u) + \frac{\partial}{\partial y}(\rho v) = 0 \tag{8.1}$$

Momentum:
$$\rho \frac{\partial u}{\partial t} + u \frac{\partial u}{\partial x} + v \frac{\partial u}{\partial y} = -\frac{\partial p}{\partial x}$$
$$\rho \frac{\partial v}{\partial t} + u \frac{\partial v}{\partial x} + v \frac{\partial v}{\partial y} = -\frac{\partial p}{\partial y} \tag{8.2}$$

Isentropic relationship:
$$p/p_0 = (\rho/\rho_0)^k \tag{8.3}$$

where $k = c_p/c_v$ is the ratio of specific heats, and p_0 and ρ_0 are the pressure and density at arbitrary reference states, usually taken as free stream values or stagnation values.

Equations (8.1) through (8.3) are independent but not unique. In place of (8.3) we could use the complete energy equation along with the equation of state. If the flow is not adiabatic such a procedure would be necessary.

Since the flow is irrotational the velocity potential, defined by $\mathbf{V} = -\nabla\phi$, may be introduced. Then the term ∇p may be written as

$$\nabla p = (\partial p/\partial \rho)_s \nabla \rho = a^2 \nabla \rho \tag{8.4}$$

where a is the sonic speed. Then the scalar product of $\mathbf{V}$ and the vector equation of motion may be formed and (8.4) and (8.1) used to eliminate p and ρ. The result is (for two-dimensional flow)

$$(u^2 - a^2)\frac{\partial u}{\partial x} + (v^2 - a^2)\frac{\partial v}{\partial y} + uv\left(\frac{\partial u}{\partial y} + \frac{\partial v}{\partial x}\right) = 0 \tag{8.5}$$

and the condition $\dfrac{\partial v}{\partial x} - \dfrac{\partial u}{\partial y} = 0$, or in terms of ϕ

$$\frac{1}{a^2}\left[\left(\frac{\partial \phi}{\partial x}\right)^2 \frac{\partial^2 \phi}{\partial x^2} + \left(\frac{\partial \phi}{\partial y}\right)^2 \frac{\partial^2 \phi}{\partial y^2} + \frac{\partial \phi}{\partial x}\frac{\partial \phi}{\partial y}\left(2\frac{\partial^2 \phi}{\partial x\,\partial y}\right)\right] = \frac{\partial^2 \phi}{\partial x^2} + \frac{\partial^2 \phi}{\partial y^2} \tag{8.6}$$

which reduces to $\nabla^2 \phi = 0$ as $a \to \infty$ which is the appropriate limit for incompressible

---

*This statement follows from Crocco's theorem which states that

$$T\nabla s + \mathbf{V} \times (\nabla \times \mathbf{V}) = \nabla h_0 + \partial \mathbf{V}/\partial t$$

where s is specific entropy. In steady flow $\nabla s = 0$ if $\nabla \times \mathbf{V} = 0$ and $\nabla h_0 = 0$. We will not prove this theorem here but it follows from the equation of motion and the thermodynamic relationship $T\,ds = dh - (1/\rho)\,dp$. In most aerodynamic flows the fluid originates in the same "reservoir," the free stream, and hence h_0 is constant.

flow. *(8.6)* is a single equation for ϕ and describes the flow, but the sonic speed a must be related to the velocity components through the energy equation and complicates the situation. In Section 8.3, when we discuss small perturbation theory, we will carry out this calculation explicitly. The method of small perturbations allows a linearization of *(8.6)* (and resultant approximate solutions) for thin bodies such as airfoils and slender bodies of revolution.

Exact shock-expansion solutions will be discussed in Section 8.2, and in Section 8.4 methods for the solution of *(8.5)* will be discussed.

8.2 SHOCK-EXPANSION THEORY

Exact solutions for flow in certain simple geometries may be obtained if the flow consists entirely of shock waves and/or expansion waves. We will discuss the oblique shock wave and simple expansion wave, then show how these solutions may be combined to describe the flow over certain simple shapes.

(a) The Oblique Shock.

Fig. 8-1 shows an oblique shock wave. By conservation of momentum the tangential component of velocity V_t is continuous across the shock so that $V_{t1} = V_{t2}$. Then V_{n1} and V_{n2} are related by the normal shock relations of Chapter 7. Hence in terms of the normal velocities an oblique shock is identical to a normal shock and the Mach numbers (in terms of V_n, $M_1 = V_{n1}/a_1$), pressure, density, etc., are related in the same way as in the normal shock. Since $V_{t1} = V_{t2}$ but $V_{n1} \neq V_{n2}$, the actual velocity vector **V** is rotated and changed in magnitude as it passes through the shock as shown in Fig. 8-2. V_{n1} is greater than the sonic speed a_1 and V_{n2} must be less than the sonic speed a_2. However, although $V_1 > a_1$, V_2 may also be greater than a_2. In an oblique shock the magnitude of the velocity does not necessarily drop to a subsonic value through the shock, although the normal component does.

Fig. 8-1.   The oblique shock.   Fig. 8-2.   Rotation of the velocity vector
                                                 through the shock.

We define M_1 as V_1/a_1 and $V_{n1} = V_1 \sin\beta$ so that $V_{n1}/a_1 = M_1 \sin\beta$. The normal shock relationships of Chapter 7 can be used with $M_1 \sin\beta$ replacing the M_1 there.* For reference we list the following:

$$\frac{V_{n1}}{V_{n2}} = \frac{\rho_2}{\rho_1} = \frac{(k+1)(M_1^2 \sin^2\beta)}{(k-1)M_1^2 \sin^2\beta + 2}$$

$$\frac{p_2 - p_1}{p_1} = \frac{2k}{k+1}(M_1^2 \sin^2\beta - 1)$$

$$\frac{T_2}{T_1} = \frac{a_2^2}{a_1^2} = 1 + \frac{2(k-1)}{(k+1)^2}\frac{M_1^2 \sin^2\beta - 1}{M_1^2 \sin^2\beta}(kM_1^2 \sin^2\beta + 1) \qquad (8.7)$$

$$\frac{s_2 - s_1}{R} = \ln\left\{\left[1 + \frac{2k}{k+1}(M_1^2 \sin^2\beta - 1)\right]^{1/(k-1)} \cdot \left[\frac{(k+1)M_1^2 \sin^2\beta}{(k-1)M_1^2 \sin^2\beta + 2}\right]^{-k/(k-1)}\right\}$$

$$M_2^2 \sin^2(\beta - \theta) = \frac{1 + \frac{1}{2}(k-1)M_1^2 \sin^2\beta}{kM_1^2 \sin^2\beta - \frac{1}{2}(k-1)}$$

---

*Normal shock tables may be used with $M_1 \sin\beta$ considered as M_1 in the tables. A brief table may be found in reference 1, page 171.

It may be noted that $0 < \beta < \pi/2$ and $M_1 \sin \beta = V_{n1}/a_1 \geqq 1$, so that β has a minimum value for a given M_1. Hence

$$\sin^{-1} 1/M_1 \leqq \beta \leqq \pi/2 \tag{8.8}$$

For a normal shock, $\beta = \pi/2$. For a weak shock, as the shock becomes a sonic wave, $\sin^{-1} 1/M = \beta$.

The value of M_2 may be found by noting that $M_2 = V_2/a_2$ and $V_{n2}/a_2 = M_2 \sin(\beta - \theta)$. From the normal shock relation

$$M_2^2 = \frac{1 + \frac{1}{2}(k-1)M_1^2}{kM_1^2 - \frac{1}{2}(k-1)}$$

we get by substituting $M_1 \sin \beta$ and $M_2 \sin(\beta - \theta)$ for M_1 and M_2 respectively,

$$M_2^2 \sin^2(\beta - \theta) = \frac{1 + \frac{1}{2}(k-1)M_1^2 \sin^2 \beta}{kM_1^2 \sin^2 \beta - \frac{1}{2}(k-1)} \tag{8.9}$$

We can relate β and θ by using the first of (8.7) and relating V_{2n} to V_{1n} by geometry, $(\tan \beta = V_{n1}/V_{t1}, \ \tan(\beta - \theta) = V_{n2}/V_{t1})$. Hence

$$\frac{\tan(\beta - \theta)}{\tan \beta} = \frac{(k-1)M_1^2 \sin^2 \beta + 2}{(k+1)M_1^2 \sin^2 \beta}$$

which can be written
$$\tan \theta = 2 \cot \beta \frac{M_1^2 \sin^2 \beta - 1}{M_1^2(k + \cos 2\beta) + 2} \tag{8.10}$$

For a given M_1, there are two values of β for each value of θ. Fig. 8-3 shows a plot of this equation.

Fig. 8-3. β versus θ for an oblique shock.

For any value of θ (less than θ_{max}) there are two solutions. In practice the weaker solution (β smaller) usually occurs (if $\theta < 45°$). These correspond to M_2 remaining > 1, except for a small region between the lines $M_2 = 1$ and $\theta = \theta_{max}$.

In practice, what determines β and θ? In other words, how are oblique shocks generated? A simple example is flow through a corner as shown in Fig. 8-4(a). A symmetrical wedge would generate the same flow pattern symmetrical about the horizontal centerline [see Fig. 8-4(b)]. The vector $\mathbf{V}_2$ is parallel to the surface of the wedge (or corner) which sets θ. Then if M_1 is specified, β must follow.

(a)   (b)

Fig. 8-4.   Oblique shock generated by flow (a) through a corner and
(b) over a symmetrical wedge.

What happens if $\theta > 45°$ (see Fig. 8-3)? Then no simple oblique shock solution exists and the shock becomes "detached" and curves back around the wedge. The solution corresponds to a normal shock at the apex and M_2 will be less than 1 (Fig. 8-5). Further, if the object is blunt the shock is always detached (since $\theta = 90°$ at the front). The dotted line where $M = 1$ (in Fig. 8-5) is called the sonic line and divides the regions of supersonic and subsonic flow.

(a)   (b)

Fig. 8-5.   A detached shock. (a) wedge, (b) blunt.

As the wedge angle θ becomes zero, β becomes $\sin^{-1} 1/M$ and the wave is called a *Mach line.* It is merely the locus of sonic disturbances since the shock strength has become zero and any infinitesimal or sonic disturbance would propagate out along this line. The angle $\sin^{-1} 1/M$, denoted as μ, is the *Mach angle.* In three dimensions the Mach lines would form a cone (from a point disturbance as discussed in Chapter 7).

In two dimensions, at any point in the flow, there are two Mach lines (at $\pm\beta = \sin^{-1} 1/M$ to the streamlines). These lines are called *characteristics* and must point downstream since there can be no upstream influence in supersonic flow (Fig. 8-6).

As the angle θ becomes small but finite the shock becomes weak, and the shock relationships may be simplified. It may be shown that across the shock $\Delta p \sim \theta$ and $\Delta s \sim \theta^3$ so that for very weak shocks the flow be-

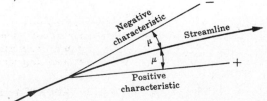

Fig. 8-6.   Characteristics in supersonic flow. ($\theta \to 0$ and $\beta \to \mu = \sin^{-1} 1/M$). The positive set runs to the right of the streamlines and the negative set to the left.

comes nearly isentropic.   The change in speed ΔV across the weak shock is approximately (for flow deflection $\Delta\theta$)

$$\frac{\Delta V}{V} = -\frac{\Delta\theta}{\sqrt{M_1^2 - 1}} \tag{8.11}$$

which is exact for isentropic flow.   If compression takes place through a continuous bend (Fig. 8-7), then a continuous set of Mach lines is formed and (*8.11*) may be written in differential form

$$\frac{dV}{V} = -\frac{d\theta}{\sqrt{M_1^2 - 1}} \tag{8.12}$$

The Mach lines coalesce to form a shock wave, but near the body the flow is approximately isentropic in the compression fan of the Mach lines.

Fig. 8-7.   Compression of supersonic flow by turning.

(b) Supersonic Expansion and the Prandtl-Meyer Function.

In flow over a convex corner or convex curved surface, no shock can form and the flow expands isentropically (Fig. 8-8).   A single wave cannot accommodate the change (it would lead to a decrease in entropy) and a fan of waves must exist.   The lines shown in Fig. 8-8 are actually Mach lines or characteristics.   At any point in the flow they are inclined at an angle $\sin^{-1} 1/M$ to the streamlines.

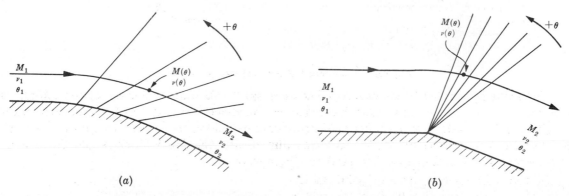

Fig. 8-8.   Supersonic expansion on a convex surface. (*a*) continuous expansion around a curve and (*b*) an expansion fan centered at a sharp corner.

Equation (*8.12*) holds throughout the expansion and the angle θ is the inclination of the streamline with respect to an arbitrary datum.   Usually we take $\theta_1 = 0$ and measure θ positive counterclockwise (see Fig. 8-8, where θ_2 is negative if we take $\theta_1 = 0$).   Equation (*8.12*) may be integrated:

$$-\theta + \text{constant} = \int_{V_1}^{V} \sqrt{M^2 - 1}\,\frac{dV}{V} = \nu(M) \tag{8.13}$$

The function $\nu(M)$ is called the Prandtl-Meyer function and may be evaluated explicitly as

$$\nu(M) \;=\; \sqrt{\frac{k+1}{k-1}}\,\tan^{-1}\sqrt{\frac{k-1}{k+1}(M^2-1)} \;-\; \tan^{-1}\sqrt{M^2-1} \qquad (8.14)$$

where ν is given in radians. We arbitrarily choose the constant in (8.13) so that $\nu = 0$ when $M = 1$, and thus we finally have

$$-(\theta - \theta_1) \;=\; \nu(M) - \nu_1(M_1) \qquad (8.15)$$

For a given value of θ_1 (usually taken as zero) and M_1, we can find $\nu(M)$ and hence M for any value of θ. $(\nu(M)$ is a monotonic function of M which varies from 0 for $M = 1$ to ν_{max} for $M \to \infty$, where $\nu_{max} = \frac{1}{2}\pi(\sqrt{(k+1)/(k-1)} - 1)$.) For supersonic expansion, θ is negative; and for compression, θ is positive (see Fig. 8-9).

(a) Supersonic Expansion   (b) Supersonic Compression

Fig. 8-9.   Supersonic expansion and compression. Locally the
angle between the Mach line and the streamline is μ.

A brief table of $\nu(M)$ is given in degrees below.*

Table 8.1.   The Prandtl-Meyer Function

ν (degrees)	0.0	26.5	49.8	65.7	77.0	85.0	91.0	95.6	99.3
M	1.00	2.00	3.00	4.00	5.00	6.00	7.00	8.00	9.00

For example, consider the flow over a convex surface (Fig. 8-8a) through a total angle of 10 degrees, with $M_1 = 2$. From Table 8.1, $\nu_1 = 26.5°$ and $\theta_2 = -10°$ so that from (8.15) $\nu_2 = 26.5° + 10° = 36.5°$ and hence M_2 is approximately 2.39. Note that the rate of curvature is irrelevant in determining the final state. A sharp corner and a smooth curve give the same final result for expansion waves. For compression, only a smooth curve is isentropic and a sharp concave corner would lead to a shock wave.

What happens when expansion occurs around a corner where $|\theta|$ is greater than ν_{max}? Then the streamlines behave as though the flow occurred over an expansion of ν_{max}, and a region of stagnant fluid lies between the "slipstream" or "tangential discontinuity" and the body. Across the slipstream the pressure and density are continuous but the velocity is discontinuous. See Fig. 8-10. (In practice, as the vortex sheet forms, the slipstream and the fluid below it may be turbulent and not stagnant.)

Fig. 8-10.   Expansion around a corner of $|\theta| > \nu_{max}$, with the formation of a slipstream.

*A more complete table may be found in reference 1, page 171.

(c) Combined Oblique Shocks and Expansions.

In supersonic flow, by patching together the oblique shock and isentropic expansion flow solutions, the flow pattern over fairly complex shapes can be obtained. Because the flow is supersonic, there is no upstream influence and it is possible to "march" over the body calculating the flow along the way. The flows over some simple bodies are shown in Fig. 8-11. The pressure plot is also shown.

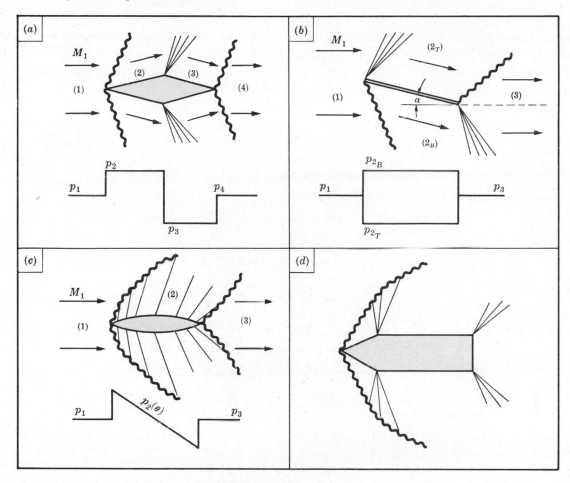

Fig. 8-11. Shock-expansion flow over two-dimensional bodies.

In Fig. 8-11(b) the fluid flowing over the top and bottom of the inclined flat plate must end up behind the body at the free stream velocity and pressure. However, the temperature (and density) may differ slightly across a "contact surface". In this figure, the pressure on the bottom is increased through the shock wave, and decreased on top through the expansion wave, giving rise to a lift on the plate. Unlike a subsonic lifting airfoil, the supersonic airfoil has a component of this pressure force in the direction of flow. This force is a drag force, known as "wave drag".

In practice, supersonic aircraft have wings which behave as subsonic wings, thus eliminating the wave drag. Subsonic wings are possible on supersonic airplanes because the sweepback on the wings gives rise to a component of velocity, normal to the wing leading edge, which is subsonic.

(d) Simple and Nonsimple Regions.

We have been discussing simple oblique shock waves and isentropic waves of expansion or compression. In regions where these waves interact and become curved (the characteristics are no longer straight lines) these simple solutions are no longer valid and the complete equations must be solved. In general these equations are nonlinear, but in some simple cases, as in the flow around thin bodies, the equations may be linearized. These solutions will be discussed in Section 8.3. An example of nonsimple flow in a nozzle is shown in Fig. 8-12.

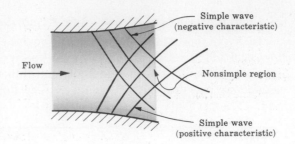

Fig. 8-12. Nonsimple flow in a nozzle. The expansion waves interact and the characteristics are no longer straight lines.

(e) Thin Airfoil Theory.

Flow over thin airfoils at small angles of attack may be considered isentropic if the shocks are weak enough, and shock-expansion theory may be simplified considerably. (The same results will be obtained later from linearized perturbation theory.) For weak shocks or expansion waves the pressure change is, from (8.7) and (8.9) approximately

$$\frac{\Delta p}{p} \approx \frac{kM^2}{\sqrt{M^2-1}}\,\Delta\theta$$

and assuming M is close to M_1 and p close to p_1,

$$\frac{p-p_1}{p_1} \approx \frac{kM_1^2}{\sqrt{M_1^2-1}}\,\theta \tag{8.16}$$

The pressure coefficient C_p is defined as

$$C_p = \frac{p-p_1}{\tfrac{1}{2}\rho_1 V_1^2} = \frac{p-p_1}{\tfrac{1}{2}kp_1M_1^2} = \frac{2}{kM_1^2}(p/p_1-1) \tag{8.17}$$

where the subscript 1 refers to free stream values. Hence we obtain from (8.16) and (8.17),

$$C_p = \frac{2\theta}{\sqrt{M_1^2-1}} \tag{8.18}$$

For a flat plate at incidence α, Fig. 8-11(b), C_p is simply $C_{p_B} = +2\alpha/\sqrt{M_1^2-1}$ for the bottom and $C_{p_T} = -2\alpha/\sqrt{M_1^2-1}$ for the top. The lift and drag coefficients are then

$$C_L = \frac{\text{lift per unit length}}{\tfrac{1}{2}\rho_1 V_1^2 c} = \frac{(p_B-p_T)c\cos\alpha}{\tfrac{1}{2}\rho_1 V_1^2 c} = (C_{p_B}-C_{p_T})\cos\alpha$$

$$C_D = \frac{\text{drag per unit length}}{\tfrac{1}{2}\rho_1 V_1^2 c} = \frac{(p_B-p_T)c\sin\alpha}{\tfrac{1}{2}\rho_1 V_1^2 c} = (C_{p_B}-C_{p_T})\sin\alpha$$

where c is the chord length (width of the airfoil). Since α is small, $\cos\alpha \approx 1$, $\sin\alpha \approx \alpha$, and we finally have

$$C_L = \frac{4\alpha}{\sqrt{M_1^2-1}}, \quad C_D = \frac{4\alpha^2}{\sqrt{M_1^2-1}} \tag{8.19}$$

for the flat plate at a small angle of attack, α.

In general it can be shown that the pressure coefficients for thin airfoils may be expressed as follows:

$$C_{p_T} = \frac{2}{\sqrt{M_1^2-1}}\left(\frac{df_T}{dx}\right), \quad C_{p_B} = \frac{2}{\sqrt{M_1^2-1}}\left(-\frac{df_B}{dx}\right) \tag{8.20}$$

where $f_T(x)$ and $f_B(x)$ are the equations of the top and bottom surfaces, respectively, of the

Fig. 8-13.   Thin airfoil at a small angle of attack. The airfoil in (a) may be decomposed into (b), (c) and (d).

airfoil. (See Fig. 8-13.)   From (8.20) the expressions for C_L and C_D can be found as

$$C_L = \frac{4\bar{\alpha}}{\sqrt{M_1^2 - 1}}, \quad C_D = \frac{4}{\sqrt{M_1^2 - 1}}\left[\overline{\left(\frac{dh}{dx}\right)^2} + (\bar{\alpha})^2 + \overline{\alpha_c^2(x)}\right] \tag{8.21}$$

where $h(x)$ is the thickness of the airfoil, $\bar{\alpha}$ is the mean angle of attack and $\alpha_c(x)$ is the local angle of attack of the camber line with respect to the mean angle of attack line inclined at angle $\bar{\alpha}$, as indicated in Fig. 8-13.

These same results may be obtained from the perturbation theory of the next section.

8.3   SMALL PERTURBATIONS AND THE LINEARIZED THEORY

(a) Perturbation Theory.

If we consider homentropic flow (isentropic throughout), that is, irrotational and frictionless and such that h_0 is the same throughout, then we can use equation (8.6) as the basic governing equation.   Shocks are not permitted, so we must confine ourselves to weak, virtually isentropic shocks and expansions.   Physically this means that the bodies over which the flow occurs must be thin two-dimensional airfoils, or thin cylindrical bodies which limit the shock strength.   Mathematically we can express this condition by saying that the velocity is everywhere close to the free stream velocity, $\mathbf{V}_0$, or $\mathbf{V}_1$ as we have called it in the previous section.   Referring to Fig. 8-14, we express the velocity at any point in the flow as the free stream velocity $\mathbf{V}_0$ plus a small perturbation velocity $\mathbf{v}'$.   Hence

$$\begin{aligned} u &= V_0 + u' & u'/V_0 &\ll 1 \\ v &= v' & v'/V_0 &\ll 1 \\ w &= w' & w'/V_0 &\ll 1 \end{aligned} \tag{8.22}$$

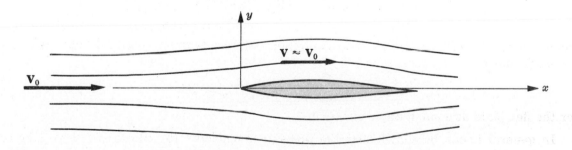

Fig. 8-14.   Thin body perturbing a uniform flow, $\mathbf{V}_0$.

Substituting into the three-dimensional form of equation (8.5) and eliminating a^2 by using the perfect gas energy equation in the form

$$\frac{(V_0 + u')^2 + v'^2 + w'^2}{2} + \frac{a^2}{k-1} = \frac{V_0^2}{2} + \frac{a_0^2}{k-1} \tag{8.23}$$

we obtain the perturbation equation for velocities which may be written

$$(1 - M_0^2)\frac{\partial u'}{\partial x} + \frac{\partial v'}{\partial y} + \frac{\partial w'}{\partial z}$$

$$= M_0^2 \left[(k+1)\frac{u'}{V_0} + \frac{k+1}{2}\frac{u'^2}{V_0^2} + \frac{k-1}{2}\frac{v'^2 + w'^2}{V_0^2} \right]\frac{\partial u'}{\partial x}$$

$$+ M_0^2 \left[(k-1)\frac{u'}{V_0} + \frac{k+1}{2}\frac{v'^2}{V_0^2} + \frac{k-1}{2}\frac{w'^2 + u'^2}{V_0^2} \right]\frac{\partial v'}{\partial y} \tag{8.24}$$

$$+ M_0^2 \left[(k-1)\frac{u'}{V_0} + \frac{k+1}{2}\frac{w'^2}{V_0^2} + \frac{k-1}{2}\frac{u'^2 + v'^2}{V_0^2} \right]\frac{\partial w'}{\partial z}$$

$$+ M_0^2 \left[\frac{v'}{V_0}\left(1 + \frac{u'}{V_0}\right)\left(\frac{\partial u'}{\partial y} + \frac{\partial v'}{\partial x}\right) + \frac{w'}{V_0}\left(1 + \frac{u'}{V_0}\right)\left(\frac{\partial u'}{\partial z} + \frac{\partial w'}{\partial x}\right) \right.$$

$$\left. + \frac{v'w'}{V_0^2}\left(\frac{\partial w'}{\partial y} + \frac{\partial v'}{\partial z}\right) \right]$$

which is an exact equation. If we assume that u', v' and w' are $\ll V_0$, then we get the simplified second order equation

$$(1 - M_0^2)\frac{\partial u'}{\partial x} + \frac{\partial v'}{\partial y} + \frac{\partial w'}{\partial z}$$

$$= M_0^2(k+1)\frac{u'}{V_0}\frac{\partial u'}{\partial x} + M_0^2(k-1)\frac{u'}{V_0}\left(\frac{\partial v'}{\partial y} + \frac{\partial w'}{\partial z}\right) \tag{8.25}$$

$$+ M_0^2 \frac{v'}{V_0}\left(\frac{\partial u'}{\partial y} + \frac{\partial v'}{\partial x}\right) + M_0^2 \frac{w'}{V_0}\left(\frac{\partial u'}{\partial z} + \frac{\partial w'}{\partial x}\right)$$

which is good for the full range of Mach numbers from subsonic through transonic to supersonic and hypersonic flow. However, a simpler linear form, good for subsonic and supersonic flow, but not for transonic flow where $M \approx 1$ nor hypersonic flow where $M \succ 6$, may be obtained by retaining only first order terms. It is

$$(1 - M_0^2)\frac{\partial u'}{\partial x} + \frac{\partial v'}{\partial y} + \frac{\partial w'}{\partial z} = 0 \tag{8.26}$$

Equation (8.25) may be simplified for transonic flow to

$$(1 - M_0^2)\frac{\partial u'}{\partial x} + \frac{\partial v'}{\partial y} + \frac{\partial w'}{\partial z} = M_0^2(k+1)\frac{u'}{V_0}\frac{\partial u'}{\partial x} \tag{8.27}$$

which is still good, actually better than (8.26), for subsonic and supersonic flow, but it is nonlinear. It is often convenient to express these perturbation equations in terms of a perturbation velocity potential defined as $\mathbf{v}' = -\nabla\phi$. (8.26) becomes

$$(1 - M_0^2)\frac{\partial^2 \phi}{\partial x^2} + \frac{\partial^2 \phi}{\partial y^2} + \frac{\partial^2 \phi}{\partial z^2} = 0 \tag{8.28}$$

and (8.27) becomes

$$(1 - M_0^2)\frac{\partial^2 \phi}{\partial x^2} + \frac{\partial^2 \phi}{\partial y^2} + \frac{\partial^2 \phi}{\partial z^2} = -\frac{M_0^2(k+1)}{V_0}\frac{\partial \phi}{\partial x}\frac{\partial^2 \phi}{\partial y^2} \tag{8.29}$$

Equation (8.28) is linear and may be easily solved for thin airfoils in the subsonic and supersonic regime. For low Mach numbers, $(1 - M_0^2) \approx 1$ and we have $\nabla^2\phi = 0$ which is exactly the equation used in Chapter 6 where we assumed the flow to be incompressible (and hence $M \ll 1$). We now can discuss compressible subsonic flow using equation (8.28). The form of (8.28) changes from elliptic for subsonic flow in which $M < 1$ (where the influence of the body is felt throughout the flow field) to hyperbolic for supersonic flow where $M > 1$ (where the body can exert no influence upstream and the solutions are wave-like disturbances propagating along characteristics).

(b) The Pressure Coefficient in the Linearized Theory.

The pressure coefficient defined by equation (8.17) and the pressure p may be written in terms of the components of $\mathbf{V}$ (using the energy equation) as

$$C_p = \frac{2}{kM_1^2}\{[1 + \tfrac{1}{2}(k-1)M_1^2(1 - V^2/V_0^2)]^{k/(k-1)} - 1\} \tag{8.30}$$

Inserting the perturbation velocities, expanding and retaining second order terms, we obtain

$$C_p = -\left[\frac{2u'}{V_0} + (1 - M_0^2)\frac{u'^2}{V_0} + \frac{v'^2 + w'^2}{V_0^2}\right] \tag{8.31}$$

For two-dimensional and planar flows it is adequate to retain only first order terms, and

$$C_p = -\frac{2u'}{V_0} \tag{8.32}$$

For flow over thin cylindrical bodies the second order term must be retained, and

$$C_p = -\frac{2u'}{V_0} - \frac{v'^2 + w'^2}{V_0^2} \tag{8.33}$$

(c) Boundary Conditions.

Physically, the boundary condition is that the velocity vector must be tangential to the body at the surface of the body. If the surface of the body is given by the equation

$$f(x, y, z) = 0$$

then this boundary condition is

$$\mathbf{V} \cdot \nabla f = 0 \tag{8.34}$$

Explicitly writing out (8.34) in terms of u', v' and w' leads to the condition, accurate to a consistent order, for two-dimensional flow in the xy plane (with small y dimension)

$$v'(x, y = 0) = V_0\,(dy/dx)_{\text{body}} \tag{8.35}$$

For "planar" flow (for thin, essentially flat three-dimensional bodies like wings) the flow is quasi-two-dimensional, and the boundary condition on the surface becomes

$$v'(x, 0, z) = V_0\,(\partial y/\partial x)_{\text{body}} \tag{8.36}$$

where the body lies in the xz plane and is almost two-dimensional in the xy plane.

For flow about thin cylindrical objects, the situation is somewhat more complicated and will not be discussed here. The reader is referred to the references.

It is interesting to note that the velocity $v'(x)$ is evaluated at $y = 0$ and not actually on the surface of the body. This approximation is consistent with the thin body approximation.

(d) Supersonic Thin Airfoil Theory.

The perturbation theory just discussed may be applied to two-dimensional thin airfoils. The results are identical to the weak shock solutions discussed previously in Section 8.2(e).

8.4 THE METHOD OF CHARACTERISTICS

In complex flows where simple shock-expansion theory or the linearized theory is not adequate, the original nonlinear equations must be solved by numerical techniques. The method of characteristics allows a simplification of these equations in the supersonic range and provides a well-established mathematical technique readily adaptable to numerical analysis.

(a) Elliptic and Hyperbolic Equations.

The equations describing subsonic flow are elliptic and those describing supersonic flow are hyperbolic, and entirely different methods of numerical analyses must be used for the two. In subsonic flow, any disturbance can be felt throughout the entire flow field and the method of relaxation must be used to solve the elliptic equations. Here the boundary conditions must be prescribed along a boundary completely enclosing the domain of interest and the entire flow field must be viewed simultaneously. However, in supersonic flow (with hyperbolic equations), disturbances and information can propagate only downstream, and boundary conditions must be specified only along a curve located upstream. Then one can "march" downstream, calculating values along the way, without the necessity of iterating back over the flow field in order to take account of a downstream condition as in subsonic flow.

A hyperbolic equation is one that gives rise to characteristics, but we will not give an exact mathematical definition here. Some differences between elliptic and hyperbolic differential equations are tabulated below, considering ϕ as the dependent variable.

Elliptic equation	Hyperbolic equation
(1) Either ϕ or $\partial\phi/\partial n$ must be prescribed on a closed boundary to avoid singularities.	(1) ϕ or $\partial\phi/\partial n$ may be specified on an open boundary. Singularities may result if boundary conditions are prescribed on a closed boundary.
(2) A change in boundary conditions affects the whole region of flow.	(2) A change in boundary condition affects only a limited domain of the flow.
(3) The solution must be analytic.	(3) Solution need not be analytic (shocks are singularities).

(b) Characteristics.

We will not discuss the general mathematical theory of characteristic and hyperbolic differential equations here. Rather, we will present a simple physical discussion of characteristics as they appear in two-dimensional gasdynamics and briefly outline the numerical method of calculation.

We begin by considering steady two-dimensional, homentropic flow. We cannot describe the structure of shock waves with the equations of such flow since shock waves involve irreversible processes. However, shocks may be admissible solutions (if the boundary conditions are of a certain type) since shocks correspond to singularities in the solution to the hyperbolic system. The flow is then homentropic within domains which do not contain shocks or which are bounded by shocks. If shocks occur, their location may necessitate some trial and error calculations. For example, in a converging-diverging nozzle under critical operation, if the inlet pressure and outlet pressure are both specified, a shock wave may occur downstream of the throat. In this section downstream of the throat the flow is supersonic and the method characteristics may be used to map the flow. However, if we were to simply march downstream to the exit, the final pressure may not be that which was specified. Only by admitting a shock in the nozzle could the pressure at the outlet be made to correspond to the prescribed value. Hence, whenever the boundary conditions are overspecified in a hyperbolic system singularities (shocks) may result. (This overspecification may be a physical one, of course, and not merely a mathematical one.) Usually the method of characteristics is most useful where shocks do not occur, and only the boundary conditions on a curve upstream are specified. Then one can simply "march" downstream, calculating along the way, without any iteration or trial and error.

Equation (8.28) in terms of ϕ,

$$(1 - M_0^2)\frac{\partial^2\phi}{\partial x^2} + \frac{\partial^2\phi}{\partial y^2} + \frac{\partial^2\phi}{\partial z^2} = 0$$

is elliptic if $M_0 < 1$ and hyperbolic if $M_0 > 1$. However, we are generally not interested in applying the method characteristic to this simple linearized equation. Rather, the complete nonlinear equations are of concern. Consider the general equations (8.5):

$$(u^2 - a^2)\frac{\partial u}{\partial x} + (v^2 - a^2)\frac{\partial v}{\partial y} + uv\left(\frac{\partial u}{\partial y} + \frac{\partial v}{\partial x}\right) = 0$$

$$\frac{\partial v}{\partial y} - \frac{\partial u}{\partial x} = 0$$

We ask the question: under what condition are these equations reducible to a form which has a one-dimensional variation (at any point in space)? That is, the variation is only normal to a characteristic, and not along it. We look for a condition such that a combination of the above equations may be put into the form

$$A\frac{\partial u}{\partial \alpha} + B\frac{\partial v}{\partial \alpha} = 0 \qquad\qquad (8.37)$$

where $\dfrac{\partial}{\partial \alpha} = \cos\chi\dfrac{\partial}{\partial x} + \sin\chi\dfrac{\partial}{\partial y}$. Let $\tan\chi = \zeta$. By multiplying the first of equation (8.5) by λ_1, and the second by λ_2, and adding we can obtain the form of (8.37) if certain conditions are satisfied by λ_1 and λ_2. These are

$$\frac{\lambda_2 - \lambda_1 uv}{\lambda_1(a^2 - u^2)} = \zeta, \qquad \frac{\lambda_1(v^2 - a^2)}{(\lambda_2 - \lambda_1 uv)} = \zeta$$

Eliminating λ_1 and λ_2 we obtain

$$(a^2 - u^2)\zeta^2 - 2uv\zeta + (a^2 - v^2) = 0 \qquad\qquad (8.38)$$

The direction α is defined by ζ which exists only if

$$(u^2 + v^2) > a^2; \quad M > 1$$

that is, the flow is supersonic with $M > 1$. The directions α defined by two roots of (8.38) are the $+$ and $-$ characteristics, which we denote as ζ_+ and ζ_-. It can be shown that

$$\zeta_+\,\zeta_- = (a^2 - v^2)/(a^2 - u^2)$$

Then by finding λ_1 and λ_2 explicitly, it is possible to show that if we take $dy = \zeta_+\,dx$ then $du = -\zeta_-\,dv$, and if we take $dy = -\zeta_-\,dx$ then $du = -\zeta_+\,dv$. Hence we arrive at the relationships, equivalent to the original differential equation (8.5), that:

on $dy = \zeta_+\,dx:$ $du = -\zeta_-\,dv$

on $dy = -\zeta_-\,dx:$ $du = -\zeta_+\,dv$

(8.39)

However, it is more convenient to work in polar coordinates. We take $u = V\cos\theta$ and $v = V\sin\theta$, Fig. 8-15, so that

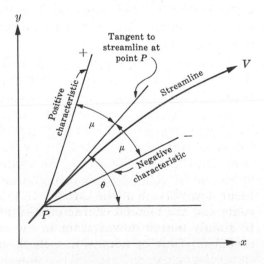

Fig. 8-15.   Polar coordinate system and characteristics.

$$du = \cos\theta\, dV - V\sin\theta\, d\theta \quad \text{and} \quad dv = \sin\theta\, dV + V\cos\theta\, d\theta$$

Substituting into (8.39) gives on the $(+)$ and $(-)$ characteristics respectively

$$\frac{\cot\mu}{V}dV = +d\theta, \qquad \frac{\cot\mu}{V}dV = -d\theta \tag{8.40}$$

and $\zeta_+ = \tan(\theta+\mu)$, $\zeta_- = \tan(\theta-\mu)$. Then the energy equation may be used to express V in terms of M and

$$\pm d\theta = \frac{\sqrt{M^2-1}\,dM}{M[1+\frac{1}{2}(k-1)M^2]} = dv(M)$$

which may be integrated to give $v(M)$. Hence since $\pm d\theta - dv = 0$, $(v-\theta)$ is constant on a $(+)$ characteristic, and $(v+\theta)$ is constant on a $(-)$ characteristic. Then if v and θ are both specified on a line L-M, we can construct a grid as we work downstream determining v and θ at points of intersection. Once v and θ are known, the Mach number, flow direction and velocity may be found. Referring to Fig. 8-16(a), let v and θ be specified along line segment L-M. Then the direction of the characteristics are known and at a set of arbitrary points $A_1, \ldots, A_n$. Let the $(+)$ and $(-)$ characteristics be drawn to the first set of intersections $B_1, \ldots, B_{n-1}$. At each of these points, $(v-\theta)$ and $(v+\theta)$ are known and hence v and θ can be found explicitly and then μ, M, V and the new direction of the $\pm$ characteristic may be drawn. This new set of lines intersect at $C_1, \ldots, C_{n-2}$. The process is continued throughout the range of influence which is bounded by the characteristics through A_1 and A_n. In general, in nonsimple flow regions the characteristics will be curved but the segments between intersections are drawn as straight lines. The finer the mesh, the more exact the solution.

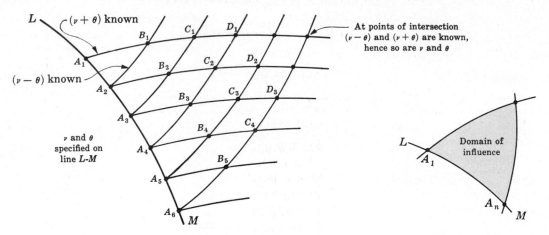

Fig. 8-16(a).   Characteristics construction in polar coordinates.

To illustrate in more detail, consider an enlarged diagram, Fig. 8-16(b), of a section of Fig. 8-16(a). At point B_1,

$$v_3 = \tfrac{1}{2}(v_1+v_2) + \tfrac{1}{2}(\theta_1-\theta_2)$$

and

$$\theta_3 = \tfrac{1}{2}(v_1-v_2) + \tfrac{1}{2}(\theta_1+\theta_2)$$

Between mesh points the characteristic lines are assumed to be straight.

The complete theory of characteristics for compressible flow is beyond the scope of this discussion and the reader is referred to the references.

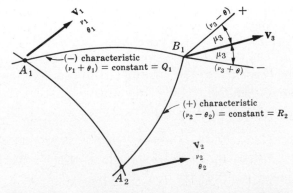

Fig. 8-16(b).   Details of the computational method.

(c) **Supersonic Aircraft.**

In actual practice, the wave drag on a wing flying supersonically, with shock-expansion wave formation, is much greater than the drag on a subsonic type wing. Consequently, supersonic aircraft are made so that the wings actually operate subsonically. This type of operation is accomplished by making the sweepback angle greater than the Mach angle. Then the component of velocity normal to the leading edge is subsonic and the wing behaves essentially as a subsonic airfoil. However, the fuselage generates a nose shock but the wave drag is minimized by tapering the nose to a needle point to weaken the shock, and by properly varying the cross sectional area of the fuselage (so that it looks something like a "coke" bottle).

The wings are three-dimensional bodies and must be treated as such in the computation of flow over them. The details are beyond the scope of this discussion, but it is important to remember that the sweepback causes the wing to behave essentially as a subsonic airfoil in terms of lifting characteristics. One effect of increasing the sweepback is to stabilize the plane in a manner similar to the effect of a positive dihedral angle. In fact in highly swept-back wings the dihedral may be negative (giving a drooping appearance).

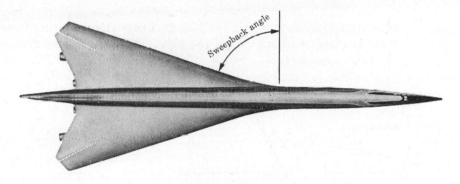

Fig. 8-17. A modern supersonic airplane. The sweepback angle is greater than the Mach angle so that the normal component of velocity on the leading edge of the wing is subsonic.

References

1. Liepmann, H. W., and Roshko, A., *Elements of Gasdynamics*, John Wiley, 1957.

2. Owczarek, J. A., *Fundamentals of Gas Dynamics*, International Textbook, 1964.

3. Howarth, L., (Editor), *Modern Developments in Fluid Dynamics, High Speed Flow*, Vols. 1 and 2, Oxford University Press, 1956.

4. Shapiro, A. H., *The Dynamics and Thermodynamics of Compressible Fluid Flow*, Vols. 1 and 2, Ronald Press, 1952.

Solved Problems

8.1. Air at 520°R and atmospheric pressure passes through an oblique shock wave inclined at 50° to the flow as shown in Fig. 8-18. The initial Mach number is 2. Determine the conditions downstream and the angle through which the flow is turned.

From Fig. 8-3, page 159, we find that θ is approximately 18°. From equations (8.7), page 158, we can find downstream conditions (at point 2) in terms of the upstream conditions (at point 1). Alternatively, we could use normal shock tables with the numerical value of M_1 in the table interpreted as our value of $M_1 \sin \beta$, and the M_2 in the table as $M_2 \sin(\beta - \theta)$. We find then:

$p_2/p_1 = 2.57$; $p_2 = 37.8$ psia

$T_2/T_1 = 1.34$; $T_2 = 697°$R

$M_2 \sin(\beta - \theta) = 0.69$; $M_2 = 1.3$

Fig. 8-18

8.2. A thin flat plate airfoil is shown in Fig. 8-19 inclined at an angle of attack of 10°. Find the fluid properties in all regions of the flow. $M_1 = 3$ and the free stream air is at $T_1 = 500°$R and $p_1 = 15$ psia.

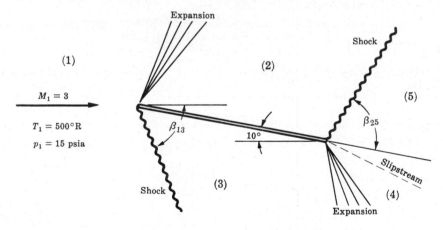

Fig. 8-19

Using equations (8.7), page 158, and Fig. 8-3, page 159, we can find conditions in region 3. We find $\beta_{13} = 27.5°$. Using $k = c_p/c_v = 1.4$ for air, we obtain

$p_3/p_1 = 2.07, \quad p_3 = 31.0$ psia; $\quad M_3 = 2.49; \quad T_3 = 1.25 T_1 = 625°$R

To find conditions in region 4 we use

$$\nu_4 = \nu_3 + |\theta_4 - \theta_3| = \nu_3 + 10° = 39.1° + 10° = 49.1°$$

and $M_4 = 2.97$ from Table 8.1, page 162. Since the expansion is isentropic, we write

$$p_4/p_3 = \left[\frac{2 + (k-1)M_3^2}{2 + (k-1)M_4^2}\right]^{k/(k-1)}$$

from which we find $p_4/p_3 = 0.48$ and $p_4 = 14.9$ psia. T_4 is found from

$$T_4/T_3 = (p_4/p_3)^{(k-1)/k}$$

and hence $T_4 = 0.81(T_3) = 0.81(1.25 T_1) = 1.01 T_1$.

Now proceeding along the upper surface of the plate, we find conditions in region 2.

$$\nu = \nu_1 + 10° = 49.8° + 10° = 59.8°$$

and hence $M_2 = 3.57$. Using the isentropic relationships we find

$$p_2 = 0.44p_1 = 6.60 \text{ psia}, \quad T_2 = 0.79T_1$$

Then through the shock to region 5 we find

$$\beta_{25} = 24°, \quad M_5 = 2.98, \quad p_5 = 2.29p_2 - 1.01p_1, \quad T_5 = 1.29T_2 = 1.02T_1$$

We see that the pressures p_5 and p_4 are approximately but not exactly equal, and the temperatures T_5 and T_4 are approximately equal. In actuality a slipstream or contact surface must extend from the rear of the airfoil separating regions of unlike temperature and density but the pressures p_4 and p_5 must be equal. Further, across this slipstream the velocities are different and a shear layer exists. It is a trial and error process to locate the exact inclination of the slipstream in order to make $p_4 = p_5 = p_1$.

The lift and drag per unit wing area are

$$L = (p_3 - p_2) \cos 10° = 24.0 \text{ psi}, \quad D = (p_3 - p_2) \sin 10° = 4.23 \text{ psi}$$

Note that since p_5 and p_1 are almost equal the contact surface comes off the airfoil nearly parallel to the free stream. In general, in order to insure that $p_5 = p_1$, as it must in reality, the contact surface may be inclined at a slight angle to the free stream.

8.3. Compute the lift and drag on the airfoil in the above problem, using thin wing theory and compare to the exact shock-expansion solution.

From equation *(8.19)*, page 164, we find C_L and C_D. $C_L = 0.247$ and $C_D = 0.043$. (Remember here, $M_1 = 3$ and α is measured in radians; $10° = 0.1745$ radians.) The lift per unit area is $\frac{1}{2}\rho_1 V_1^2 C_L$ or $\frac{1}{2}kM_1^2 p_1 C_L$. Knowing T_1 and p_1 we find ρ_1 as 0.00253 slugs/ft³ from the perfect gas law, and $V_1 = a_1 M_1 = (1090 \text{ ft/sec})(3) = 3270 \text{ ft/sec}$.

$$L = \tfrac{1}{2}\rho_1 V_1^2 C_L = \tfrac{1}{2}(0.00253)(3270)^2(0.247) = 3340 \text{ psf} = 23.2 \text{ psi}$$

and

$$D = \tfrac{1}{2}\rho_1 V_1^2 C_D = 4.04 \text{ psi}$$

Comparing these results to those of the previous problem, we see that they are off by less than 5 percent.

8.4. Using shock expansion theory determine the flow over the two-dimensional double wedge profile shown in Fig. 8-20. The Mach number of the free stream is 2.

Fig. 8-20

A contact surface will extend from the trailing edge. The exact angle this contact surface makes with the free stream must be determined by imposing the condition that the pressure at 4 is the same as the pressure at 1. This would mean a slight turning of the free stream flow on the bottom, at the trailing edge. We neglect this effect here for the moment and assume the bottom flow to be undisturbed.

For flow through the leading shock, 1-2, $\theta = 10°$, and from Fig. 8-3, page 159, $\beta = 39.5°$. We find from shock tables or equations *(8.7)*, page 158,

$$p_2/p_1 = 1.72, \quad T_2/T_1 = 1.17, \quad M_2 = 1.63$$

Then through the expansion fan 2-3 we find

$$\nu_2 = 15.9°, \quad \nu_3 = \nu_2 + 20° = 35.9°, \quad M_3 = 2.37$$

$$p_3/p_2 \;=\; \left[\frac{2 + (k-1)M_2^2}{2 + (k-1)M_3^2}\right]^{k/(k-1)} \;=\; 0.32, \qquad T_3/T_2 \;=\; (p_3/p_2)^{(k-1)/k} \;=\; 0.72$$

Through the shock 3-4, $\theta = 10°$ and $\beta = 34°$, and

$$p_4/p_3 \;=\; 1.88, \quad T_4/T_3 \;=\; 1.21, \quad M_4 \;=\; 1.90$$

Clearly then, $p_4 = 1.03 p_1$, and the flow cannot leave the airfoil parallel to the free stream flow since p_4 would not then be the same as p_1. Hence the shock 3-4 must take place through slightly less than a $10°$ deflection angle and the flow on the bottom is slightly compressed through a shock. The determination of the exact angle of the contact surface may be done by trial and error, such that $p_4 = p_1$. The details are left as an exercise for the reader.

8.5. A shock wave impinging on a wall shown in Fig. 8-21 will be reflected so that the final flow is parallel to the wall. Consider a shock reflecting as shown.

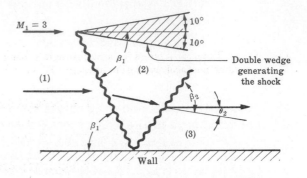

For $\theta = 10°$ and $M_1 = 3$, we find $\beta_1 = 28°$ and $M_2 = 2.5$ from (8.7) or appropriate tables. Then for $\theta_2 = 10°$ and $M_2 = 2.5$ we find $\beta_2 = 32°$. Remember, if we use standard normal shock tables we insert $M_1 \sin \beta_1$ and $M_2 \sin(\beta_1 - \theta)$ for M_1 and M_2 in the tables respectively.

Fig. 8-21

Supplementary Problems

8.6. Air flows over a corner as shown in Fig. 8-22. Find the air properties and Mach number downstream. Draw in the expansion fan. What happens when the angle θ becomes larger and larger?

Fig. 8-22   Fig. 8-23

8.7. Air flows through a corner shown in Fig. 8-23. Find the properties and Mach number downstream. What happens as θ becomes larger and larger?

8.8. Find the shock pattern of the wedge of Fig. 8-24 with standard air flowing in at Mach 5.

Fig. 8-24

8.9. Find the properties downstream and plot the Mach angle μ as a function of θ for the flow of Fig. 8-25.

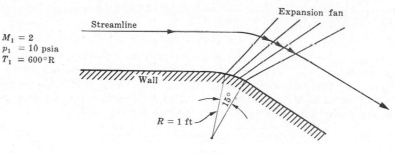

$M_1 = 2$
$p_1 = 10 \text{ psia}$
$T_1 = 600°\text{R}$

Streamline

Expansion fan

Wall

$R = 1 \text{ ft}$

15°

Fig. 8-25

8.10. Two-dimensional flow occurs through a bend as shown in Fig. 8-26. Locate the downstream bend so that no shock reflection obtains. What is the width D_2?

$M_1 = 3$
$p_1 = 5 \text{ psia}$
$T_1 = 500°\text{R}$

D_1

Shock

Locate this point

10°

D_2

Fig. 8-26

8.11. Similar to Problem 8.10 is the expanding turn as shown in Fig. 8-27. Specify the shape of the top wall so that the expansion wave is not reflected. (*Hint.* The shape follows a streamline through the turn.) What is D_2 in terms of relevant parameters?

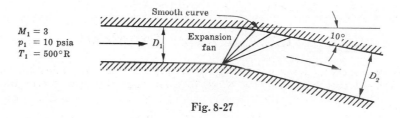

$M_1 = 3$
$p_1 = 10 \text{ psia}$
$T_1 = 500°\text{R}$

Smooth curve

D_1

Expansion fan

10°

D_2

Fig. 8-27

8.12. What happens in Problem 8.5 where the shock is reflected when the angle of the first shock, β_1, becomes larger and larger? Can a simple reflection turn the flow parallel to the wall, or does something strange happen?

8.13. Flow occurs over a triangular shaped surface as shown in Fig. 8-28. For $M_1 > 1$ find the flow pattern over the wall by the linearized theory of small perturbations (assuming $\epsilon \ll \lambda$).

M_1

y

ϵ

λ

x

Fig. 8-28

8.14. A regular diamond shaped airfoil (Fig. 8-29 below) is inclined at an angle of 10° to a supersonic flow of Mach 2. The wedge angle of the airfoil is 20° so that the top and bottom surfaces are horizontal.

Compute the lift on the airfoil by shock expansion theory and sketch in the shocks and waves. What is the wave drag?

Compute the lift by thin airfoil linearized theory and compare the results to those obtained by the more exact theory.

What does the flow pattern look like as indicated by linearized theory?

Fig. 8-29　　　　　　　　　　　　　　　　　　　　Fig. 8-30

8.15. The Busemann biplane shown in Fig. 8-30 consists of two parallel airfoils, each of which is a half diamond as shown in the sketch. At zero angle of attack the wave drag can be made effectively zero by correctly spacing the airfoils for a given Mach number M_1. Assuming two-dimensional linear theory $(t \ll c)$, find the maximum spacing G (as a function of M_1) for drag cancellation at zero angle of attack. (At certain sub-multiples of the maximum critical spacing G, cancellation is also achieved.)

Is there any lift at zero angle of attack?

Is there wave drag cancellation if the angle of attack is changed, keeping M_1 and G constant?

8.16. Find the lift and drag coefficient for the half diamond shaped (cross section) airfoil of Problem 8.4. Discuss the character of the contact surface in thin airfoil theory.

8.17. Using the theory of thin airfoils, find the flow pattern and the lift and drag coefficients over the two-dimensional airfoil shown in cross section in Fig. 8-31.

$$h(x) = H \sin \pi x / c$$

Equation of center line:
$$y = Y \sin 2\pi x / c$$
H and $Y \ll c$. $\bar{\alpha}$ is known.

Fig. 8-31

8.18. Using thin airfoil theory make a plot of C_L and C_D versus M for a two-dimensional thin flat plate airfoil inclined at an angle of attack of 5°.

8.19. Make a similar plot to the one in Problem 8.18 but assume $M = 2$ and plot C_L and C_D versus the angle of attack.

8.20. Flow expands around a sharp corner as shown in Fig. 8-32. Locate the slipstream.

Fig. 8-32　　　　　　　　　　　　　　　　　　Fig. 8-33

8.21. Make a plot of C_L versus C_D for a thin airfoil of the shape shown in Fig. 8-33. (Treat $\bar{\alpha}$ as an independent variable and M as a constant.) t is the maximum thickness and the airfoil is symmetrical, top and bottom.

8.22. As shown in Fig. 8-34, a piston is contained in a cylinder which has a closed end. The piston is suddenly set in motion at a constant velocity towards the closed end of the tube. A shock wave will then be initiated, travel to the end of the tube, and be reflected back toward the piston.

Determine the velocity of the shock before and after reflection and the pressures in all regions of flow at all times. Qualitatively explain briefly what happens after the shock reflects off the piston face.

The air in the cylinder is initially at atmospheric pressure and at 520°R. The piston is moved at a constant velocity of 100 ft/sec. *Hint.* Refer back to Chapter 7.

$U_p = 100$ ft/sec　(velocity of piston)

Fig. 8-34

8.23. In Problems 8.1 and 8.2, find the velocity of the air in the various regions of flow.

NOMENCLATURE FOR CHAPTER 8

a　=　sonic speed

c　=　chord length (width of airfoil)

c_p　=　specific heat at constant pressure

c_v　=　specific heat at constant volume

C_D　=　drag coefficient

C_L　=　lift coefficient

C_P　=　pressure coefficient

D　=　drag

h　=　specific enthalpy

h_0　=　total (or stagnation) specific enthalpy

k　=　ratio of specific heats, c_p/c_v

L　=　lift

M　=　Mach number

M_0　=　Mach number of the free stream

p　=　pressure

s　=　specific entropy

u　=　x component of velocity

u'　=　x component of perturbation velocity

v　=　y component of velocity

v'　=　y component of perturbation velocity

$\mathbf{V}$　=　velocity vector

V_0　=　free stream velocity

w　=　z component of velocity

w'　=　z component of perturbation velocity

α　=　angle of attack

β　=　shock angle

θ　=　deflection angle

μ　=　Mach angle

ν　=　Prandtl-Meyer function

ρ　=　density

ϕ　=　velocity potential

Chapter 9

Incompressible Turbulent Flow

9.1 INTRODUCTION

Although we have previously considered flows which are turbulent (much of Chapter 5 was devoted to turbulent flows and many of the results of Chapters 7 and 8 are valid for turbulent flow), we will now consider the important problem of turbulent fluid motion in more depth in the present chapter.

The problems of fluid motion might be arranged in a sequence going from the least to the most difficult in the following way: potential flow $\longrightarrow$ viscous laminar flow $\longrightarrow$ turbulent flow. Historically, the early work in the field was primarily concerned with potential flow and laminar flow, with very little research effort devoted to the difficult problems of turbulent flow. This was unfortunate because most of the flows of engineering importance are turbulent. In recent years, however, the research effort in the area of turbulent flow has increased substantially. These problems, nevertheless, are far from being solved and will be with us for a long time.

Before we go further, let us answer two questions: What is turbulent flow? Where does it occur? Turbulent fluid motion is defined by Hinze (see reference 3, page 192) as "an irregular condition of flow in which various quantities (for example, velocity and pressure) show a random variation with time and space, so that statistically distinct average values can be discerned". One finds that this kind of motion predominates in most flows which occur in nature. When objects such as ships, automobiles, aircraft and re-entry vehicles move through fluids, the flow is nearly always turbulent. In these flows one finds that there is a fluctuating motion superimposed on the main or average flow.

Turbulence also occurs when a fluid moves through enclosures such as fans, pumps, ducts and pipes. The important criterion as to when the flow will be turbulent is the magnitude of the Reynolds number, as was previously indicated in Chapter 5.

We are seeking (1) a physical understanding and (2) a quantitative description of turbulent fluid motion. The former will rely heavily (although, of course, not entirely) on experiment, while the latter will rely heavily on mathematical models. Both are important to the engineer.

There are two basically different approaches used in describing and seeking an understanding of turbulent motion. They are (1) phenomenological and (2) statistical. In the former, one establishes an expression for shear stress in terms of some empirical exchange coefficient and in the latter one studies the equations of motion in terms of time average quantities.

9.2 EQUATIONS OF MEAN VELOCITY

Equations of mean velocity distribution were obtained for turbulent flows in Section 5.2(d), page 81. They are summarized here for convenience. The reader may refer back to Chapter 5 for definitions of the symbols used here.

(a) **Power Law:**

$$u/U = (y/\delta)^{m/(2-m)} = (y/\delta)^{1/n} \tag{5.13}$$

Here y is the distance from the wall, δ is the boundary layer thickness, U is the free stream velocity, and u is the velocity in the boundary layer. The power law applies for flow with a negligible pressure gradient over a flat plate. It also applies for fully developed flow in a pipe. The exponent varies weakly with Reynolds number.

(b) **Logarithmic Form of Law of the Wall:**

$$u/u_\tau \;=\; 2.44 \ln (yu_\tau/\nu) \,+\, 4.9 \qquad\qquad (5.16)$$

where u_τ is the friction velocity, $\sqrt{\tau_0/\rho}$, and τ_0 is the wall shear stress. The equation is valid over most of the boundary layer. It does not apply to a small region right at the wall $(0 < yu_\tau/\nu < 50)$ and to the outermost portion of the boundary layer. It does apply for a nonzero pressure gradient, but the larger the pressure gradient the more the region over which it applies is reduced.

(c) **Logarithmic Form of the Velocity Defect Law:**

$$(U - u)/u_\tau \;=\; -2.44 \ln (y/\delta) \,+\, 2.5 \qquad\qquad (5.17)$$

This equation applies to the intermediate portion of the boundary layer for zero or moderate pressure gradients. In the above equations *(5.13)*, *(5.16)* and *(5.17)*, u, as in Chapter 5, denotes the time average velocity in a steady turbulent flow, although in the remainder of this chapter we will use a bar to indicate mean values (i.e. $\bar{u}$).

9.3 STATISTICAL APPROACH

(a) **Turbulent Velocities and Averaging.**

Consider turbulent flow in a pipe. If we choose a particular point in the flow and observe the velocity at that point as a function of time, we obtain a random curve as shown in Fig. 9-1. We define the time average velocity $\bar{u}$ as

$$\bar{u} \;\equiv\; \frac{1}{T_1} \int_0^{T_1} u\, dt \qquad (9.1)$$

where T_1 is a time large enough such that $\bar{u}$ is the same for any larger time for a steady mean flow. The bar over the quantity indicates the time average of the type indicated by equation *(9.1)*. The instantaneous velocity u may be written in terms of a time average velocity $\bar{u}$ which we call the mean velocity and a fluctuating velocity u'. $(u = \bar{u} + u'.)$

Fig. 9-1. Velocity as a function of time at a fixed point in a turbulent flow. u' is a random quantity superimposed on the mean velocity $\bar{u}$.

We will have need to combine fluctuating quantities in various ways in the next section. The following set of rules will aid in these operations. If a and b are fluctuating quantities and c is a constant, we have the following set of rules (Reynolds' rules of averages):

$$\overline{a + b} \;=\; \bar{a} + \bar{b}$$

$$\overline{ca} \;=\; c\bar{a}$$

$$\overline{ab} \;=\; \bar{a}\bar{b} + \overline{a'b'}$$

$$\overline{\frac{\partial a}{\partial x}} \;=\; \frac{\partial \bar{a}}{\partial x}$$

where $a = \bar{a} + a'$, $b = \bar{b} + b'$. (The mean value of a fluctuation is zero, $\bar{a}' = \bar{b}' = 0$.)

(*b*) **Equations of Motion for Turbulent Flow.**

We will now develop the equations of motion for turbulent flow. The method is basically the same in every case. First, the equations are written for the instantaneous quantities. Then we take the time average of both sides, noting that if the equality is valid instantaneously then it is also valid on the average for some period of time. Finally we simplify the equations such that only time average quantities appear.

(i)   *Continuity Equation for Turbulent Flow.*

The differential form of the continuity equation as derived in Chapter 3 is (in cartesian tensor form)

$$\frac{\partial \rho}{\partial t} + \frac{\partial}{\partial x_i}(\rho u_i) = 0 \tag{3.30}$$

where ρ is the density and u_i is the ith component of velocity. This equation is valid for turbulent flow, and the dependent variables (ρ and u_i) represent instantaneous fluctuating quantities. If we take the time average of this equation, we obtain

$$\overline{\frac{\partial \rho}{\partial t} + \frac{\partial}{\partial x_i}(\rho u_i)} = 0$$

By replacing the instantaneous quantities with the time average plus the fluctuating part, and by applying Reynolds' rules of averages as given in the previous section, we obtain

$$\frac{\partial \bar{\rho}}{\partial t} + \frac{\partial}{\partial x_i}(\bar{\rho}\bar{u}_i) + \frac{\partial}{\partial x_i}(\overline{\rho' u_i'}) = 0 \tag{9.2}$$

For incompressible flow, equation (*9.2*) becomes

$$\frac{\partial \bar{u}_i}{\partial x_i} = 0 \tag{9.3}$$

(ii)   *Momentum Equation for Turbulent Flow.*

The momentum equation in differential form was determined in Chapter 3 (equation (*3.47*)). We will assume that the flow is incompressible and the viscosity is constant. Then equation (*3.47*) becomes, in cartesian tensor notation with the summation convention used,

$$\rho\left(\frac{\partial u_i}{\partial t} + u_j\frac{\partial u_i}{\partial x_j}\right) = -\frac{\partial p}{\partial x_i} + \mu\frac{\partial^2 u_i}{\partial x_j\,\partial x_j} + B_i \tag{9.4}$$

where B_i is the body force and μ is the viscosity. This equation is assumed to be valid for turbulent as well as laminar flow. For turbulent flow, however, the dependent variables all vary as functions of time. They are not averaged quantities such as would be indicated by pitot tube measurements. We will now proceed to establish the equations in terms of time average quantities.

Let us substitute $u_i = \bar{u}_i + u_i'$ and $p = \bar{p} + p'$ into equation (*9.4*). We have

$$\rho\left[\frac{\partial(\bar{u}_i + u_i')}{\partial t} + (\bar{u}_j + u_j')\frac{\partial}{\partial x_j}(\bar{u}_i + u_i')\right] = B_i - \frac{\partial(\bar{p} + p')}{\partial x_i} + \mu\frac{\overline{\partial^2(\bar{u}_i + u_i')}}{\partial x_j\,\partial x_j}$$

Simplifying and taking the time average of both sides gives

$$\rho\left(\frac{\partial \bar{u}_i}{\partial t} + \bar{u}_j\frac{\partial \bar{u}_i}{\partial x_j} + \overline{u_j'\frac{\partial u_i'}{\partial x_j}}\right) = -\frac{\partial \bar{p}}{\partial x_i} + \mu\frac{\partial^2 \bar{u}_i}{\partial x_j\,\partial x_j} + \bar{B}_i \tag{9.5}$$

The third term on the left side of equation (*9.5*) is usually written in a different form. From the continuity equation for incompressible flow, we have $\partial u_j'/\partial x_j = 0$. Thus

$$u_i'\frac{\partial u_j'}{\partial x_j} = 0 \quad \text{and} \quad \overline{u_i'\frac{\partial u_j'}{\partial x_j}} = 0$$

Then by adding $\overline{u_i' \dfrac{\partial u_j'}{\partial x_j}}$ (i.e. zero) to both sides of equation (9.5) we have

$$\overline{u_j' \frac{\partial u_i'}{\partial x_j}} + \overline{u_i' \frac{\partial u_j'}{\partial x_j}} = \frac{\partial}{\partial x_j} \overline{u_i' u_j'}$$

and equation (9.5) becomes (with the turbulence term on the right side)

$$\rho\left(\frac{\partial \bar{u}_i}{\partial t} + \bar{u}_j \frac{\partial \bar{u}_i}{\partial x_j}\right) = -\frac{\partial \bar{p}}{\partial x_i} + \frac{\partial}{\partial x_j}\left(\mu \frac{\partial \bar{u}_i}{\partial x_j} - \rho \overline{u_i' u_j'}\right) + \bar{B}_i \tag{9.6}$$

Equation (9.6) is the momentum equation for turbulent flow written in terms of time average quantities. It differs from the equation for instantaneous quantities, equation (9.4), only by the addition of the last term. This term is often referred to as the Reynolds stresses or turbulent stresses. When the turbulent flow equation is written in this form, it gives the appearance of being the same as the laminar flow equation except for a term added to the laminar stress term. Strictly speaking, this term is not a stress but is an inertia (or momentum exchange) effect (recall that it came from the left side of the equation) and is only referred to as a stress because of the way in which the laminar flow equation is modified.

(iii) *Energy Equation for Turbulent Flow.*

Starting with the momentum equation for a constant viscosity and constant density fluid, equation (9.4), we multiply by u_i and simplify, obtaining

$$\frac{\partial}{\partial t}\left(\frac{u_i u_i}{2}\right) = -\frac{\partial}{\partial x_i}\left[u_i\left(\frac{p}{\rho} + \frac{u_j u_j}{2}\right)\right] + \nu \frac{\partial}{\partial x_j}\left[u_i\left(\frac{\partial u_i}{\partial x_j} + \frac{\partial u_j}{\partial x_i}\right)\right] - \nu\left(\frac{\partial u_i}{\partial x_j} + \frac{\partial u_j}{\partial x_i}\right)\frac{\partial u_i}{\partial x_j} \tag{9.7}$$

Equation (9.7) has units of energy and is referred to as an energy equation. However, it is not to be confused with the first law of thermodynamics. The first law of thermodynamics is a statement of the conservation of energy of all forms. The turbulence energy equation comes from the conservation of momentum and does not involve any forms of thermal energy.

Now we will write (9.7) in terms of time average plus fluctuating quantities

$$u_i = \bar{u}_i + u_i'$$

$$p = \bar{p} + p'$$

$$u_i u_i = \bar{u}_i \bar{u}_i + 2\bar{u}_i u_i' + u_i' u_i'$$

and take time average of both sides. Then we combine (subtract) with equation (9.6) after it has been multiplied by $\bar{u}_i$ and obtain

$$\overbrace{\frac{\partial}{\partial t}\left(\frac{\overline{u_i' u_i'}}{2}\right)}^{1} + \overbrace{\frac{\partial}{\partial x_i}\left(\bar{u}_i \frac{\overline{u_j' u_j'}}{2}\right)}^{2} = -\overbrace{\frac{\partial}{\partial x_i}\overline{u_i'\left(\frac{p'}{\rho} + \frac{u_j' u_j'}{2}\right)}}^{3}$$

$$\underbrace{-\overline{u_i' u_j'}\frac{\partial \bar{u}_j}{\partial x_i}}_{4} + \underbrace{\nu \frac{\partial}{\partial x_j}\overline{u_i'\left(\frac{\partial u_i'}{\partial x_j} + \frac{\partial u_j'}{\partial x_i}\right)}}_{5} - \underbrace{\nu \overline{\left(\frac{\partial u_i'}{\partial x_j} + \frac{\partial u_j'}{\partial x_i}\right)\frac{\partial u_j'}{\partial x_i}}}_{6} \tag{9.8}$$

Equation (9.8) is called the turbulence energy equation and each term is identifiable as a certain type of energy:

1, time rate of increase of turbulent kinetic energy.

2, convective diffusion of turbulent kinetic energy by the mean flow.

3, convective diffusion of total turbulent energy by turbulence.

4, production of turbulence (energy taken from the mean flow).

    5, work done by the viscous shear stresses of the turbulent motion.

    6, dissipation of turbulence by turbulent motion.

We will come back to this equation later in this chapter. In particular, we will look at the various terms for simple flows in order to gain some insight into the mechanism of turbulence.

9.4 PHENOMENOLOGICAL THEORIES

    In the previous section we determined the equations for turbulent flow. The usefulness of these equations is somewhat restricted from an engineering point of view. There is no way to solve these equations even for very simple flows. Thus we must go to a more direct approach which involves models of the flow which are physically somewhat inexact but which allow approximate solutions for some flows of engineering interest.

    The shear stress tensor τ_{ij} (laminar τ_{ij_l} plus turbulent τ_{ij_T}) is

$$\tau_{ij} = \mu\left(\frac{\partial \overline{u}_i}{\partial x_j} + \frac{\partial \overline{u}_j}{\partial x_i}\right) - \rho\,\overline{u_i' u_j'} = \tau_{ij_l} + \tau_{ij_T} \tag{9.9}$$

$$\tau_{ij_l} = \mu\left(\frac{\partial \overline{u}_i}{\partial x_j} + \frac{\partial \overline{u}_j}{\partial x_i}\right), \qquad \tau_{ij_T} = -\rho\,\overline{u_i' u_j'}, \qquad \text{for } i \neq j$$

There is little hope in obtaining a solution for the Reynolds stresses. Thus the problem is to relate in some way the turbulent stresses to the mean velocity. This approach has been successful in describing free turbulent flows such as jets and wakes. All of these models are restricted to two dimensional flow.

(a) Eddy Viscosity or Turbulent Viscosity.

    By writing the shear stress in terms of the laminar viscosity plus an additional term to account for the turbulent or macroscopic motion, we have (for two dimensional flow)

$$\tau_{ij} = (\mu + \rho\epsilon)\frac{\partial \overline{u}_i}{\partial x_j} \tag{9.10}$$

where ϵ is referred to as the eddy viscosity and is related to the Reynolds stresses by

$$\epsilon = \frac{-1}{\partial \overline{u}_i/\partial x_j}\,\overline{u_i' u_j'}$$

    The advantage of defining an eddy viscosity as in equation (9.10) is that if ϵ is a quantity which can be numerically determined (or expressed in terms of the mean velocity), then this form of the shear stress may be substituted into the momentum equation, thereby reducing the number of dependent variables. This procedure would lead to a substantial simplification of the problem. The difficulty is, however, that for most cases ϵ is different for each different flow condition and is not spatially constant for a given flow. We will consider the eddy viscosity for some actual flows later in this chapter.

(b) Prandtl Momentum Mixing Length.

    Prandtl determined a length for transfer of momentum between layers of different mean velocity. This transfer process is illustrated in Fig. 9-2 and given by equation (9.11).

$$\tau = \rho l^2 \left|\frac{d\overline{u}}{dy}\right|\frac{d\overline{u}}{dy} \tag{9.11}$$

The length l represents the distance that a fluid particle must travel in order to produce the ap-

Fig. 9-2. Illustration of Prandtl momentum mixing length.

parent turbulent shear stress for the given velocity gradient. The momentum mixing length model of turbulence is analogous to kinetic theory where the microscopic or molecular viscosity is equal to a velocity (mean molecular velocity) times a length (mean free path). There are inconsistencies in applying the kinetic theory analogy to turbulence in that for turbulent flow, dissipation occurs, and bits of fluid do not maintain their identity. The mixing length may be applied to two dimensional flows such as pipe flow, flow over a flat plate, free jet and wake flow.

The mixing length approach suffers from the same difficulties as the eddy viscosity approach for most flows, i.e. it is different for different flow conditions and is spatially variable for a given flow. In addition, in the derivation of the equations for mixing length the assumption is made that it is small. However, measurements have indicated that for many flows the mixing length is quite large.

(c) Other Phenomenological Theories.

There are other models of turbulent flow similar to the two previously mentioned. One of these is Taylor's vorticity transfer theory which assumes that the vorticity of each particle is constant. In this case one obtains a mixing length for vorticity in a manner similar to the momentum mixing length in Prandtl's model.

9.5 TURBULENCE CORRELATIONS

Bypassing the problem of solving the equations for the moment, let us ask the question: What would one need to know to have a complete description of a turbulent flow field? The instantaneous velocity components at every point in the flow (say $u_i(x, y, z, t)$) would yield much information. But, as we have previously noted, u_i is a random function of time and itself has limited practical utility. Also,

- $\overline{u}_i$ describes mean velocity field.

- $\overline{u'_i}$ does not help since it is zero.

- $\overline{u'^2_i}$ gives information about the intensity of the fluctuations.

- $\overline{u'_i u'_j}$ gives more information about the flow at a point (9 quantities which includes the 3 quantities $\overline{u'^2_i}$). These quantities appear in the equations of motion and are called one point double velocity correlations.

If all of these quantities were known, then the flow would still not be completely described. This is the same as saying that if we completely solved the momentum equation, we still would not have a complete description of the flow. The reason for this is that one point velocity correlations do not give information regarding the size of the turbulent eddies and the way in which energy is transferred from an eddy of one size to an eddy of a different size.

Two point velocity correlations do give information regarding the size of turbulent eddies. Here we want to establish the dependence of the velocity at one point, A, $(u'_i)_A$ on the velocity at another point $(u'_j)_B$, i.e.,

$$\overline{(u'_i)_A (u'_j)_B}$$

If there is no correlation, that is, no dependence of one velocity on the other, then this quantity is zero.

9.6 ISOTROPIC TURBULENCE

Isotropic turbulence requires that the various turbulence quantities be unaltered by rotation of the coordinate system, i.e. given quantities are the same (at a point) no matter which direction one takes in measuring this quantity. The condition of isotropy requires that the flow be homogeneous (i.e. the same at every point).

Isotropic turbulence is an idealization which can only be approximated by real flows. One example of nearly isotropic turbulence is flow with a uniform velocity downstream of a screen. Any flow having a mean velocity variation is a nonisotropic flow. Most real flows are far from isotropic and the only reason for studying isotropic flow is that to some extent it is a mathematically tractable problem which aids in understanding the more complicated nonisotropic flow. Much of the recent research has been in the area of isotropic turbulence. References 2 and 3, page 192, consider this subject in considerable depth.

9.7 WALL TURBULENCE

Wall turbulence may be described as turbulent flow which is influenced by a solid boundary. The flow is retarded by the solid boundary such that there is a mean velocity variation between the surface and the free stream. As a result of the mean velocity variation the flow must be anisotropic.

Wall turbulence is divided into two types: (1) external (boundary layer) and (2) internal (flow in pipes and ducts). In this chapter we will consider one simple example of each of these. First we will consider flow over a flat plate with zero pressure gradient and then we will consider fully developed pipe flow. While most flows are more complicated than these, they contain basically the same features and aid substantially in leading to a physical understanding of the more complicated boundary layer and channel flows.

(a) Boundary Layer Flow along a Flat Plate.

(i) *Regions of the Turbulent Boundary Layer.*

We have considered methods of describing mean velocity distribution in Chapter 5. The results of the law of the wall apply especially well for the flat plate problem. For example, these results which are shown in Fig. 5-8, page 83, indicate that there are three distinct regions across the boundary layer. They are:

1. Wall Layer on Viscous Sublayer.

   This region is very small ($0 < yu_\tau/\nu < 5$). It is a region close to the wall where the viscous stresses are much larger than the turbulent stresses. The velocity distribution in this region is a linear function of distance from the wall, $u/u_\tau = yu_\tau/\nu$.

2. Wall Turbulent or Transition Region.

   This region is an intermediate region ($5 < yu_\tau/\nu < 30$) where viscous and turbulent stresses are of about the same magnitude.

3. Free Turbulent Region.

   This region is by far the largest of the three ($yu_\tau/\nu > 30$). The turbulent stresses are much larger than the viscous stresses and the mean velocity distribution is described by the logarithmic form of the law of the wall (equation (*5.16*)) except for the outermost part of the boundary layer.

(ii) *Measurements of Turbulence Quantities in the Boundary Layer.*

The turbulence velocities have been measured with hot wire anemometers. As shown in Fig. 9-3 below, they increase rapidly from zero at the wall to a maximum value relatively close to the plate surface. Fig. 9-3 also shows that the degree of anisotropy increases in going from the boundary layer edge toward the wall. The component normal to the wall, v', has the smallest value. This is a result of the wall having a more restrictive influence in this direction.

Fig. 9-4 below shows the distribution of Reynolds stress in the boundary layer. Here we note that there is a region close to the wall where the Reynolds stress is essentially constant. Also, the viscous stresses are important for only about 2% of the boundary layer.

Fig. 9-3. Turbulence velocities for flow along a wall with zero pressure gradient (from reference 4, page 192).

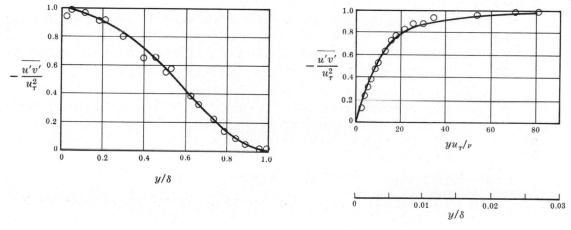

(a) Distribution of turbulent shear stress across the boundary layer.

(b) Distribution of turbulent shear stress close to the wall.

Fig. 9-4. Turbulent stress for flow over a flat plate with zero pressure gradient (from reference 4, page 192).

The energy equation for flow over a flat plate (except close to the wall where viscous stresses are important) is

$$\bar{u}\frac{\partial}{\partial x}\left(\frac{\overline{q^2}}{2}\right) + \bar{v}\frac{\partial}{\partial y}\left(\frac{\overline{q^2}}{2}\right) + \overline{u'v'}\frac{\partial \bar{u}}{\partial y} + \frac{\partial}{\partial y}\left[\overline{v'\left(\frac{p'}{\rho} + \frac{q^2}{2}\right)}\right]$$

$$-\nu\left[\frac{\partial^2}{\partial y^2}\left(\frac{\overline{q^2}}{2}\right) - \overline{\frac{\partial u'_j}{\partial x_i}\frac{\partial u'_j}{\partial x_i}}\right] = 0 \qquad (9.12)$$

where q^2 is the turbulent kinetic energy, $u'_i u'_i$. Fig. 9-5 below shows the experimental results for the various terms of equation (9.12). Production and dissipation are seen to be the important terms over most of the boundary layer. These terms are largest in the region close to the wall.

Fig. 9-5. Turbulence energy distribution in the boundary layer (from reference 3, page 192).

Fig. 9-6. Instantaneous picture of the turbulent boundary layer showing sharp division between turbulent and nonturbulent regions and intermittency.

The preceding experimental results are given in terms of time average quantities. However, based on instantaneous hot wire anemometer measurements, the model for the boundary layer was postulated as shown in Fig. 9-6. There is a sharp, irregular boundary between the turbulent and nonturbulent flow regions. The figure shows an instantaneous picture, and the boundary moves irregularly with time between the limits $0.4 < y/\delta < 1.2$. Thus these are three distinct regions: a region close to the surface which is fully turbulent, $y/\delta < 0.4$; a region which is intermittently turbulent and nonturbulent, $0.4 < y/\delta < 1.2$; and a nonturbulent region, $y/\delta > 1.2$.

(b) Fully Developed Turbulent Flow in a Pipe.

The meaning or definition of the length required, and other influencing factors regarding the attainment of fully developed flow were discussed in Chapter 5. The equations for this flow are greatly simplified since all terms (except pressure) of the form $\partial/\partial x$ are zero. The entrance length required to attain fully developed flow in terms of the mean velocity is between 20 and 100 diameters depending on entrance conditions, Reynolds number, wall roughness and inlet turbulence. The entrance length for satisfying the definition of fully developed flow in terms of the turbulence quantities is substantially longer.

Fully developed pipe flow is similar to the flat plate flow in some respects. For example, both are two dimensional flows and both have the three basic regions (viscous, wall turbulent and free turbulent) for the same range of y/δ distances from the wall.

The essential differences are that in pipe flow (1) there is no transverse (radial) mean velocity, $\bar{v}$, (2) the mean velocity in the main flow direction, $\bar{u}$, does not depend on the coordinate in that direction, (3) there is no free stream and thus no intermittency, and (4) the shear stress varies linearly with distance from the wall. Thus fully developed pipe flow is one of the simplest turbulent flows and for this reason it has received extensive experimental investigation.

The momentum equations for this case (in cylindrical coordinates) are, where u, v and w are respectively the velocities in the axial x direction, the radial direction v, and the azimuthal direction θ,

$$\frac{1}{\rho}\frac{\partial \bar{p}}{\partial x} + \frac{1}{r}\frac{d}{dr}(r\overline{u'v'}) - \nu\left(\frac{d^2\bar{u}}{dr^2} + \frac{1}{r}\frac{d\bar{u}}{dr}\right) = 0 \qquad (9.13)$$

$$\frac{1}{\rho}\frac{\partial \bar{p}}{\partial r} + \frac{1}{r}\frac{d}{dr}(r\overline{v'^2}) - \frac{\overline{w'^2}}{r} = 0 \qquad (9.14)$$

where r is the radial coordinate measured from the axis.

The energy equation is

$$\overline{u'v'}\frac{d\bar{u}}{dr} + \frac{1}{r}\frac{d}{dr}\overline{\left[rv'\left(\frac{p'}{\rho} + \frac{q^2}{2}\right)\right]}$$

$$-\frac{\nu}{r}\frac{d}{dr}\left[r\frac{d}{dr}\left(\frac{\overline{q^2}}{2}\right)\right] + \nu\,\overline{\frac{\partial u_i'}{\partial x_j}\frac{\partial u_i'}{\partial x_j}} = 0 \qquad (9.15)$$

where q^2, the turbulence kinetic energy, is $(u'u' + v'v' + w'w')$.

Fig. 9-7 shows the turbulence velocities and Fig. 9-8 the Reynolds stress distribution for fully developed flow in a pipe of radius R. Fig. 9-9 shows the distribution of the turbulence energy. y is the distance from the wall of the pipe and U is the mean centerline velocity.

From these results we are able to construct a model of turbulent pipe flow. Many of the results of this model also apply to boundary layer flow. The degree of similarity between the two flows decreases with distance from the wall, mainly due to the intermittent character of the boundary layer.

Fig. 9-7. Turbulence velocities for fully developed flow in a pipe (from reference 5, page 192). R is the pipe radius and y is the distance from the wall. U is the velocity (mean centerline velocity).

Fig. 9-8. Distribution of turbulence shear stress for fully developed flow in a pipe (from reference 5, page 192).

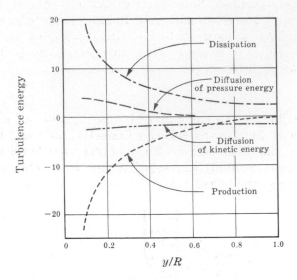

Fig. 9-9. Distribution of turbulence energy for fully developed pipe flow (from reference 5, page 192).

The important characteristics of pipe flow are presented in Fig. 9-10. Production and dissipation are the largest terms over most of the boundary layer. The turbulent kinetic energy, production and dissipation all show a sharp maximum in the wall turbulent or transition region.

Fig. 9-10. Description of fully developed turbulent flow in a pipe.

There is a transport of turbulent kinetic energy down the gradient toward the center of the pipe where the kinetic energy is a minimum. This energy is balanced by dissipation at the centerline.

9.8 FREE TURBULENCE

Turbulent fluid motion which is not being influenced directly by a solid boundary is called free turbulence. Examples of free turbulent flows are wakes behind objects in a moving fluid and jets emitting from a nozzle into a stagnant or slower moving fluid.

The problems of engineering interest are to determine the rate of spreading with distance in the flow direction, mean velocity and transport of momentum and energy during mixing with the surrounding fluid.

A characteristic of free turbulent flows is that viscosity effects have no controlling influence on the mean motion. The mean motion is dictated entirely by the turbulent eddies. In this sense, jet and wake flows are similar to the outer portion of the turbulent boundary layer. The only role that viscosity plays in free turbulent flows is in the final stage of dissipation of turbulent energy through the small scale eddies.

(a) Wake Flows.

Consider the turbulent flow in the wake of a circular cylinder of diameter d as shown in Fig. 9-11. The problem is: for a given cylinder diameter, fluid and fluid velocity, determine $u = u(x, y)$, $b = b(x)$ the wake half width, and the turbulence quantities. We are unable to determine a completely analytical solution, but with some experimental results useful generalizations may be established.

(a) Time average velocity as measured with a pitot tube

(b) Instantaneous picture

Fig. 9-11. Turbulent wake of the circular cylinder.

The momentum equations far from the cylinder become

$$U \frac{\partial \bar{u}}{\partial x} = -\frac{\partial}{\partial y}(\overline{u'v'}) \qquad (9.16)$$

$$0 = \frac{\partial \bar{p}}{\partial y} + \rho \frac{\partial}{\partial y}(\overline{v'^2}) \qquad (9.17)$$

where it has been assumed $\tau_T \gg \tau_l$, $\bar{u} \gg \bar{v}$, $\partial/\partial x \ll \partial/\partial y$, $\nabla \bar{p} = 0$. τ_T is the turbulent shear stress defined by equation (9.9) and τ_l is the laminar shear stress.

Even as simple as equations (9.16) and (9.17) are compared to the original equations, they are inadequate in yielding a solution. Thus the general approach in seeking solutions to jet and wake flow problems is to assume similar velocity profiles in conjunction with replacing the Reynolds stress with one of the phenomenological models such as eddy viscosity or Prandtl mixing length.

By a similar velocity profile we mean a velocity distribution having the form

$$\bar{u}/U = f(y/b) \tag{9.18}$$

Schlichting (see reference 7, page 192) used the similarity argument in conjunction with the Prandtl momentum mixing length. By assuming that the mixing length is proportional to the wake width, he solved the differential equation and used the momentum integral equation to obtain

$$b = \sqrt{10}\,\beta(xC_D\,d)^{1/2} \tag{9.19}$$

$$\frac{U - \bar{u}}{U} = \frac{\sqrt{10}}{18\beta}[x/C_D\,d]^{-1/2}[1 - (y/b)^{3/2}]^2 \tag{9.20}$$

where $\beta = 0.18$, a constant determined from experimental measurements. C_D is the drag coefficient.

Equation (9.19) is in good agreement with experimental results for $x/d > 10$ and (9.20) for $x/d > 50$.

(b) Jet Flows.

Let us consider the turbulent circular jet as shown in Fig. 9-12. The flow may be separated into three regions, each having a distinctly different character. Region I consists of a potential core of uniform mean velocity U_P bounded by a shear layer which in turn is bounded by a fluid having a uniform mean velocity U_S. This region starts at the nozzle exit and has a length of 4 or 5 nozzle diameters. Region II is characterized by both the absence of a potential core and absence of similarity in the mean velocity distribution. This region is followed by region III which starts at about 8 nozzle diameters and is characterized by similar velocity distributions.

Fig. 9-12. Different regions and velocity profiles for a turbulent jet.

There have been a large number of investigations of turbulent jets mainly because of their engineering importance, simplicity and relevance to other turbulent flows. Two books have been published which are largely devoted to this subject (see references 1 and 6, page 192).

Hinze (reference 3, page 192) used the similarity method and an eddy viscosity to obtain a solution for the mean velocity distribution. Using the momentum equation (differential form) and the momentum integral equation, he found that for $(U_P - \bar{u})/U_S \gg 1.0$, b is proportional to $(x + a)$ and

$$\frac{U_P - \bar{u}}{U_P - \bar{u}_c} = \left[1 + \frac{(U_P - \bar{u}_c)r^2}{8\epsilon(x + a)} \right]^{-2}$$

For $(U_P - \bar{u})/U_S \ll 1.0$, b is proportional to $(x + a)^{1/2}$. Here ϵ is assumed constant and a is an experimental constant. U_P and U_S are shown on Fig. 9-12 and $\bar{u}_c$ is the centerline velocity.

The results for the rate of growth of the wake and jet and the centerline velocities are summarized in Table 9-1.

Table 9.1. WAKE WIDTH AND CENTERLINE VELOCITY

	Width, Proportional to	Centerline velocity defect, $(\bar{u}_c - U_S)$, Proportional to
Plane two-dimensional jet	x	$x^{-1/2}$
Circular jet	x	x^{-1}
Plane two-dimensional wake	$x^{1/2}$	$x^{-1/2}$
Circular wake	$x^{1/3}$	$x^{-1/3}$

Of course, these results are not valid in the near wake and close to the nozzle.

9.9 SUMMARY

We have considered the subject of incompressible turbulent flow in terms of "isotropic turbulence" and "shear turbulence". Isotropic turbulence is a highly idealized flow which requires that there be no mean velocity variation. While isotropic turbulence is rarely approximated by real flows of engineering importance, it does lend itself to some mathematical tractability and as a result it is the subject of extensive study in an attempt to gain some understanding of the more complicated nonisotropic flows.

Shear turbulence is further subdivided into "wall turbulence" such as boundary layer flows and "free turbulence" such as wakes and jets. The problems are to determine mean velocity, shear stress, and the turbulence quantities. There are two approaches: (1) the phenomenological approach of defining exchange coefficients such as eddy viscosity and mixing length to relate the turbulent stress to the mean velocity field and (2) the statistical approach of writing the basic differential equations in terms of time average quantities. Both approaches are useful from an engineering standpoint.

The reader may consult references 2, 3 and 9, page 192, for more details and depth regarding the material of this chapter.

References

1. Abramovich, G. N., *The Theory of Turbulent Jets*, (USSR), MIT Press, 1963.

2. Batchelor, G. K., *The Theory of Homogeneous Turbulence*, Cambridge University Press, 1960.

3. Hinze, J. O., *Turbulence*, McGraw-Hill, 1959.

4. Klebanoff, P. S., "Characteristics of Turbulence in a Boundary Layer with Zero Pressure Gradient", NACA TN 3178, 1954.

5. Laufer, J., "The Structure of Turbulence in Fully Developed Pipe Flow", NACA R. 1174, 1954.

6. Pai, S. I., *Fluid Dynamics of Jets*, Van Nostrand, 1954.

7. Schlichting, H., *Boundary Layer Theory*, McGraw-Hill, 1962.

8. Schubauer, G. B. and Tchen, C. M., *Turbulent Flow*, Princeton University Press, 1961.

9. Townsend, A. A., *The Structure of Turbulent Shear Flow*, Cambridge University Press, 1956.

Supplementary Problems

9.1. Derive the equations of motion for constant density and viscosity for fully developed turbulent flow in concentric annuli. The flow is in the axial direction.

9.2. Show that the incompressible continuity equation is satisfied by the instantaneous deviations alone.

9.3. Consider two-dimensional fully developed flow between parallel walls, one stationary and one moving at a constant velocity U. Assume $\partial \bar{p}/\partial x = 0$ where x is measured in the direction of flow.

(a) Determine the general shape of the mean velocity curve.

(b) Determine the shear stress distribution.

(c) Determine the approximate distribution of the eddy viscosity ϵ and mixing length l.

(d) Determine approximately the pressure distribution.

9.4. Consider the flow of air ($p = 14.7$ psi, $T = 59°$F, $\rho = 0.00238$ slug/ft^3, $\mu = 0.0373(10)^{-5}$ slug/ft-sec, $\nu = 1.57 \times 10^{-4}$ ft^2/sec) with a free stream velocity of 50 ft/sec over a flat plate. At one section $\delta = 2.8$ in. and the wall shear stress $\tau_0 = 0.00813$ lb/ft^2. Assume that the velocity distribution for $20 < y u_\tau/\nu < 1000$ is given by

$$\bar{u}/u_\tau = 2.44 \ln y u_\tau/\nu + 4.9$$

Assuming further that the shear stress is constant, calculate (a) the Prandtl mixing length and (b) the ratio ϵ/ν at $y = 0.05$ in. and at $y = 0.10$ in.

NOMENCLATURE FOR CHAPTER 9

a = constant

b = wake or jet half width

B_i = body force per unit volume

C_D = drag coefficient

d = diameter of cylinder

f = functional notation

l = Prandtl momentum mixing length

m = exponent for power law velocity distribution

n = exponent for power law velocity distribution

p = pressure

q^2 = turbulence kinetic energy, $\overline{u_i' u_i'}$

r = radial coordinate

R = radius of pipe

t = time

T_1 = length of time for averaging

U = free stream velocity, mean centerline velocity in a pipe

U_P = velocity of jet

U_S = velocity of secondary stream

$\bar{u}_c$ = mean centerline velocity

u_i = $u_1, u_2, u_3 = u, v, w$ velocity components

u_τ = friction velocity, $\sqrt{\tau_0/\rho}$

x_i = $x_1, x_2, x_3 = x, y, z$ cartesian coordinates

y = distance from wall

$\overline{u_i' u_j'}$ = one point double velocity correlation

$\overline{(u_i')_A (u_j')_B}$ = two point double velocity correlation

δ = boundary layer thickness

ϵ = eddy viscosity

μ = viscosity

ν = kinematic viscosity, μ/ρ

ρ = density

τ_{ij} = shear stress tensor

τ_{ij_T} = turbulent shear stress tensor = $-\rho\,\overline{u_i' u_j'}$

τ_{ij_l} = laminar shear stress tensor = $\mu\dfrac{\partial \bar{u}_i}{\partial x_j}$

τ = one component of shear stress relevant to a particular problem

τ_0 = shear stress at the wall

$(\bar{\ })$ = denotes mean value

$(\ )'$ = denotes fluctuating component

Chapter 10

Hypersonic Boundary Layer Flow

10.1 INTRODUCTION

Hypersonic flow has become very important because of interest in missiles and space-craft. When an object enters or flies within the earth's atmosphere at very high Mach numbers, dissociation of molecules may occur as a result of the high temperature of the gas in the region surrounding the body. Hypersonic flow is defined as a high speed flow where the Mach number is so high that dissociation occurs ($M > 6$ for the earth's atmosphere).

Let us begin the study of hypersonic flow by considering an example, the different flow regimes around a vehicle entering the earth's atmosphere at very high speed as shown in Fig. 10-1. A *bow shock* wave forms ahead of and wraps around the body. The flow is undisturbed ahead of the shock. This shock is strongest on the axis of symmetry since it is normal to the flow there. Behind the shock there is a region where dissociation will occur. Immediately behind the shock is a region where viscous effects are not important, but close to the body surface is the boundary layer where viscous stresses are important and where the flow may be laminar or turbulent. As the fluid passes over the rear portion of the body, it has a tendency to turn in toward the axis as in a Prandtl-Meyer expansion. This is followed by a turning of the flow in the opposite direction (a straightening) as a result of the fluid from opposite sides coming together. The straightening of the flow results in an oblique shock called a *wake shock*. The flow following the wake shock consists of a wake containing a turbulent core surrounded by a nonturbulent flow region. In the wake the velocity is reduced (it is a minimum on the axis) but increases with distance behind the body until eventually the velocity is nearly uniform and equal to the free stream velocity. However, the turbulent core will persist for long distances behind the body (thousands of body diameters).

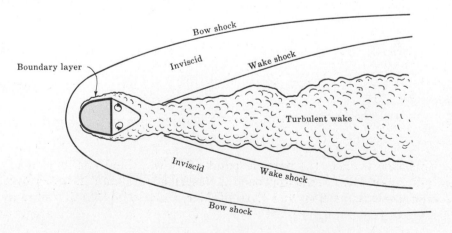

Fig. 10-1. Hypersonic flow regimes.

194

In this chapter we will consider the boundary layer and wake flows but will not discuss the determination of the shock shape and the inviscid flow regions, since they involve (ultimately) a numerical approach for solving the equations. We have mentioned the basic ideas of supersonic flow in Chapter 8 which will give some idea of the methods that must be used for these calculations.

The turbulent hypersonic boundary layer problem is one of the most complicated in fluid mechanics. It has all of the difficulties (and as we saw in Chapter 9 there were many) of incompressible turbulent flow, but in addition there are the added complications of large density and temperature variations, dissociation and recombination of molecules and diffusion.

We will approach the problem by writing the important equations and considering the way in which the results of simpler flows are used, and briefly discuss the methods of solving the equations.

10.2 BOUNDARY LAYER EQUATIONS

The boundary layer equations are the same as written in Chapter 5 except that now the effects of chemical reactions and diffusion must be included. The simple equations of Chapter 5 are not adequate for fluids which are not homogeneous in the concentrations of particles of various kinds. For hypersonic flow there are large temperature gradients and large diffusion gradients, and hence transport of mass, momentum and energy by diffusion will take place.

As we have mentioned before, there are two approaches to developing the equations of fluid mechanics. The first, and the one which has found more use, is the continuum approach. The equations of momentum and energy, for example, are derived assuming that the fluid is a continuum. Then, phenomenological equations relate shear and rate of strain, heat flux and temperature gradient, and mass diffusion and concentration gradient. These relationships are (to first order) for two-dimensional plane (xy) flow with velocity u in the x direction.

$$\tau_{yx} = \mu \frac{\partial u}{\partial y} \qquad \text{Stokes' law} \qquad (10.1)$$

$$q_y = -\kappa \frac{\partial T}{\partial y} \qquad \text{Fourier's law} \qquad (10.2)$$

$$V_{iy} = -D_{ij} \frac{1}{C_i} \frac{\partial C_i}{\partial y} \qquad \text{Fick's law} \qquad (10.3)$$

The coefficients, μ the viscosity, κ the thermal conductivity, and D_{ij} the binary diffusion coefficient (for diffusion of species i into a mixture of species i and j) are known as transport coefficients, and

τ_{yx} = shear stress

q_y = heat flux rate in the y direction

V_{iy} = diffusion velocity in y direction for species i diffusing into a mixture of species i and j [see equation (10.4)].

C_i = mass fraction of species i = ratio of mass of species i per unit volume to total mass density.

The second approach is from the particle point of view. Here one must deal with the dynamics of colliding particles. This approach is described in detail in books by Chapman and Cowling (reference 2, page 203) and Hirschfelder, Curtiss and Bird (reference 3), and will not be considered here except in that it does yield the conservation of species equation (see reference 1, page 203):

$$\rho \frac{DC_i}{Dt} = \dot{w}_i - \nabla \cdot (\rho C_i \mathbf{V}_i) \tag{10.4}$$

where $\mathbf{V}_i = \mathbf{v}_i - \mathbf{V}$ = diffusion velocity of species i.

       $\mathbf{v}_i$ = average velocity of species i.

       $\mathbf{V}$ = mass average velocity of all species = $\dfrac{\sum\limits_i \rho C_i \mathbf{v}_i}{\sum\limits_i \rho C_i} = \dfrac{\sum\limits_i \rho_i \mathbf{v}_i}{\sum\limits_i \rho_i}$ where ρ_i is the

       mass density of species i. $\mathbf{V}$ has components u and v.

       $\dot{w}_i$ = mass rate of production of species i per unit volume by chemical reactions.

       ρ = total mass density = $\sum\limits_i \rho_i$.

Assuming plane two-dimensional steady boundary layer flow and neglecting diffusion terms in the x direction and using Fick's law, the *conservation* of *species equation* becomes

$$\rho \left[u \frac{\partial C_i}{\partial x} + v \frac{\partial C_i}{\partial y} \right] = \dot{w}_i + \frac{\partial}{\partial y}\left(\rho D_{12} \frac{\partial C_i}{\partial y} \right) \tag{10.5}$$

where u and v are the x and y components of the mass average velocity $\mathbf{V}$, and we have replaced D_{ij} by D_{12}, the binary diffusion coefficient. It can be shown that $D_{12} = D_{21}$ and for most systems of gases of interest the binary coefficient is adequate. We usually have two types of species, heavy ones and light ones. For example, in air we have the heavy particles O_2 and N_2 and the light ones O and N. D_{12} adequately describes diffusion of O or N through O_2 and N_2. The total continuity equation is

$$\frac{\partial(\rho u)}{\partial x} + \frac{\partial(\rho v)}{\partial y} = 0 \tag{10.6}$$

and the momentum equation is for the total fluid

$$\rho \left[u \frac{\partial u}{\partial x} + v \frac{\partial u}{\partial y} \right] = -\frac{\partial p}{\partial x} + \frac{\partial}{\partial y}\left(\mu \frac{\partial u}{\partial y} \right) \tag{10.7}$$

The total energy equation is for the total fluid (where the kinetic energy contribution $v^2/2$ is neglected compared to $u^2/2$),

$$\rho \left[u \frac{\partial}{\partial x}(h + u^2/2) + v \frac{\partial}{\partial y}(h + u^2/2) \right]$$
$$= \frac{\partial}{\partial y}\left[\frac{\mu}{P_r} \frac{\partial}{\partial y}(h + u^2/2) + \mu \left(1 - \frac{1}{P_r}\right) \frac{1}{2} \frac{\partial u^2}{\partial y} \right] - \frac{\partial}{\partial y}\left[\left(\frac{1}{L} - 1 \right) \rho D_{12} \sum_i h_i \frac{\partial C_i}{\partial y} \right] \tag{10.8}$$

where $h = \sum\limits_i C_i h_i$

       $h_i = \int_0^T c_{pi}\, dT + h_i^0$

       h_i^0 = heat of formation of species i

       $P_r = \dfrac{\mu c_{pf}}{\kappa}$,   the Prandtl number

       $L = \dfrac{\rho D_{12} c_{pf}}{\kappa}$,   the Lewis number

       $c_{pf} = \sum\limits_i C_i c_{pi}$,   the frozen specific heat at constant pressure

For a derivation and discussion of the energy equation the reader may refer to reference 4, page 203. Since the energy equation is of importance in hypersonic flow, we will "outline" the derivation here.

Consider an infinitesimal control volume at a point in the flow as shown in Fig. 10-2. We will write the energy equation for this control volume. Consider the following fluxes.

1. Net internal and kinetic energy flux out of control volume:

$$\nabla \cdot \left[(\rho \mathbf{V}) \left(\sum_i C_i e_i + u^2/2 \right) \right]$$

where $e_i = \int_0^T c_{vi}\, dT$, the specific internal energy for the ith species assuming it to be a perfect gas.

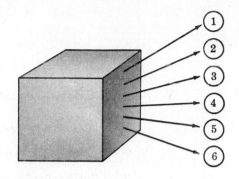

Fig. 10-2.   Infinitesimal control volume for energy equation.

2. Net molecular transfer of energy out due to temperature gradient:

$$-\nabla \cdot (\kappa \nabla T)$$

3. Rate of work done by fluid per unit volume by pressure forces:

$$\nabla \cdot (p\mathbf{V})$$

4. Rate of work done by fluid per unit volume by viscous forces:

$$\nabla \cdot [\tau \cdot \mathbf{V}] = \frac{\partial}{\partial x_i} (\tau_{ij} u_j)$$

5. Energy carried out by mass diffusion of species i:

$$\nabla \cdot \left(\sum_i \rho \mathbf{V}_i C_i h_i \right)$$

where

$$\mathbf{V}_i = -\frac{D_{12}}{C_i} \nabla C_i$$

6. Energy added due to formation of a species:

$$-\sum_i \dot{w}_i h_i^0$$

where $h_i^0 = 0$, for molecules; $h_i^0 =$ a positive value for atoms.

Then the energy equation becomes, adding the six above effects,

$$\rho \mathbf{V} \cdot \nabla \left(\sum_i C_i e_i + u^2/2 \right) + \left(\sum_i C_i e_i + u^2/2 \right) \nabla \cdot (\rho \mathbf{V}) - \nabla \cdot (\kappa \nabla T)$$
$$+ \nabla \cdot (p\mathbf{V}) + \nabla \cdot (\tau \cdot \mathbf{V}) + \nabla \cdot \left(\sum_i \rho \mathbf{V}_i C_i h_i \right) + \sum_i \dot{w}_i h_i^0 = 0 \qquad (10.9)$$

In addition to equation (10.9), the other equations which are used in the derivation are the equation of state

$$p_i = \rho_i R_i T \qquad (10.10)$$

where all species are assumed to be at the same temperature and $p = \sum_i p_i = \rho \bar{R} T$, $\bar{R} = \sum_i C_i R_i$,

$$h_i = e_i + R_i T \qquad (10.11)$$

and continuity

$$\nabla \cdot \rho \mathbf{V} = 0 \qquad (10.12)$$

Using equations (10.4), (10.9), (10.10), (10.11) and (10.12) and assuming $h_i = f(T)$, the energy equation is obtained in the form of equation (10.8).

The total energy equation for boundary layer flow in terms of the temperature becomes

$$c_{pf}\left[\rho u\frac{\partial T}{\partial x} + \rho v\frac{\partial T}{\partial y}\right]$$

$$= \frac{\partial}{\partial y}\left(\kappa\frac{\partial T}{\partial y}\right) + u\frac{\partial p}{\partial x} + \mu\left(\frac{\partial u}{\partial y}\right)^2 - \sum_i \dot{w}_i h_i^0 + \sum_i c_{pi}\left(D_{ij}\rho\frac{\partial C_i}{\partial y}\right) \qquad (10.13)$$

Equations (10.4) through (10.8) then, are the basic equations of hypersonic (laminar) boundary layer flow.

10.3 HYPERSONIC LAMINAR BOUNDARY LAYER

Although it is likely that transition will occur at some point on the body resulting in the flow going from laminar to turbulent, we will consider laminar flow only in this section and turbulent flow will be treated in the next section.

Consider an ideal dissociating gas. The molecule A_2 dissociates into the atom A

$$A_2 \rightleftarrows 2A$$

where $\rho_A/\rho = \alpha$, the mass fraction of atoms

$\rho_M/\rho = (1-\alpha)$, the mass fraction of molecules.

The subscripts A and M refer to the atom and molecule, respectively. An alternative form of the energy equation (10.8) is

$$\rho u\frac{\partial h}{\partial x} + \rho v\frac{\partial h}{\partial y}$$

$$= u\frac{\partial p}{\partial x} + \frac{\partial}{\partial y}\left(\kappa\frac{\partial T}{\partial y}\right) + \frac{\partial}{\partial y}\left(\rho D_{12}\sum_i h_i\frac{\partial C_i}{\partial y}\right) + \mu\left(\frac{\partial u}{\partial y}\right)^2 \qquad (10.14)$$

Then, for the ideal dissociating gas, we have

$$\rho u\frac{\partial h}{\partial x} + \rho v\frac{\partial h}{\partial y}$$

$$= u\frac{\partial p}{\partial x} + \frac{\partial}{\partial y}\left(\kappa\frac{\partial T}{\partial y}\right) + \frac{\partial}{\partial y}\left[\rho D_{12}h_A\frac{\partial \alpha}{\partial y} - \rho D_{12}h_M\frac{\partial \alpha}{\partial y}\right] + \mu\left(\frac{\partial u}{\partial y}\right)^2 \qquad (10.15)$$

The conservation of species equation becomes

$$\rho u\frac{\partial \alpha}{\partial x} + \rho v\frac{\partial \alpha}{\partial y} = \frac{\partial}{\partial y}\left(\rho D_{12}\frac{\partial \alpha}{\partial y}\right) + \dot{w}_A \qquad (10.16)$$

The conservation of species, continuity, momentum and energy equations, i.e. (10.16), (10.6), (10.7) and (10.15), along with property relationships define the problem if the particular boundary conditions are given. Also, one would need to determine the appropriate values for the transport coefficients.

The solution to these equations present enormous difficulties. Therefore let us consider a related problem of somewhat lesser difficulty. Consider the flow of a nonreacting gas on a flat plate with zero pressure gradient and constant properties (see Schlichting, reference 6, page 203). The equations become

$$\rho u\frac{\partial h}{\partial x} + \rho v\frac{\partial h}{\partial y} = \frac{\partial}{\partial y}\left(\kappa\frac{\partial T}{\partial y}\right) + \mu\left(\frac{\partial u}{\partial y}\right)^2$$

$$\rho u\frac{\partial u}{\partial x} + \rho v\frac{\partial u}{\partial y} = \mu\frac{\partial^2 u}{\partial y^2}$$

$$\frac{\partial u}{\partial x} + \frac{\partial v}{\partial y} = 0$$

The boundary conditions are

$$y = 0; \quad u = v = 0, \ T = T_w$$

$$y = \infty; \quad u = U_\infty, \ T = T_\infty$$

The result for the heat transfer at the wall is

$$q \ = \ -\kappa \frac{\partial T}{\partial y} \ = \ \frac{C_f}{2}(P_r)^{-2/3}\rho_\infty U_\infty \left[h_\infty \ + \ (P_r)^{1/2}\frac{U_\infty^2}{2} \ - \ h_w \right]$$

where $C_f = 1.328\sqrt{\nu/U_\infty x}, \ P_r = \mu c_p/\kappa$.

The additional complications of variable properties, dissociation and diffusion make the problem considerably more difficult. And, although we cannot obtain a solution, we can determine some of the physical characteristics of hypersonic flow.

The heat flux without dissociation is $q = -\kappa\,\partial T/\partial y$. The total heat flux with dissociation is [see equation (10.15)]

$$q \ = \ -\kappa\frac{\partial T}{\partial y} \ - \ \rho D_{12}(h_A - h_M)\frac{\partial \alpha}{\partial y} \tag{10.17}$$

But

$$h_A \ - \ h_M \ = \ h_A^0 \ + \ \int_0^T (c_{pA} - c_{pM})\,dT$$

which is approximately h_A^0, and

$$q \ - \ \kappa\frac{\partial T}{\partial y} \quad \rho D_{12}h_A^0\frac{\partial \alpha}{\partial y}$$

Now consider an adiabatic wall, $q = 0$, and

$$\frac{\partial T}{\partial y} \ = \ - \ \frac{\rho D_{12}h_A^0}{\kappa}\frac{\partial \alpha}{\partial y}$$

Thus there may be a nonzero temperature gradient at the wall when the heat flux is zero as shown in Fig. 10-3.

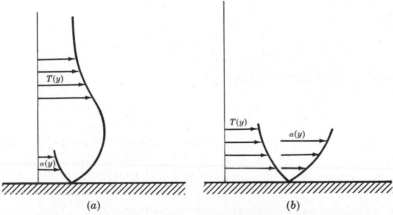

Fig. 10-3. Velocity and concentration distributions for an adiabatic wall. (a) Cold wall, (b) hot wall.

Dorrance (reference 1, page 203) shows that heat transfer of the wall for a dissociating gas on a flat plate is

$$q \ = \ -\frac{C_f}{2}\rho_\infty U_\infty P_r^{-2/3}\left(h_\infty \ - \ h_w \ + \ P_r^{1/2}\frac{U_\infty^2}{2} \right)\left[1 + \frac{(L-1)(\alpha_\infty - \alpha_w)h_A^0}{h_\infty - h_w + P_r^{1/2}U_\infty^2/2} \right]^{2/3} \tag{10.18}$$

We note in equation (10.18) that if $L = 1.0$ or $\alpha_\infty = \alpha_w$, the equation is the same as that for no dissociation. The subscripts ∞ and w refer to free stream and wall conditions, respectively. L is the Lewis number.

The previous discussion was for flow over a flat plate. There has been much interest in the heat transfer for flows over blunt nosed bodies, particularly in the region of the stagnation point where the heat flux is large. These problems have been considered in detail by Dorrance, by Lees, by Fay and Riddell and by others (see references 1, 5 and 4, page 203). We will not pursue this problem in depth here.

The method that is used is to set up coordinate transformations which result in changing the problem from one involving partial differential equations to one involving ordinary differential equations. The equations are then solved by numerical techniques for (1) frozen flow (i.e. for a sufficiently small recombination rate where the concentration of atoms is determined wholly by diffusive flow) and (2) equilibrium flow (i.e., for a sufficiently large recombination rate where the temperature would determine the concentration throughout). Results for particular values of Lewis and Prandtl numbers and wall temperature are shown in Fig. 10-4.

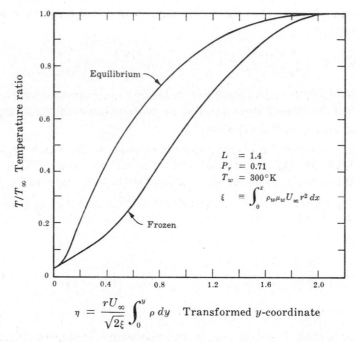

$$\eta = \frac{rU_\infty}{\sqrt{2\xi}} \int_0^y \rho \, dy \quad \text{Transformed } y\text{-coordinate}$$

Fig. 10-4. Temperature distribution in the boundary layer for hypersonic flow (from reference 4, page 203). The flow is assumed to occur over a cylindrical blunt-nosed object and r is the radius of the cylinder. y is the distance from the surface or wall.

For the same wall temperature and free stream temperature, the intermediate temperature of equilibrium flow is higher than for frozen flow. This results from the atoms recombining as they move into an area of lower temperature.

10.4 HYPERSONIC TURBULENT BOUNDARY LAYER

When an object enters the earth's atmosphere, the flow field surrounding the object goes through several phases. The initial stage of re-entry consists of flow through a low density medium where the continuum assumptions are not valid. This is followed by a more dense medium where the flow behaves as a continuum and is laminar. As the penetration of the atmosphere further progresses, random velocity fluctuations appear in the form of turbulence in the downstream wake. A further increase in density results in the boundary between laminar and turbulent flow moving upstream to the point where eventually most of the boundary layer is turbulent. When this has occurred the flow is as shown in Fig. 10-1.

We will not consider the problem of transition. Rather, we will assume that a turbulent boundary layer exists, then proceed to describe the flow. The method here will be quite similar to that of Chapter 9 on turbulence.

Consider the continuity, species, momentum and energy equations of the previous sections. If we multiply the continuity equation (*10.6*) by C_i and add the species equation (*10.5*), we obtain

$$\frac{\partial}{\partial x}(\rho u C_i) + \frac{\partial}{\partial y}(\rho v C_i) = -\frac{\partial}{\partial y}(\rho C_i V_{iy}) + \dot{w}_i \tag{10.19}$$

Combining the continuity and momentum equation (*10.7*) gives

$$\frac{\partial}{\partial x}(\rho u^2) + \frac{\partial}{\partial y}(\rho v u) = \frac{\partial}{\partial y}\left(\mu \frac{\partial u}{\partial y}\right) \tag{10.20}$$

Multiplying the continuity equation by I, the stagnation enthalpy $(h + u^2/2)$, and adding the energy equation gives

$$\frac{\partial}{\partial x}(\rho u I) + \frac{\partial}{\partial y}(\rho v I) = \frac{\partial}{\partial y}\left[\frac{\mu}{P_r}\frac{\partial I}{\partial y} + \mu\left(1 - \frac{1}{P_r}\right)\frac{1}{2}\frac{\partial(u^2)}{\partial y}\right] + \frac{\partial}{\partial y}\left[\left(\frac{1}{L} - 1\right)\sum_i V_{iy} h_i\right] \tag{10.21}$$

Equations (*10.19*), (*10.20*) and (*10.21*) are valid for laminar flow. We will assume that they are valid also for turbulent flow as long as we consider the instantaneous quantities for the dependent variables in the equations.

However, in their present form there does not seem to be much hope for solving the equations as a function of space and time even for simple flows. Thus we will use the method of Chapter 9 to obtain associated equations involving time average quantities.

We will write the instantaneous quantities in terms of time average and fluctuating quantities as follows:

$$u = \bar{u} + u' \qquad\qquad C_i = \bar{C}_i + C_i'$$

$$\rho u = \overline{\rho u} + (\rho u)' \qquad\qquad h_i = \bar{h}_i + h_i'$$

$$\rho v = \overline{\rho v} + (\rho v)' \qquad\qquad \rho V_{iy} = \overline{\rho V_{iy}} + (\rho V_{iy})'$$

$$h = \bar{h} + h'$$

where the bar indicates time average values and the prime indicates fluctuating quantities. Now we substitute the above expressions into the continuity and equations (*10.19*), (*10.20*) and (*10.21*) and take the time average of each. We obtain:

Total Continuity:
$$\frac{\partial}{\partial x}(\overline{\rho u}) + \frac{\partial}{\partial y}(\overline{\rho v}) = 0 \tag{10.22}$$

Species Continuity:
$$\overline{\rho u}\frac{\partial \bar{C}_i}{\partial x} + \overline{\rho v}\frac{\partial \bar{C}_i}{\partial y} = \frac{\partial}{\partial y}\left[\bar{\rho}D_{12}\frac{\partial \bar{C}_i}{\partial y} - \overline{(\rho v)' C_i'}\right] + \dot{w}_i \tag{10.23}$$

where it was assumed $\frac{\partial}{\partial x}\overline{[(\rho u)' C_i']} \ll \frac{\partial}{\partial y}\overline{[(\rho v)' C_i']}$ and $\overline{[(\rho V_{iy})' C_i']} \ll \overline{[\rho V_{iy} C_i]}$.

Momentum:
$$\overline{\rho u}\frac{\partial \bar{u}}{\partial x} + \overline{\rho v}\frac{\partial \bar{u}}{\partial y} = \frac{\partial}{\partial y}\left[\mu\frac{\partial \bar{u}}{\partial y} - \overline{(\rho v)' u'}\right] \tag{10.24}$$

where it is assumed $\frac{\partial}{\partial x}\overline{[(\rho u)' u']} \ll \frac{\partial}{\partial y}\overline{[(\rho v)' u']}$.

Energy:
$$\overline{\rho u}\frac{\partial \overline{h}}{\partial x} + \overline{\rho v}\frac{\partial \overline{h}}{\partial y} = \mu\left(\frac{\partial \overline{u}}{\partial y}\right)^2 - \overline{(\rho v)'u'}\frac{\partial \overline{u}}{\partial y}$$
$$+ \frac{\partial}{\partial y}\left[\kappa\frac{\partial \overline{T}}{\partial y} - \sum_i \overline{h}_i\overline{\rho_i V_{iy}} - \sum_i \overline{C}_i\overline{h_i'(\rho v)'} - \sum_i \overline{(\rho v)'C_i'}\,\overline{h}_i\right] \qquad (10.25)$$

It is interesting to note that there are additional terms which appear in the equations as a result of the turbulent fluctuations. These terms have a definite physical interpretation. For example,

$$-\overline{(\rho v)'C_i'} \qquad \text{is turbulent mass transfer}$$
$$-\overline{(\rho v)'u'} \qquad \text{is turbulent momentum transfer}$$
$$-\overline{(\rho v)'h_i'} \qquad \text{is turbulent energy transfer}$$

With some algebraic manipulations and after defining new terms such as

$$\epsilon = -\frac{\overline{(\rho v)'u'}}{\partial \overline{u}/\partial y}, \qquad \epsilon_T = -\frac{\overline{(\rho v)'h_i'}}{\partial \overline{T}/\partial y}, \qquad \overline{\rho}D_T = -\frac{\overline{(\rho v)'C_i'}}{\partial \overline{C}_i/\partial y},$$

$$P_{rT} = \frac{c_{pf}\epsilon}{\epsilon_T}, \qquad L_T = \frac{c_{pf}\overline{\rho}D_T}{\epsilon_T}$$

we have

Species Continuity:
$$\overline{\rho u}\frac{\partial \overline{C}_i}{\partial x} + \overline{\rho v}\frac{\partial \overline{C}_i}{\partial y} = \frac{\partial}{\partial y}\left[(\rho D_{12} + \rho D_T)\frac{\partial \overline{C}_i}{\partial y}\right] + \dot{w}_i \qquad (10.26)$$

Momentum:
$$\overline{\rho u}\frac{\partial \overline{u}}{\partial x} + \overline{\rho v}\frac{\partial \overline{u}}{\partial y} = \frac{\partial}{\partial y}\left[(\mu + \epsilon)\frac{\partial \overline{u}}{\partial y}\right] \qquad (10.27)$$

Energy:
$$\overline{\rho u}\frac{\partial \overline{h}}{\partial x} + \overline{\rho v}\frac{\partial \overline{h}}{\partial y} = (\mu + \epsilon)\left(\frac{\partial \overline{u}}{\partial y}\right)^2 + \frac{\partial}{\partial y}\left[\left(\frac{\mu}{P_r} + \frac{\epsilon}{P_{rT}}\right)\frac{\partial \overline{h}}{\partial y}\right]$$
$$+ \frac{\partial}{\partial y}\left\{\left[\frac{\kappa}{c_{pf}}(L-1) + \frac{\epsilon_T}{c_{pf}}(L_T-1)\right]\sum_i h_i\frac{\partial \overline{C}_i}{\partial y}\right\} \qquad (10.28)$$

The equations are now in terms of the microscopic and macroscopic transport coefficients. The solutions to the equations are considered in reference 1, page 203. The general procedure is to consider the simple case where

$$P_r = P_{rT} = L = L_T = 1.0$$

Then the results are extended to the more general case.

10.5 SUMMARY AND DISCUSSION

The turbulent reacting boundary layer is one of the most complicated problems in fluid mechanics, one which will probably receive considerable attention as we progress into the space age.

There are two kinds of transport coefficients in the equations. The transport coefficients μ, κ and D_{12} are due to microscopic effects and are properties of the fluid. They do not depend on the flow conditions. However, the transport coefficients ϵ, ϵ_T and D_T are the result of macroscopic effects and they are not properties of the fluid. They depend on the flow conditions and should be considered as unknowns in the equations just as are velocity, entropy, etc. Determination of the transport coefficients (microscopic and macroscopic) remains one of the major problems in turbulent hypersonic boundary layer flow.

References

1. Dorrance, W. H., *Viscous Hypersonic Flow*, McGraw-Hill, 1962.

2. Chapman, S. and Cowling, T. G., *The Mathematical Theory of Non-Uniform Gases*, Cambridge University Press, 1958.

3. Hirschfelder, J. O., Curtiss, C. F. and Bird, R. B., *Molecular Theory of Gases and Liquids*, John Wiley, 1954.

4. Fay, J. A. and Riddell, F. R., "Theory of Stagnation Point Heat Transfer in Dissociated Air", *J. Aero. Sci.*, 25, No. 2, pp. 73-85, 1958.

5. Lees, L., "Laminar Heat Transfer over Blunt Nosed Bodies at Hypersonic Flight Speeds", *Jet Propulsion*, April, 1956.

6. Schlichting, H., *Boundary Layer Theory*, McGraw-Hill, 1960.

7. Hall, J. G., Editor, *Fundamental Phenomena in Hypersonic Flow*, Cornell University Press, 1966.

The reader who desires further study in hypersonic flow will find that reference 1 will provide an excellent introduction and discussion of the problems. Also, reference 7 considers some of the important specific problems of hypersonic flow. Both of these books list many of the important publications in hypersonic flow.

NOMENCLATURE FOR CHAPTER 10

C_f = skin friction coefficient

C_i = species mass fraction

c_p = specific heat at constant pressure

c_{pi} = specific heat at constant pressure for species i

c_{pA} = specific heat at constant pressure for atoms

c_{pf} = the frozen specific heat, $\sum_i C_i c_{pi}$, at constant pressure

C_{pM} = specific heat at constant pressure for molecules

c_{vi} = specific heat at constant volume for species i

D_{12} = binary diffusion coefficient

D_T = turbulent diffusion coefficient

e_i = specific internal energy of species i

h = specific enthalpy

h_i = specific enthalpy of species i

h_i^0 = specific enthalpy of formation of species i

h_w = specific enthalpy at the wall

h_∞ = specific enthalpy of free stream

I $\quad = u^2/2 + h,\ $ total or stagnation specific enthalpy

L $\quad =$ Lewis number

L_T $\quad =$ turbulent Lewis number

M $\quad =$ Mach number

p $\quad =$ pressure

p_i $\quad =$ partial pressure of species i

P_r $\quad =$ Prandtl number $\ = \mu c_{pf}/\kappa$

P_T $\quad =$ turbulent Prandtl number

q $\quad =$ heat flux in the y direction

$\bar{R}$ $\quad =$ gas constant for total gas $\ = \sum_i C_i R_i$

R_i $\quad =$ gas constant for species i

t $\quad =$ time

T $\quad =$ temperature

T_∞ $\quad =$ temperature of the free stream

u $\quad =$ mass average velocity in x direction

U_∞ $\quad =$ velocity of the free stream

v $\quad =$ mass average velocity in y direction

$\mathbf{V}$ $\quad =$ mass average velocity $\ = \dfrac{\sum_i C_i \rho_i \mathbf{v}_i}{\sum_i C_i \rho_i}$

V_{iy} $\quad =$ diffusion velocity of species i in y direction

$\mathbf{V}_i$ $\quad =$ diffusion velocity of species i

$\mathbf{v}_i$ $\quad =$ average velocity of species i

w $\quad =$ mass average velocity in z direction

$\dot{w}_i$ $\quad =$ mass rate of production of species i per unit volume, by chemical reaction

x, y, z $\quad =$ coordinates

α $\quad =$ mass fraction of atoms

α_∞ $\quad =$ mass fraction of atoms for free stream

α_w $\quad =$ mass fraction of atoms at the wall

ϵ $\quad =$ turbulent viscosity

ϵ_T $\quad =$ turbulent energy transfer coefficient

κ $\quad =$ thermal conductivity

μ $\quad =$ viscosity

ρ $\quad =$ density

ρ_A $\quad =$ density of atoms

ρ_M $\quad =$ density of molecules

τ_{yx} $\quad =$ shear stress

$(\ )_A$ $\quad$ refers to the property of an atom

$(\ )_M$ $\quad$ refers to the property of a molecule

$(\ )_w$ $\quad$ refers to the property at the wall

$(\ )_\infty$ $\quad$ refers to the property in the free stream

Chapter 11

Magnetohydrodynamics

11.1 INTRODUCTION

Magnetohydrodynamics (MHD) is a relatively new but important branch of fluid dynamics. It is concerned with the interaction of electrically conducting fluids and electromagnetic fields. When a conducting fluid moves through a magnetic field, an electric field and consequently a current may be induced and, in turn, the current interacts with the magnetic field to produce a body force on the fluid.

Such interactions occur both in nature and in new man-made devices. MHD flow occurs in the sun, the earth's interior, the ionosphere, and the stars and their atmosphere, to mention a few. In the laboratory many new devices have been made which utilize the MHD interaction directly, such as propulsion units and power generators; or which involve fluid-electromagnetic field interactions, such as electron beam dynamics, traveling wave tubes, electrical discharges, and many others.

There are two basic approaches to this problem, the macroscopic, fluid continuum model known as MHD, and the microscopic statistical model known as plasma dynamics. We will be concerned here only with MHD, that is, electrically conducting liquids and fairly dense ionized gases.

11.2. ELECTRODYNAMICS OF MOVING MEDIA

Before we begin the study of MHD itself, a thorough understanding of classical electromagnetic field theory is necessary. A brief review is presented here, although it is assumed that the reader has some familiarity with Maxwell's equations.

The basic laws of electromagnetic theory may be presented in a mathematical form known as the Maxwell equations. These equations relate the basic field quantities and show how they are produced. In addition to the Maxwell equations, for a complete description of an electromagnetic system, we must relate the field quantities seen by observers in relative motion. These laws are all contained in the Special Theory of Relativity, but we will confine ourselves here to nonrelativistic problems, that is, we will always assume that all velocities are small compared to the speed of light, c (mathematically, $V^2/c^2 \ll 1$). We will use RMKS units throughout.

(a) The Maxwell Equations.

The four basic Maxwell equations are the following. The displacement field $\mathbf{D}$ is given by the source equation

$$\int_{\mho} \rho_e \, d\mho = \int_A \mathbf{D} \cdot d\mathbf{A} \qquad (11.1a)$$

which states that the true space charge density ρ_e generates the total $\mathbf{D}$ field. $\mathbf{D}$ lines must always terminate on charges and cannot just end in space. In differential form,

$$\nabla \cdot \mathbf{D} = \rho_e \qquad (11.1b)$$

205

The source equation for the magnetic field **H**, which is known as Ampere's law, is

$$\oint \mathbf{H} \cdot d\mathbf{l} \;=\; \int_A \mathbf{J} \cdot d\mathbf{A} \;+\; \int_A \frac{\partial \mathbf{D}}{\partial t} \cdot d\mathbf{A} \tag{11.2a}$$

where **J** is the true current density and $\partial \mathbf{D}/\partial t$ is the displacement current. In differential form,

$$\nabla \times \mathbf{H} \;=\; \mathbf{J} + \frac{\partial \mathbf{D}}{\partial t} \tag{11.2b}$$

Faraday's law states
$$\oint \mathbf{E} \cdot d\mathbf{l} \;=\; -\int_A \frac{\partial \mathbf{B}}{\partial t} \cdot d\mathbf{A} \tag{11.3a}$$

or
$$\nabla \times \mathbf{E} \;=\; -\frac{\partial \mathbf{B}}{\partial t} \tag{11.3b}$$

Finally, for the magnetic induction field **B**,

$$\int_A \mathbf{B} \cdot d\mathbf{A} \;=\; 0 \tag{11.4a}$$

which states that all **B** lines must form closed loops. In differential form,

$$\nabla \cdot \mathbf{B} = 0 \tag{11.4b}$$

These Maxwell equations hold for any observer, regardless of his motion, so long as he measures all field quantities in his frame of reference. Such equations which have the same form for all observers, regardless of their relative motion, are said to be covariant. The field quantities as measured by the various observers are related by the Lorentz transformations. Further, the quantities of mass, length, and time and their derivatives must also be related by the Lorentz transformations among various observers in relative motion. For low velocities (compared to that of light) the Galilean transformations relate distance (time and mass are then the same), but even then the electromagnetic field quantities must be related by the low velocity limit of the Lorentz transformations. These transformations may be derived from the principles of special relativity. Beginning with the postulate of the invariance of the speed of light and the covariance of the laws of nature all the appropriate transformations follow, but they will not be derived here.

Consider two frames of reference S and S' shown in Fig. 11-1. Frame S' moves with velocity **V** with respect to frame S. We will use S' throughout to denote the rest frame of material media so that the observer in S' moves locally with the medium (fluid in MHD). In the rest frame (and only in the rest frame, in general) can the necessary constitutive equations be written. These equations relate **D'** to **E'**, **B'** to **H'**, and usually are considered to include Ohm's law which relates **J'** to **E'**. We will use primes throughout to designate quantities measured in the rest frame. Hence we can write

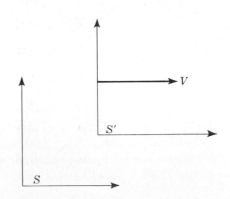

Fig. 11-1. Observers in relative motion. Frame S' moves with velocity **V** relative to frame S.

$$\mathbf{D'} = \epsilon \mathbf{E'} = \epsilon_0 \kappa \mathbf{E'} = \mathbf{P'} + \epsilon_0 \mathbf{E'}$$

$$\mathbf{B'} = \mu \mathbf{H'} = \mu_0 \kappa_m \mathbf{H'} = \mu_0 (\mathbf{H'} + \mathbf{M'}) \tag{11.5}$$

$$\mathbf{J'} = \sigma \mathbf{E'}$$

where ϵ is the permittivity, ϵ_0 the permittivity of free space, and κ the relative permittivity. Similarly, μ is the permeability,* μ_0 the permeability of free space, and κ_m the relative

---

*In this chapter the viscosity is denoted as μ_f to avoid confusion with permeability.

permeability. σ is the scalar electrical conductivity. **P** is the polarization and **M** the magnetization. The first two equations of (11.5) are generally true, ϵ and μ being only functions of temperature and pressure for linear media and also functions of the fields if the material is nonlinear. Ohm's law is a phenomenological equation and is not generally true. The form given here for a scalar σ is good for liquids and dense gases, but in rarefied gases the conductivity becomes a tensor.

In any frame of reference we can write

$$\mathbf{D} = \mathbf{P} + \epsilon_0 \mathbf{E}$$
$$\mathbf{B} = \mu_0(\mathbf{M} + \mathbf{H}) \tag{11.6}$$

but (11.5) is only true in the rest frame. In free space or in media where $\kappa = \kappa_m = 1$ we see that $\mathbf{P} = \mathbf{M} = 0$ and thus

$$\mathbf{D} = \epsilon_0 \mathbf{E}$$
$$\mathbf{B} = \mu_0 \mathbf{H} \tag{11.7}$$

in any frame of reference.

In any MHD problem we usually need all four Maxwell equations and the constitutive equations. However, it is often convenient not to use the equation $\nabla \cdot \mathbf{D} = \rho_e$, but instead the equation

$$\frac{\partial \rho_e}{\partial t} + \nabla \cdot \mathbf{J} = 0 \tag{11.8}$$

(or in steady state or in cases where ρ_e is negligible in this equation, $\nabla \cdot \mathbf{J} = 0$ as is the case in MHD). Equation (11.8) follows directly from Maxwell's equations and is not independent.

(b) The Lorentz Transformations.

The Lorentz transformations are now listed below. **V** is the velocity of the rest frame S' with respect to S and $\perp$ and $\parallel$ indicate the components of the quantities perpendicular to and parallel to the vector **V** respectively.

$$
\begin{aligned}
\mathbf{E}'_\perp &= \beta(\mathbf{E} + \mathbf{V} \times \mathbf{B})_\perp & \mathbf{E}'_\parallel &= \mathbf{E}_\parallel \\
\mathbf{D}'_\perp &= \beta(\mathbf{D} + \mathbf{V} \times \mathbf{H}/c^2)_\perp & \mathbf{D}'_\parallel &= \mathbf{D}_\parallel \\
\mathbf{H}'_\perp &= \beta(\mathbf{H} - \mathbf{V} \times \mathbf{D})_\perp & \mathbf{H}'_\parallel &= \mathbf{H}_\parallel \\
\mathbf{B}'_\perp &= \beta(\mathbf{B} - \mathbf{V} \times \mathbf{E}/c^2)_\perp & \mathbf{B}'_\parallel &= \mathbf{B}_\parallel \\
\mathbf{J}'_\perp &= \mathbf{J}_\perp & \mathbf{J}'_\parallel &= \beta(\mathbf{J} - \rho_e \mathbf{V})_\parallel \\
\rho'_c &= \beta(\rho_e - \mathbf{V} \cdot \mathbf{J}/c^2) & & \\
\mathbf{P}'_\perp &= \beta(\mathbf{P} - \mathbf{V} \times \mathbf{M}/c^2)_\perp & \mathbf{P}'_\parallel &= \mathbf{P}_\parallel \\
\mathbf{M}'_\perp &= \beta(\mathbf{M} + \mathbf{V} \times \mathbf{P})_\perp & \mathbf{M}'_\parallel &= \mathbf{M}_\parallel
\end{aligned}
\tag{11.9}
$$

where $\beta = 1/\sqrt{1 - V^2/c^2}$.

In the nonrelativistic limit, which is the case of interest in MHD, the transformations reduce to:

$$
\begin{aligned}
\mathbf{E}' &= \mathbf{E} + \mathbf{V} \times \mathbf{B} & \mathbf{J}' &= \mathbf{J} - \rho_e \mathbf{V} \\
\mathbf{D}' &= \mathbf{D} + \mathbf{V} \times \mathbf{H}/c^2 & \rho'_e &= \rho_e - \mathbf{V} \cdot \mathbf{J}/c^2 \\
\mathbf{H}' &= \mathbf{H} - \mathbf{V} \times \mathbf{D} & \mathbf{P}' &= \mathbf{P} - \mathbf{V} \times \mathbf{M}/c^2 \\
\mathbf{B}' &= \mathbf{B} - \mathbf{V} \times \mathbf{E}/c^2 & \mathbf{M}' &= \mathbf{M} + \mathbf{V} \times \mathbf{P}
\end{aligned}
\tag{11.10}
$$

(c) **The Boundary Conditions.**

The boundary conditions on the field quantities at an interface are the same as in stationary media. Across an interface the following conditions hold in any frame of reference. We need only write the conditions with *all* the field quantities measured in any arbitrary frame of reference. (See Fig. 11-2.)

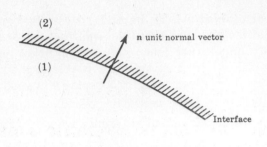

Fig. 11-2. The interface between two media, 1 and 2.

$$n \times (E_2 - E_1) = 0 \qquad n \times (H_2 - H_1) = J_s$$

$$n \cdot (D_2 - D_1) = \rho_s \qquad n \cdot (B_2 - B_1) = 0$$

$$(11.11)$$

where ρ_s is the surface charge density on the interface and J_s is the surface current on the interface. Physically then, the tangential component of **E** and the normal component of **B** are continuous across the interface. The tangential component of **H** jumps if a surface current is present, and the normal component of **D** jumps if a surface charge exists.

11.3 THE INDUCED EMF AND TERMINAL VOLTAGE

In MHD problems we are often interested in the terminal potential or voltage between two electrodes. The question is: given two electrodes, what is the terminal voltage between them if an electrically conducting fluid flows between them?

In general we define the emf about a closed loop (in a laboratory frame of reference in which we locate the terminals) as

$$\text{emf} = \oint E' \cdot dl \qquad (11.12)$$

where **E'** is the local electric field seen by an observer moving locally with the fluid, but dl is fixed in the laboratory frame. Using Maxwell's equations and the nonrelativistic Lorentz transformations, we obtain

$$\text{emf} = \oint (V \times B) \cdot dl - \int_A \frac{\partial B}{\partial t} \cdot dA \qquad (11.13)$$

where $\partial B/\partial t$ must *not* be taken outside the integral. **V** is the velocity of the conductor instantaneously coincident with dl.

The terminal potential V_{AB} is then the emf minus the IR drop between the electrodes A and B:

$$V_{AB} = \text{emf} - \int_A^B E' \cdot dl \qquad (11.14)$$

where V_{AB} is the voltage at B with respect to A and the line integral is taken between the electrodes, through the fluid. It should be noted that the emf may be dependent on the integration path used to determine it (if eddy currents are present in AC systems), but the terminal potential is always independent of the path of integration.

In steady MHD problems such as generators, pumps, etc., we obtain the simplified form of (11.14) which follows directly by using the fact that $\partial/\partial t = 0$ and the Lorentz transformations. We get

$$V_{AB} = - \int_A^B E \cdot dl \qquad (11.15)$$

Note that in (*11.15*) $\mathbf{E}$ is measured in the laboratory frame of reference, and (*11.15*) also follows from the fact that (since $\nabla \times \mathbf{E} = 0$ in steady state) $\mathbf{E} = -\nabla \phi$, and hence

$$\phi_{AB} = -\int_A^B \mathbf{E} \cdot d\mathbf{l}$$

and ϕ is the potential, identical with V_{AB}.

11.4 THE ELECTROMAGNETIC BODY FORCE

The electromagnetic body force is derivable from the Coulomb force law, since basically this is the only interaction that occurs.

The electromagnetic force on a particle of charge q in the local rest frame of the particle is $\mathbf{F} = q\mathbf{E}'$. Now, if we transform to the laboratory frame, $\mathbf{E}' = \mathbf{E} + \mathbf{V} \times \mathbf{B}$ (non-relativistic) so that $\mathbf{F} = q(\mathbf{E} + \mathbf{V} \times \mathbf{B})$ which is the familiar Lorentz force law. $\mathbf{V}$ is the velocity of the particle with respect to the laboratory frame.

(a) The Body Force in a Fluid.

The complete electromagnetic body force in a conducting fluid may be derived, microscopically, from the Coulomb law, or by a virtual work and energy method. We will only present the result here. The body force density $\mathbf{f}_e'$ in the rest frame (because the constitutive equations have been used) is

$$\mathbf{f}_e' = \rho_e'\mathbf{E}' + \mathbf{J}' \times \mathbf{B}' - \tfrac{1}{2}\epsilon_0 E'^2 \nabla'\kappa - \tfrac{1}{2}\mu_0 H'^2 \nabla'\kappa_m$$
$$+ \tfrac{1}{2}\epsilon_0 \nabla'\left(E'^2 \frac{\partial\kappa}{\partial\rho}\rho\right) + \tfrac{1}{2}\mu_0 \nabla'\left(H'^2 \frac{\partial\kappa_m}{\partial\rho}\rho\right) \qquad (11.16)$$

However, in MHD, only the first two terms are important. These two terms are covariant and the expression holds in any frame of reference. In MHD then,

$$\mathbf{f}_e = \rho_e\mathbf{E} + \mathbf{J} \times \mathbf{B} \qquad (11.17)$$

and nonrelativistically, $\mathbf{f}_e = \mathbf{f}_e'$ so that we can compute $\rho_e'\mathbf{E}' + \mathbf{J}' \times \mathbf{B}'$ or $\rho_e\mathbf{E} + \mathbf{J} \times \mathbf{B}$ and obtain the same numerical result. As we will see, $\rho_e\mathbf{E}$ is usually negligible compared to $\mathbf{J} \times \mathbf{B}$.

(b) The Stress Tensor.

An alternative but equivalent description of the body force is the electromagnetic stress tensor T_{ij}. The body force is then $f_j = \dfrac{\partial T_{ij}}{\partial x_i} - \dfrac{\partial g_j}{\partial t}$ where g_i is the electromagnetic momentum flux vector. A covariant expression for T_{ij} (neglecting striction effects) is

$$T_{ij} = -\tfrac{1}{2}(\mathbf{D} \cdot \mathbf{E} + \mathbf{B} \cdot \mathbf{H})\delta_{ij} + D_i E_j + B_i H_j \qquad (11.18)$$

For all practical purposes the term $\partial g_i/\partial t$ is negligible and is of no concern in MHD. The most important use of the stress tensor concept is the physical interpretation of the body force which it permits. If the stress tensor is diagonalized (the principal stresses determined) we get an interesting result. If we make the assumptions, which are valid in MHD, that the electric terms in the stress tensor are negligible, and that B and H are collinear (they will be collinear in the rest frame or in any frame in MHD since there $\mathbf{B} = \mathbf{B}'$ and $\mathbf{H} = \mathbf{H}'$ for nonrelativistic speeds), we obtain the result that the three principal stresses, λ_i, are

$$\lambda_1 = \tfrac{1}{2}\mathbf{H} \cdot \mathbf{B}, \quad \lambda_2 = \lambda_3 = -\tfrac{1}{2}\mathbf{H} \cdot \mathbf{B} \qquad (11.19)$$

and the principal axes are oriented so that λ_1 is a tension along the magnetic lines of force, and λ_2 and λ_3 represent a compression normal to the field lines. Alternatively, we can say that there is a hydrostatic compression of $\mathbf{H} \cdot \mathbf{B}/2$ with a tension of $\mathbf{H} \cdot \mathbf{B}$ (along the field lines) superposed on the hydrostatic compression.

The concept of magnetic pressure is based on these results. It should be remembered, however, that this body force is not a physical tension or pressure in the fluid, but enters into the momentum equation as a body force and consequently may generate mechanical stresses. In static equilibrium, the pressure gradient must be balanced out by the tensor divergence of the electromagnetic stress tensor (which, physically, is a body force). The situation is similar to pressure in a fluid being generated in a static fluid because of a gravitational field.

Another way to arrive at the idea of magnetic pressure is to write the body force $\mathbf{J} \times \mathbf{B}$ as $(\nabla \times \mathbf{H}) \times \mathbf{B}$ (where we have used the Maxwell equation $\nabla \times \mathbf{H} = \mathbf{J} + \dot{\mathbf{D}}$ and $\dot{\mathbf{D}}$ is negligible as we shall show). $(\nabla \times \mathbf{H}) \times \mathbf{B}$ may be written (using $\mathbf{B} = \mu \mathbf{H}$)

$$(\nabla \times \mathbf{H}) \times \mathbf{B} = -\nabla \left(\frac{B^2}{2\mu}\right) + \frac{1}{\mu}(\mathbf{B} \cdot \nabla)\mathbf{B} \qquad (11.20)$$

Hence the first term on the right is the irrotational part of the body force and adds directly to pressure in the momentum equation, and the second term is the rotational part (corresponding to the tension along the magnetic field lines) and is generally not zero in MHD.

11.5 BASIC CONCEPTS OF MHD FLOW

We will now review the basic assumptions of MHD and the relevant principles and equations.

(a) Assumptions.

The MHD assumptions which are usually made are the following:

1. All velocities are small compared to that of light, so that $V^2/c^2 \ll 1$.

2. The electric field is of order $\mathbf{V} \times \mathbf{B}$. Any $\mathbf{E}$ fields involved are induced or of the order of the induced field. We must always write $\mathbf{E}' = \mathbf{E} + \mathbf{V} \times \mathbf{B}$ and distinguish between $\mathbf{E}'$ and $\mathbf{E}$.

3. $\mathbf{H} \cong \mathbf{H}'$ and $\mathbf{B} \cong \mathbf{B}'$, since

$$\mathbf{B}' = \mathbf{B} - \frac{\mathbf{V} \times \mathbf{E}}{c^2} \cong \mathbf{B} - 0\left[\frac{V^2}{c^2}\mathbf{B}\right]$$

Liquid metals and ionized gases have permeability μ_0, so that we write $\mathbf{B} = \mu_0 \mathbf{H}$ in any frame of reference.

4. The displacement current $\dot{\mathbf{D}}$ is negligible with respect to $\mathbf{J}$.

5. Ohm's law is $\mathbf{J} = \sigma \mathbf{E}' = \sigma(\mathbf{E} + \mathbf{V} \times \mathbf{B})$, and $\mathbf{J}' \cong \mathbf{J}$ since $\rho_e \mathbf{V}$ is neglected compared to $\sigma(\mathbf{E} + \mathbf{V} \times \mathbf{B})$.

6. The space charge ρ_e' is zero, but $\rho_e \neq 0$. We must write $\nabla \cdot \mathbf{D} = \rho_e$, and *not* set $\nabla \cdot \mathbf{D}$ to zero. Since ρ_e is not usually known, $\nabla \cdot \mathbf{D} = \rho_e$ is not a useful equation. It is better and more convenient to use $\nabla \cdot \mathbf{J} = 0$ (even in unsteady problems, since space charge transport is negligible compared to $\mathbf{J}$).

7. The force $\rho_e \mathbf{E}$ is negligible compared to $\mathbf{J} \times \mathbf{B}$. The electric stress and energy, proportional to $\mathbf{E} \cdot \mathbf{D}$, is negligible compared to $\mathbf{H} \cdot \mathbf{B}$.

8. For high conductivity, $\sigma \rightarrow \infty$, Ohm's law indicates that for finite $\mathbf{J}$, $\mathbf{E}' = 0$, and $\mathbf{E} = -\mathbf{V} \times \mathbf{B}$. The current is then determined by $\nabla \times \mathbf{H} = \mathbf{J}$ and not by Ohm's law.

(b) Equations.

The basic equations of MHD can be written then as the Maxwell equations, Ohm's law, the equation of continuity, the equation of motion with the $\mathbf{J} \times \mathbf{B}$ body force, and the energy equation with Joule heating. In addition, we must use the nonrelativistic Lorentz transformations. The equation of state for a perfect gas can still be used under the MHD approximations. We can list the equations as:

Maxwell's:

$$\begin{aligned}
\nabla \times \mathbf{H} &= \mathbf{J} \\
\nabla \cdot \mathbf{B} &= 0 \\
\nabla \times \mathbf{E} &= -\partial \mathbf{B}/\partial t \\
\nabla \cdot \mathbf{J} &= 0
\end{aligned}$$

(11.21)

Ohm's Law:

$$\mathbf{J} = \sigma(\mathbf{E} + \mathbf{V} \times \mathbf{B})$$

(11.22)

Motion:

$$\begin{aligned}
\rho \left[\frac{\partial \mathbf{V}}{\partial t} + (\mathbf{V} \cdot \nabla)\mathbf{V} \right] &= -\nabla p + \nabla \cdot \tau + \mathbf{J} \times \mathbf{B} - \rho \nabla \psi \\
&= -\nabla(p + B^2/2\mu) + (\mathbf{B} \cdot \nabla)\mathbf{B}/\mu + \nabla \cdot \tau - \rho \nabla \psi
\end{aligned}$$

(11.23)

where τ is the mechanical stress tensor and ψ is the gravitational potential.

Energy:

$$\rho \frac{Du}{Dt} = -p \nabla \cdot \mathbf{V} + \kappa_T \nabla^2 T + \Phi + \mathbf{E}' \cdot \mathbf{J}'$$

(11.24)

We use κ_T for thermal conductivity here to avoid confusion with relative permittivity. u is the specific internal energy. The Joule heat $(\mathbf{E}' \cdot \mathbf{J}' \cong \mathbf{E}' \cdot \mathbf{J} = J^2/\sigma)$ is the only interaction if the material is linear, that is, ϵ and μ are not functions of temperature. The reader is referred to reference 2, page 225, for a detailed discussion of this equation.

State:

$$p = \rho R T$$

(11.25)

(c) Parameters.

These equations may be put into dimensionless form, as discussed in Chapter 4, and the relevant dimensionless parameters obtained. We will not go through the calculations here, but will list the parameters. In addition to all the parameters of ordinary flow (of Chapter 4) we have two additional independent parameters. We list several (not independent) below.

R_m = Magnetic Reynolds number = $V_0 L \sigma \mu$, which is a measure of the ratio of magnetic convection to magnetic diffusion. If $R_m \ll 1$, it can be shown that the induced magnetic field is small compared to the applied magnetic field.

M_m = Magnetic Mach number = V_0/A, where A is the Alfvén speed, defined as $\sqrt{\mathbf{B} \cdot \mathbf{H}/\rho}$ which will be discussed presently.

M = Hartmann number = $\sqrt{\sigma B_0^2 L^2/\mu_f} = \sqrt{N_R R_m/M_m}$, which is a measure of the ratio of the magnetic body force to the viscous force.

P_m = Magnetic Prandtl number = $\nu/\eta = R_m/N_R$, which is a measure of the ratio of vorticity diffusion to magnetic diffusion.

N = The interaction parameter, which is a measure of the ratio of the magnetic body force to the inertia force. For finite conductivity N is taken as $\sigma B_0^2 L/\rho V_0 = R_m/M_m^2$, and for very high or infinite conductivity $N = M_m^{-2}$.

(d) **Magnetic Transport.**

A very important equation may be derived by combining Maxwell's equations and Ohm's law. $\nabla \times \mathbf{H} = \mathbf{J} = \sigma(\mathbf{E} + \mathbf{V} \times \mathbf{B})$, and $\mathbf{E}$ may be eliminated by taking the curl of the above equation and using $\nabla \times \mathbf{E} = -\dot{\mathbf{B}}$. Then making use of a few vector identities and $\nabla \cdot \mathbf{B} = 0$, we arrive at

$$\frac{\partial \mathbf{B}}{\partial t} = \eta \nabla^2 \mathbf{B} + \nabla \times (\mathbf{V} \times \mathbf{B}) \tag{11.26}$$

which is the equation of transport, diffusion and convection, of the magnetic field. η is the magnetic diffusivity, $1/\sigma\mu$. This equation may be used simultaneously with the equation of motion [with the body force written as $(\nabla \times \mathbf{H}) \times \mathbf{B}$] in certain problems where it is not convenient to introduce the electric field.

By introducing the dimensionless variables

$$\mathbf{B}^* = \mathbf{B}/\mathbf{B}_0, \qquad t^* = tV_0/L, \qquad \mathbf{r}^* = \mathbf{r}/L$$

the transport equation becomes

$$\frac{\partial \mathbf{B}^*}{\partial t^*} = -\frac{1}{R_m} \nabla^* \times (\nabla^* \times \mathbf{B}^*) + \nabla^* \times (\mathbf{V}^* \times \mathbf{B}^*) \tag{11.27}$$

which indicates the significance of R_m. The first term on the right side is a diffusion term and the second a convection. If no motion is present, $\mathbf{V} = 0$, and (11.26) becomes

$$\frac{\partial \mathbf{B}}{\partial t} = \eta \nabla^2 \mathbf{B} \tag{11.28}$$

a diffusion equation where η is the diffusivity. On a laboratory scale the diffusion usually dominates, $(R_m \ll 1)$, but on an astronomical scale (for example in the sun) convection dominates $(\sigma \to \infty$, and $R_m \gg 1)$. In fact, as $\sigma \to \infty$, the magnetic field is transported entirely by convection and there is no diffusion of the field lines through the conducting media. Hence it is said that then the magnetic field lines are "frozen" in the fluid and move along with it.

There is an exact analogy between the transport of the magnetic field here and the transport of vorticity in ordinary fluid mechanics. The classical Kelvin theorems, etc., may be applied here to the magnetic field.

We may think of the field lines as being elastic, and the flowing fluids drag them until they are in static equilibrium. This is the case when a magnetic field is induced (which then adds to the original applied magnetic field). The induced field is caused by the distortion of the applied field lines because of the fluid convecting them. As $\sigma \to \infty$ the lines lose their ability to resist being dragged along by the fluid.

(e) **Alfvén Waves.**

As we have shown earlier, stress tensor considerations show that the body force is equivalent to a hydrostatic pressure plus a tension of $\mathbf{H} \cdot \mathbf{B}$ along the field lines. As we will show later, these lines behave like taut strings and transverse waves will propagate along them at what is called Alfvén speed, $\sqrt{\mathbf{H} \cdot \mathbf{B}/\rho}$. Coupled with this transverse field disturbance must be a transverse velocity wave which is 90° out of phase with the magnetic wave. These waves, which are called Alfvén or magnetohydrodynamic waves, travel without dispersion or attenuation if $\sigma \to \infty$ and viscosity is neglected.

(f) **The Bernoulli and Kelvin Theorems.**

The equation of motion (11.23) may be written for an inviscid fluid and may be integrated along a streamline to yield (for a compressible fluid in steady flow)

$$\frac{V_2^2 - V_1^2}{2} + \psi_2 - \psi_1 + \int_1^2 \frac{d(p + B^2/2\mu)}{\rho} = \frac{1}{\mu} \int_1^2 \frac{(\mathbf{B} \cdot \nabla)\mathbf{B} \cdot d\mathbf{s}}{\rho} \tag{11.29}$$

If $(\mathbf{B} \cdot \nabla) \mathbf{B} = 0$, the classical Bernoulli theorem is valid with the pressure replaced by $(p + B^2/2\mu)$ which is then the total (mechanical plus magnetic) pressure.

By forming the circulation, the equation of motion yields the MHD form of Kelvin's theorem as

$$\frac{D\Gamma}{Dt} = \frac{D}{Dt} \int_A (\nabla \times \mathbf{V}) \cdot d\mathbf{A} = \int_A \nabla \times \left[\frac{1}{\mu} (\mathbf{B} \cdot \nabla) \mathbf{B} \right] \cdot d\mathbf{A} \qquad (11.30)$$

The force $(\mathbf{B} \cdot \nabla)\mathbf{B}$ is rotational and may generate vorticity even though the fluid is inviscid.

11.6 INCOMPRESSIBLE VISCOUS MHD FLOW

As one of the simplest examples of MHD flow we will now discuss the steady flow of an electrically conducting, viscous, incompressible fluid between parallel plates with an applied transverse magnetic field. The configuration is shown in Fig. 11-3. The details of this problem provide an excellent illustration of method and in particular of the construction of an equivalent electric circuit. We assume the flow to be fully developed so that only pressure varies in the x direction. The channel extent in the z direction is much greater than that in the y direction so that no variations occur with z. The electrodes are assumed to be perfect conductors, and the fluid has conductivity σ. The applied magnetic field $\mathbf{B}_0$ is steady and uniform. This problem is known as the Hartmann problem, after the Danish physicist.

Fig. 11-3. Flow between parallel plates. The Hartmann problem.

On a laboratory scale the magnetic Reynolds number for such a problem is very small and the induced magnetic field would be small and could be thought of as produced by a slight dragging of the $\mathbf{B}_0$ lines by the flowing fluid. However, we will see that for this problem the induced field (which will be entirely in the x direction) does not couple into the equations of motion at all and may be found as the final step in the problem. In many problems (which are not one-dimensional) the induced field may couple into the basic equations and make a solution very difficult. Even then it is often possible, if $R_m \ll 1$, to assume that the induced field is negligible compared to $\mathbf{B}_0$.

We begin the Hartmann problem by writing the Maxwell equations, Ohm's law, and the equations of motion. From continuity, $v = w = 0$. From $\nabla \cdot \mathbf{J} = 0$ we conclude that J_z must only depend on y and be equal to (by Ohm's law)

$$J_z = \sigma(E_z + uB_0)$$

From $\nabla \times \mathbf{E} = 0$ we conclude that E_x is a constant which we arbitrarily take as zero since no electric field is applied in the x direction. Also, since the electrodes have high conductivity, $E_y = 0$ in the electrodes and hence everywhere. It follows that E_z is a function only of y.

The pressure gradient $\partial p/\partial x$ is a constant, but a gradient $\partial p/\partial y$ will also exist due to a "pinch" effect.

The equation of motion in the x direction becomes

$$0 \; = \; -\frac{\partial p}{\partial x} + \mu_f \frac{d^2 u}{dy^2} - \sigma(E_z + uB_0)B_0 \qquad (11.31)$$

which can be integrated immediately with the boundary conditions

$$u = 0, \;\; y = \pm y_0$$

to give the velocity profile as

$$u \; = \; \frac{y_0^2}{M^2}\left(\frac{1}{\mu_f}\frac{\partial p}{\partial x} + \frac{M}{y_0}\sqrt{\frac{\sigma}{\mu_f}}E_z\right)\left(\frac{\cosh My/y_0}{\cosh M} - 1\right) \qquad (11.32)$$

where M, the Hartmann number is $\sqrt{B_0^2 y_0^2 \sigma/\mu_f}$.

The y equation of motion is

$$0 \; = \; -\frac{\partial p}{\partial y} + J_z B_x$$

and allows determination of $\partial p/\partial y$ once B_x, the induced magnetic field, is found later. From (11.32) and Ohm's law we find J_z as

$$J_z \; = \; \sigma E_z \frac{\cosh My/y_0}{\cosh M} + \frac{y_0}{M}\sqrt{\frac{\sigma}{\mu_f}}\frac{\partial p}{\partial x}\left(\frac{\cosh My/y_0}{\cosh M} - 1\right) \qquad (11.33)$$

The total current (per unit channel length in the x direction) is given by

$$\mathcal{I} \; = \; \int_{-y_0}^{+y_0} J_z\,dy \; = \; 2\sigma y_0 E_z \frac{\tanh M}{M} + \frac{2y_0^2}{M}\sqrt{\frac{\sigma}{\mu_f}}\frac{\partial p}{\partial x}\left(\frac{\tanh M}{M} - 1\right) \qquad (11.34)$$

The terminal voltage V_t (voltage of electrode at $+z_0$ with respect to the one at $-z_0$) is defined as

$$V_t \; = \; -\int_{-z_0}^{+z_0} E_z\,dz \; = \; -2z_0 E_z$$

and using (11.34) to solve for E_z in terms of $\mathcal{I}$, we find

$$V_t \; = \; -\frac{z_0 M \mathcal{I}}{\sigma y_0 \tanh M} + \frac{2y_0 z_0}{M\sqrt{\sigma\mu_f}}\frac{\partial p}{\partial x}\left(1 - \frac{M}{\tanh M}\right) \qquad (11.35)$$

Now we can construct an equivalent circuit of the device by adding the open circuit voltage in series with the effective internal resistance R_i which is defined as the ratio of the open circuit voltage $V_{t_{oc}}$ to the short circuit current I_{sc}. From (11.35) $V_{t_{oc}}$ is found by setting $\mathcal{I} = 0$ to get

$$V_{t_{oc}} \; = \; \frac{2y_0 z_0}{M\sqrt{\sigma\mu_f}}\frac{\partial p}{\partial x}\left(1 - \frac{M}{\tanh M}\right) \qquad (11.36)$$

(which is a negative number) and I_{sc} is found by setting $E_z = 0$ in (11.34) to get

$$\mathcal{I}_{sc} \; = \; \frac{2y_0^2}{M}\sqrt{\frac{\sigma}{\mu_f}}\frac{\partial p}{\partial x}\left(\frac{\tanh M}{M} - 1\right) \qquad (11.37)$$

which is a negative number, which indicates current flows from the $+z_0$ to the $-z_0$ terminal through the channel. Hence for a device of length L, I_{sc} (the total short circuit current for the entire device) is $L\mathcal{I}_{sc}$ so that R_i is

$$R_i \; = \; \frac{V_{t_{oc}}}{I_{sc}} \; = \; \frac{z_0}{L\sigma y_0}\frac{M}{\tanh M} \qquad (11.38)$$

The equivalent circuit then is, by Thévenin's theorem, as shown by Fig. 11-4. A load resistor R_L may be attached to the terminals as indicated, and by using Kirchhoff's law we get

$$V_{t_{oc}} + I(R_L + R_i) = 0 \qquad (11.39)$$

Note that R_L may also be replaced by an external generator. The sign on V_t and I depends on whether a load R_L or an external generator is attached.

Fig. 11-4. The equivalent circuit of an MHD flow device with sign conventions. For the Hartmann problem, $V_{t_{oc}}$ is negative and hence the polarity of $V_{t_{oc}}$ is the reverse of that shown.

The above circuit method may be used to analyze generators, pumps, and meters in incompressible or compressible flow for any channel shape and lays the groundwork for the MHD generator analysis.

Now the induced magnetic field H_x may be found from $\nabla \times \mathbf{H} = \mathbf{J}$, since $\mathbf{J}$ is known. From (11.33),

$$\frac{dH_x}{dy} = -J_z = -\sigma E_z \frac{\cosh My/y_0}{\cosh M} - \frac{y_0}{M}\sqrt{\frac{\sigma}{\mu_f}}\frac{\partial p}{\partial x}\left(\frac{\cosh My/y_0}{\cosh M} - 1\right)$$

which may be integrated to find $H_x(y)$. The boundary condition depends on the geometric configuration of the return circuit, and can be determined by applying Ampere's circuital law. If the return circuit is symmetric in y (consisting of two plates as shown in Fig. 11-3), the value of $H_x(y=0) = 0$ and H_x is antisymmetric in y. H_x has a constant value between the insulating walls and the return path plates, then it drops to zero through the plates. Integration of the above equation gives

$$H_x = \frac{y_0^2}{M}\sqrt{\frac{\sigma}{\mu_f}}\frac{\partial p}{\partial x}\cdot\frac{y}{y_0} - \left(\frac{y^2}{M}\sqrt{\frac{\sigma}{\mu_f}}\frac{\partial p}{\partial x} + \frac{I}{2L}\right)\frac{\sinh My/y_0}{\sinh M} \qquad (11.40)$$

In Hartmann flow, the flow rate is reduced as the external load R_L is increased (for a given Hartmann number). If an external voltage source is applied, the flow rate may be further reduced (and even made to flow against the pressure gradient) or it may be increased, depending on the polarity of the applied voltage. For a fixed value of R_L, the profile is flattened as the Hartmann number is increased, as shown in Fig. 11-5. However, if an external voltage is applied, the curve may not flatten but steepen. In general, an increasing Hartmann number means an increasing interaction.

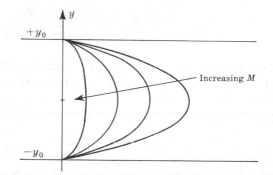

Fig. 11-5. The velocity profile in Hartmann flow for a load resistor R_L and a constant pressure gradient.

This analysis of the Hartmann problem may be applied to generators and pumps, the device acting as either depending on the terminal conditions and pressure gradient. These methods will be applied to the compressible flow in an MHD generator channel in Section 11.7. The extension to pipes and channels of finite cross section will not be made here, but the reader is referred to reference 2, page 225.

11.7   WAVES AND SHOCKS IN MHD

Earlier, we mentioned a new type of wave that occurs in MHD, the Alfvén wave. Now we will investigate general plane wave motion and see that the Alfvén wave is just one of several new phenomena that arise because of electromagnetic field-fluid interactions. We will confine our attention here to plane waves, since these are the only type that are amenable to simple description, but the conclusions that may be reached by this analysis suffice to give a good picture of the waves that propagate in MHD.

If we assume that a wave propagates in the x direction, a plane wave is characterized by the fact that no variations of any variable occur in the y or z directions. True plane waves do not exist in nature; but at least over small regions of space, waves may exhibit plane wave behavior. And, in any case, more complex wave geometries may always be thought of as a superposition of waves which behave like plane waves.

There are two types of plane waves, transverse and longitudinal. Transverse waves, such as shear waves and TEM (electromagnetic waves), involve only y and z components of vector variables in the wave (assuming propagation in the x direction). Pressure and density variations do not accompany transverse waves. Longitudinal waves are those that have only x components of variables, or pure scalars, entering into the wave motion. A common example is the acoustic or sound wave which carries with it a pressure and density disturbance. In MHD we will find that the transverse shear waves couple with the field quantities to give a new type of wave (the Alfvén wave), and the ordinary acoustic wave is split into fast, slow and intermediate magnetoacoustic waves.

In our study we will assume that the fluid is a continuum and that Ohm's law holds. In rarefied gases, a more complex fluid model must be used and the results, particularly at high frequency, are different. The study of radio waves in the ionosphere is based on these rarefied ionized gas (or plasma) oscillations, but we cannot discuss them here. Another assumption which we will make which is valid for liquids and dense gases is that the displacement current is negligible compared to the conduction current. This assumption amounts to saying that $\sigma/\omega\epsilon \gg 1$ where ω is the angular frequency and ϵ is the dielectric constant. For mercury (in RMKS units), $\sigma \cong 10^6$, $\epsilon \cong 10^{-12}$, so that for frequencies even into the microwave region the assumption is quite good. Even for poorly ionized gases at $\sigma \cong 1$, the frequency would have to be of order 10^{12} hertz before displacement current would become significant.

The approach here will be to assume that the waves consist of small disturbances or perturbations in the variables. We perturb the governing equations, linearize, and assume phasor solutions. Then a characteristic value problem may be set up and a dispersion equation derived. We assume that all disturbances may be expressed in the form $e^{j(\omega t - kx)}$ for propagation in the x direction. j is $\sqrt{-1}$.

(a) Plane Waves in Gases.

Neglecting displacement current and assuming the fluid to be initially at rest, we can derive the appropriate dispersion equation as follows. Referring to Fig. 11-6, the applied magnetic field is assumed to have components H_{0x} and H_{0y}, with propagation in the x direction. There is no loss of generality in leaving H_{0z} out, since we can always rotate the coordinate system about the x axis so that H_{0z} is zero.

The relevant equations are three motion, three magnetic transport, continuity, energy,

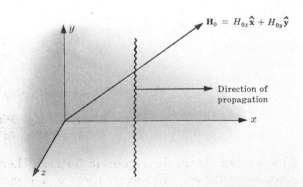

Fig. 11-6.   Plane wave propagation in the presence of an applied magnetic field.

and state, a total of nine equations. We assume perturbation quantities are represented by small letters and the perturbation pressure, density and temperature are represented by primes:

$$\mathbf{H} = \mathbf{H}_0 + \mathbf{h} \qquad\qquad \rho = \rho_0 + \rho'$$

$$\mathbf{V} = \mathbf{v}, \ (\mathbf{V}_0 = 0) \qquad\qquad T = T_0 + T'$$

$$p = p_0 + p'$$

The components of $\mathbf{v}$ are u, v, and w.

The continuity equation is
$$\frac{\partial \rho}{\partial t} + \nabla \cdot (\rho \mathbf{V}) = 0$$

which becomes
$$\frac{\partial}{\partial t}(\rho_0 + \rho') + \nabla \cdot [(\rho_0 + \rho')\mathbf{v}] = 0$$

The first order linearized equation is

$$\frac{\partial \rho'}{\partial t} + \rho_0 \frac{\partial u}{\partial x} = 0$$

Then the algebraic form (assuming a phasor solution $\rho' = \rho'^* e^{j(\omega t - kx)}$ and $u = u^* e^{j(\omega t - kx)}$, where ρ'^* and u^* are phasors) is

$$u^* \rho k - \rho'^*{}_\omega - u^* \rho_0 k = 0 \qquad\qquad (11.41)$$

Similarly, we can write these algebraic forms of the remaining eight linearized equations. The first order equations become:

State:
$$\frac{p'}{p_0} = \frac{T'}{T_0} + \frac{\rho'}{\rho_0} \qquad\qquad (11.42)$$

Motion:

(a) $\quad \rho_0 \dfrac{\partial u}{\partial t} = -\dfrac{\partial p'}{\partial x} + (\zeta + \tfrac{4}{3}\nu\rho_0)\dfrac{\partial^2 u}{\partial x^2} - \mu H_{0y}\dfrac{\partial h_y}{\partial x}$

(b) $\quad \rho_0 \dfrac{\partial v}{\partial t} = \nu\rho_0\dfrac{\partial^2 v}{\partial x^2} + \mu H_{0x}\dfrac{\partial h_y}{\partial x} \qquad\qquad (11.43)$

(c) $\quad \rho_0 \dfrac{\partial w}{\partial t} = \nu\rho_0\dfrac{\partial^2 w}{\partial x^2} + \mu H_{0x}\dfrac{\partial h_z}{\partial x}$

Energy (the dissipation is second order):

$$\rho_0 c_p \frac{\partial T'}{\partial t} = \frac{\partial p'}{\partial t} + \kappa_T \nabla^2 T' \qquad\qquad (11.44)$$

Magnetic Transport:

(a) $\quad \dfrac{\partial h_x}{\partial t} = \eta\dfrac{\partial^2 h_x}{\partial x^2}$

(b) $\quad \dfrac{\partial h_y}{\partial t} = \eta\dfrac{\partial^2 h_y}{\partial x^2} + H_{0x}\dfrac{\partial v}{\partial x} - H_{0y}\dfrac{\partial u}{\partial x} \qquad\qquad (11.45)$

(c) $\quad \dfrac{\partial h_z}{\partial t} = \eta\dfrac{\partial^2 h_z}{\partial x^2} + H_{0x}\dfrac{\partial w}{\partial x}$

Now we can obtain the algebraic forms. There result nine algebraic equations for the nine phasor quantities. However, these equations are not linearly independent and the determinant of the coefficients of the phasors must be zero. This equation is then the dispersion equation. The determinental form is

	h_x^*	h_z^*	w^*	u^*	v^*	h_y^*	p'^*	ρ'^*	T'^*
$(12.45a)$									
$(12.43c)$		2×2							
$(12.45c)$									
(12.41)									
$(12.43a)$				6×6					
$(12.43b)$									
$(12.45b)$									
(12.42)									
(12.44)									

$$= 0 \qquad (11.46)$$

There are three uncoupled terms. The first term is not important and merely indicates that $h_x = 0$. The 2×2 determinant represents two transverse waves and the 6×6 represents a set of coupled longitudinal and transverse waves. We will not go into the details of these general waves, but will look at some special cases.

(b) Transverse Waves.

The 2×2 determinant may be written out as

$$\nu \eta k^4 + [A_x^2 + j(\nu + \eta)\omega]k^2 - \omega^2 = 0 \qquad (11.47)$$

which represents two transverse modes since it is quadratic in k^2. These modes are due to a coupling between viscous and magnetic diffusion and the Alfvén wave. (A + or − sign indicates a forward or backward wave.) A_x is the x component of Alfvén velocity, $\sqrt{B_{0x}H_{0x}/\rho_0}$. If $A_x = 0$, then we get two uncoupled waves given by

$$(\eta k^2 + j\omega)(\nu k^2 + j\omega) = 0 \qquad (11.48)$$

which represents pure viscous diffusion and pure magnetic diffusion (since k^2 is imaginary).

If $\nu = \eta = 0$ (no dissipation), then we get $A_x^2 k^2 - \omega^2 = 0$ so that the phase velocity, $v_p = \omega/(\text{Re } k)$, is the Alfvén speed, that is, $v_p = \pm A_x$. Then the k is real and no attenuation occurs.

The transverse waves are identical for gases or liquids.

(c) Coupled Longitudinal Waves.

The 6×6 determinant of (11.46) written out explicitly is

$$\left[\kappa_T \left\{\frac{1}{\rho_0} + j\frac{\omega}{\rho_0 p_0}(\tfrac{4}{3}\nu\rho_0 + \zeta)\right\} k^4 - \left\{\frac{\omega^2 \kappa_T}{p_0} - j\omega c_p + \frac{\omega^2 c_p}{a_0^2 \rho_0}(\tfrac{4}{3}\nu\rho_0 + \zeta)\right\} k^2 - j\frac{\omega^3 c_p}{a_0^2}\right]$$

$$\cdot [\nu \eta k^4 + \{A_x^2 + j(\nu + \eta)\omega\}k^2 - \omega^2] - k^2 A_y^2 (j\omega + \nu k^2)\left(\frac{\omega^2 c_p}{a_0^2} - \frac{j\omega \kappa_T k^2}{p_0}\right) = 0 \qquad (11.49)$$

where $A_x = \sqrt{B_{0x}H_{0x}/\rho_0}$, $A_y = \sqrt{B_{0y}H_{0y}/\rho_0}$, and $a_0 =$ the sonic speed, $\sqrt{kRT_0}$.

We will not discuss the general case, but will look at some special cases of particular interest.

If we set the field $\mathbf{H}_0 = 0$ $(A_x = A_y = 0)$ then we get ordinary acoustic waves in a viscous, heat conducting fluid. If we further set $\nu = \zeta = \kappa_T = 0$ we get ordinary simple acoustic waves and (11.49) reduces to

$$a_0^2 k^2 - \omega^2 = 0$$

so that $v_p = \pm a_0$, the ordinary sonic velocity.

If $\nu = \eta = \kappa_T = \zeta = 0$, then there is no dissipation and we get "ideal" magnetoacoustic waves. These waves may be examined in detail and are of extreme importance in MHD. We note that *(11.49)* reduces to two factors, one identical to the Alfvén wave of the previous section, and the other quadratic in k^2:

$$[(a_0^2 k^2 - \omega^2)(A_x^2 k^2 - \omega^2) - k^2 A_y^2 \omega^2](A_x^2 k^2 - \omega^2) = 0 \qquad (11.50)$$

The two roots of the quadratic expression represent two longitudinal waves (magneto-acoustic waves), a fast and slow wave. The phase velocities are:

Longitudinal:

$$v_{p_{\text{fast}}} = \pm[\tfrac{1}{2}(A_x^2 + A_y^2 + a_0^2) + \sqrt{\tfrac{1}{4}(A_x^2 + A_y^2 + a_0^2)^2 - a_0^2 A_x^2}]^{1/2}$$

$$v_{p_{\text{slow}}} = \pm[\tfrac{1}{2}(A_x^2 + A_y^2 + a_0^2) - \sqrt{\tfrac{1}{4}(A_x^2 + A_y^2 + a_0^2)^2 - a_0^2 A_x^2}]^{1/2}$$

$$(11.51)$$

Transverse: $\qquad\qquad\qquad v_p = \pm A_x$

The character of these waves can best be seen physically by looking at a plot of the phase velocity as a function of direction of propagation relative to the magnetic field. In Fig. 11-7 we show a plot of the phase velocity in a three-dimensional polar diagram. We see that, in general, there are the three waves, and for propagation at right angles to $\mathbf{H}_0$ ($H_{0x} = 0$, then) there is only one wave which is a modified acoustic wave.

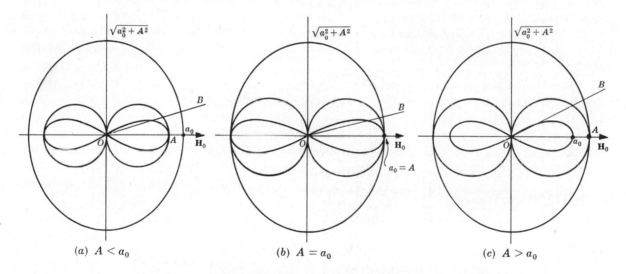

(a) $A < a_0$ (b) $A = a_0$ (c) $A > a_0$

Fig. 11-7. Phase velocity of ideal magnetoacoustic waves. The radius vector OB represents the phase velocity of plane wave propagation in that direction relative to the applied magnetic field $\mathbf{H}_0$. The diagram should be imagined rotated about $\mathbf{H}_0$ to form three-dimensional surfaces. $A^2 = A_x^2 + A_y^2$.

From a practical standpoint, A is usually much smaller than a_0 in liquid metals and the effect on acoustic behavior is difficult to measure in the laboratory. On an astronomical and planetary scale, however, such is not the case and these waves become important.

Another type of diagram of interest is the ray-normal diagram for the ideal magneto-acoustic waves. These are called Friedrichs diagrams and are shown in Fig. 11-8 below. These diagrams are the envelope of plane waves traveling outward from the origin and hence represent the unit time development in space of a pulse at the origin. In ordinary acoustics such a diagram would be a sphere of radius a_0. (The Mach cone is the develop-

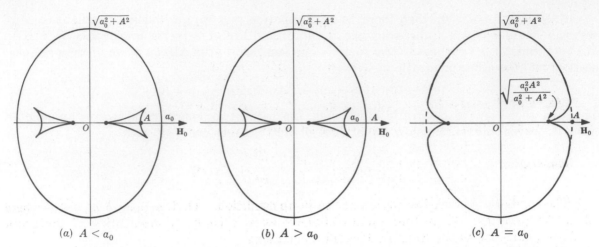

Fig. 11-8.   The ray-normal, or Friedrichs diagrams for ideal
magnetoacoustic waves.   A sound pulse at the origin
develops into these surfaces in unit time.   They
should be rotated about $\mathbf{H_0}$ to form three-dimensional surfaces.

ment of a sound pulse emanating from a supersonically moving source.)   These diagrams
may be constructed geometrically from Fig. 11-7.   The perpendiculars are drawn to the
rays (such as OB) where they cross the phase velocity locus curve.   We form a continuous
set of these perpendicular planes as OB sweeps through all angles.   The envelopes of these
planes then form the sound disturbance surfaces which are generated by a pulse at the
origin.

The disturbance surface generated by a moving source (as an aircraft) becomes rather
complicated, and there are more than just two distinct cases (as subsonic and supersonic in
ordinary flow).   Now there are four regions of flow depending on the magnitude of the
moving objects' velocity relative to the three wave speeds and orientation with respect to
the magnetic field.   We will not discuss magneto-aerodynamics here but refer the reader
to the references.

(d) MHD Shock Waves.

We will discuss here only a special case of
the MHD shock, which we will call the normal
MHD shock.   We assume that the applied
magnetic field on both sides of the shock is
parallel to the shock front, and further that
the conductivity of the fluid is infinite.   The
velocity *may be oblique* to the shock front, so
that we are concerned only with velocity components normal to the shock front.   The normal MHD shock is a generalization of the ordinary oblique shock.   The more general case
of an arbitrary magnetic field will not be discussed here.

We will carry out the analysis in the shock
frame of reference and assume that B is the
same in all frames.   Referring to Fig. 11-9
we can write the following conservation equations across the shock.

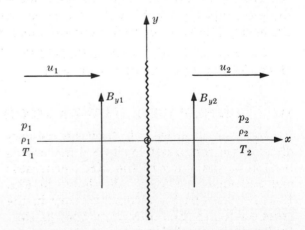

Fig. 11-9.   The normal MHD shock.   We orient the
coordinate system so that $B_{z1} = 0$,
without loss of generality. B_{z2} must also
be zero to satisfy magnetic transport.

Continuity:
$$[\rho u]_1^2 = 0$$

Momentum:
$$\left[\rho u^2 + p + \frac{1}{2\mu} B_y^2\right]_1^2 = 0$$

Magnetic Transport: $[uB_y]_1^2 = 0,$ $B_{z1} = B_{z2} = 0$

Also, v and w, the y and z velocity components must be continuous.

Energy:
$$\left[\frac{p}{\rho}\left(\frac{k}{k-1}\right) + \frac{u^2}{2} + \frac{B_y^2}{\rho\mu}\right]_1^2 = 0$$

The symbol $[\ \ ]_1^2$ is used to represent the jump condition. That is, $[A]_1^2 = A_2 - A_1$, where A is any quantity. These four equations above allow a complete description of the shock and are analogous to the Rankine-Hugoniot equations.

A current sheet exists in the shock to effect the change in B_y.

Solving, we find the shock speed a_s into still air (the same as u_1 in Fig. 11-9) as

$$a_s = \frac{2}{k+1} \cdot \frac{a_1^2 + A_1^2[1 + (1 - k/2)(\rho_2/\rho_1 - 1)]}{\rho_1/\rho_2 - (k-1)/(k+1)} \tag{11.52}$$

where a_1 is the sonic speed upstream and A_1 the upstream Alfvén speed, $\sqrt{B_{y1}^2/\mu\rho_1}$. As A_1 goes to zero we get the shock speed of ordinary gas dynamics. The shock speed is increased by the presence of the magnetic field. As the strength becomes small, $\rho_2/\rho_1 \to 1$, $a_s^2 = a_1^2 + A_1^2$, which gives the magnetosonic velocity in a perpendicular field.

The pressure jump $[p]_1^2 = p_2 - p_1$ is given by

$$p_2 - p_1 = a_s^2 \rho_1 (1 - \rho_1/\rho_2) + \frac{B_{y1}^2}{2\mu}(1 - \rho_2^2/\rho_1^2) \tag{11.53}$$

and a magnetosonic Mach number, $M_t^2 = a_s^2/(a_1^2 + A_1^2)$, can be expressed as

$$M_t^2 = \frac{2}{k+1} \cdot \frac{1 + [A_1^2/(a_1^2 + A_1^2)](1 - k/2)(\rho_2/\rho_1 - 1)}{\rho_1/\rho_2 - (k-1)/(k+1)} \tag{11.54}$$

As $\rho_2/\rho_1 \to 1$, $M_{t1} \to 1$. For $M_{t1} < 1$, no shock can occur; and for $M_{t1} > 1$ and $a_s^2 > a_1^2$ there can exist a shock. For $a_s^2 < a_1^2$ no shock can occur for any value of A_1. Hence as the field is increased beyond a critical value, no shock can occur.

For a general oblique magnetic field the situation is more complicated and a multiplicity of shocks and discontinuities can occur.

11.8 COMPRESSIBLE FLOW—MAGNETOGASDYNAMIC CHANNEL FLOW

In this section we will discuss quasi-one-dimensional compressible channel flow which is vital to the study of the MHD generator and propulsion systems. As shown in Fig. 11-10 we assume the channel to vary in the cross section in the x direction, and the electrodes to be parallel perfect conductors and form two opposite channel walls. The other walls are assumed to be insulators. The velocity components, v and w, are assumed $\ll u$, and the induced field effects are neglected.

Fig. 11-10. The one-dimensional channel with compressible flow.

The terminal potential V_t is related to the electric field E_z (E_y and E_x are zero) by

$$E_z = -V_t/l$$

so that E_z is constant throughout the channel, and $J_z = \sigma(E_z + uB_0)$ is a function only of x (since u is a function of x). We could let l vary with x, then E_z would be a function of x but we confine our discussion here to parallel electrodes.

Under open circuit conditions the total external current I is zero, but $\mathscr{I}(x)$ (the current density per unit length) is not necessarily zero and currents can circulate in the channel. We cannot determine $V_{t_{oc}}$ without knowing the function $u(x)$. However, on a local scale, (at a given value of x) the local open circuit conditions ($J_z = 0$) is given by $E_z = -uB_0$. Under local short circuit, $E_z = 0$. Hence any given local portion of the channel operates as a generator if $-uB_0 < E_z < 0$. In a full channel this condition must be satisfied at every value of x. By considering the sign of E_z, we can show that E_z must also be negative for the channel to act as a pump or flow meter. We will confine our study to negative E_z.

(a) Basic One-Dimensional Flow.

The basic channel flow equations can be obtained by averaging the differential equations across the channel. We assume steady flow, σ to be a scalar constant, a perfect gas, and no variations across the channel, and adiabatic flow.

Continuity:
$$\rho u A = m \text{ (a constant)} \tag{11.55}$$

Motion:
$$\rho u \frac{du}{dx} = -\frac{dp}{dx} - \sigma(E_z + uB_0)B_0 \tag{11.56}$$

Energy:
$$\rho u \left[c_p \frac{dT}{dx} + u \frac{du}{dx} \right] = \sigma(E_z + uB_0)E_z \tag{11.57}$$

State:
$$p = \rho R T \tag{11.58}$$

Here, A is the cross sectional area of the channel.

These equations cannot be solved explicitly for a general area variation $A(x)$, but a useful first integral may be obtained. By suitably combining the above equations we obtain

$$\frac{du}{dx} = \frac{(u/A)(dA/dx) - (\sigma B_0^2/p)(u - u_3)(u - u_1)}{M^2 - 1} \tag{11.59}$$

$$\frac{dM}{dx} = \frac{1}{(M^2 - 1)} \left\{ \left(1 + \frac{k-1}{2}M^2\right) \frac{M}{A} \frac{dA}{dx} - \left(1 + \frac{k-1}{2}M^2\right) \frac{\sigma B_0^2}{ap}(u - u_3)(u - u_2) \right\} \tag{11.60}$$

where the critical velocities u_1, u_2, and u_3 are defined as

$$u_1 = -\frac{k-1}{k} \cdot \frac{E_z}{B_0} = \frac{k-1}{k} u_3, \qquad u_2 = \frac{1 + kM^2}{2 + (k-1)M^2} u_1, \qquad u_3 = -\frac{E_z}{B_0} = \frac{V_t}{B_0 l} \tag{11.61}$$

and M is the local Mach number.

Now the net effect of the electromagnetic interaction with the fluid is not merely the $\mathbf{J} \times \mathbf{B}$ force, but the Joule heat also enters into the interaction. The net effect then can be determined from (11.59) and (11.60). For $u < u_3$ the body force, alone, accelerates the flow, and for $u > u_3$ the body force, alone, decelerates the flow. The speed u_1 is that speed at which the body force and Joule heat cancel each other. The net effect then is: if $M > 1$ the flow is accelerated if u lies between u_3 and u_1, and decelerated if u lies outside that region. If $M < 1$, the flow follows the converse behavior. The net effect on M may be seen from (11.60). If $M > 1$, M increases with x if u lies between u_2 and u_3 and decreases with x if M lies outside this region. For $M < 1$, the reverse is true.

For operation at $E_z < 0$ and for various values of u_0 (inlet velocity at $x = 0$), we can plot qualitatively the behavior of u and M along the channel. This behavior is shown in Fig. 11-11 and 11-12. For generator operation, $u > u_3$, and from the figures we see that in only cases $1A$ and $2A$ is $u > u_3$. In $2A$, u is $> u_3$ throughout and in $1A$ there is the possibility for the channel to act as a generator only over a portion of its length (case $1Ab$). We must remember, however, that $u > u_3$ is the local requirement for generator operation, and the overall channel behavior ($V_{t_{oc}}$, I_{sc} and R_t) can only be calculated after $u(x)$ is known.

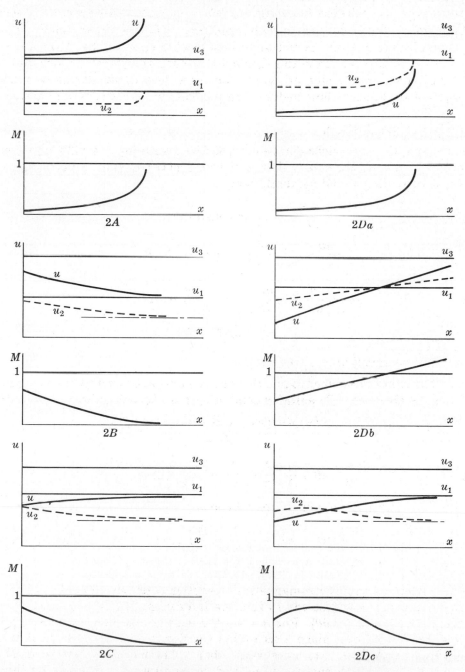

Fig. 11-11. The qualitative behavior of u and M along a constant area channel for various subsonic initial conditions. $2A$: $u_2 < u_1 < u_3 < u_0$. $2B$: $u_2 < u_1 < u_0 < u_3$. $2C$: $u_2 < u_0 < u_1 < u_3$. $2Da, 2Db, 2Dc$: $u_0 < u_2 < u_1 < u_3$.

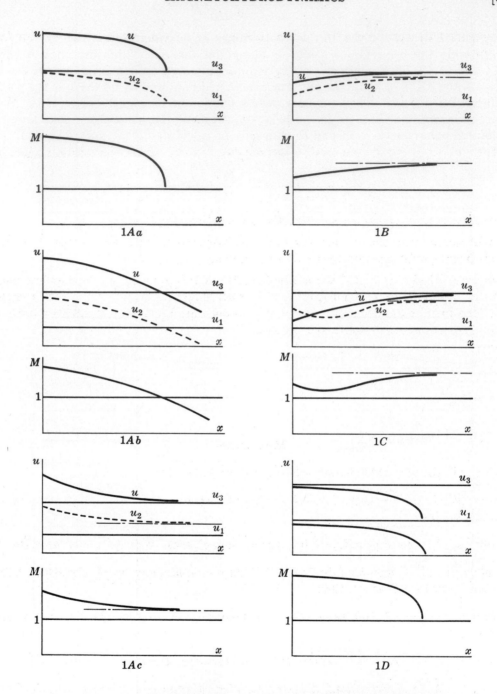

Fig. 11-12. The qualitative behavior of u and M along a constant area channel for various supersonic initial conditions. $1Aa, 1Ab, 1Ac$: the three possibilities when $u_1 < u_2 < u_3 < u_0$. $1B$: $u_1 < u_2 < u_0 < u_3$. $1C$: $u_1 < u_0 < u_2 < u_3$. $1D$: $u_0 < u_1 < u_2 < u_3$.

(b) Generator Operation.

We will not discuss the general solution of the basic equations, but only discuss one special simple, but practical problem, the constant velocity generator. $A(x)$ must vary in a special way to give rise to $u(x)$ being a constant.

By imposing constant velocity, u_0, on the basic equations we can derive the following relationship:

$$p_0 - p = xB_0^2\sigma(u_0 - u_3), \qquad T/T_0 = (p/p_0)^{(k-1)u_3/ku_0}, \qquad A/A_0 = (p_0/p)^{1-(k-1)u_3/ku_0} \qquad (11.62)$$

The total current I is then

$$I = \int_0^L \sigma(-V_t + u_0B_0)\frac{A}{l}\,dx \qquad (11.63)$$

so that for a given V_t (or u_3) the total power output P is IV_t which, upon integration, becomes

$$P = \frac{A_0p_0ku_0}{(k-1)}\left[1 - \left\{1 - \frac{B_0\sigma}{p_0}(u_0 - u_3)L\right\}^{(k-1)u_3/ku_0}\right] \qquad (11.64)$$

Equation (11.62) may be optimized directly for u_3 (for a fixed u_0).

We will not pursue the matter further here because integration of the flow equations under arbitrary conditions becomes rather complex.

From a practical standpoint the analysis of the MHD generator is somewhat more complex. The conductivity is a tensor (giving rise to Hall currents) and varies with temperature. However, the principles of one-dimensional channel flow have been presented here and are the same, even for more complicated devices.

References

1. Cowling, T. G., *Magnetohydrodynamics*, Interscience, 1957.

2. Hughes, W. F. and Young, F. J., *The Electromagnetodynamics of Fluids*, John Wiley, New York, 1966.

3. Jeffrey, A., *Magnetohydrodynamics*, Interscience (John Wiley), Oliver and Boyd, 1966.

4. Kulikovskiy, A. G. and Lyubimov, G. A., *Magnetohydrodynamics*, (translated from the Russian), Addison-Wesley, 1965.

5. Landau, L. D. and Lifschitz, E. M., *Electrodynamics of Continuous Media*, Addison-Wesley, 1960.

6. Shercliff, A., *A Textbook of Magnetohydrodynamics*, Pergamon Press, 1965.

7. Sutton, G. W. and Sherman, A., *Engineering Magnetohydrodynamics*, McGraw-Hill, 1965.

Solved Problems

11.1. The Faraday disk generator is shown in Fig. 11-13. Consider a conducting thin disk rotating with uniform angular velocity ω in the presence of a uniform steady magnetic field $\mathbf{B}_0$ in the axial direction. The perfectly conducting axle (of radius a) and periphery of the disk are connected by sliding contacts to a meter. What open circuit voltage does the meter read?

Since the motion is steady, there are no eddy currents and the emf is the same as the terminal voltage. Hence

$$V_{AB} = -\int_a^b E_r \cdot dr$$

and under open circuit, $J_r = 0 = \sigma(E_r + r\omega B_0)$. Hence

$$V_{AB} = \int_a^b r\omega B_0\, dr = \tfrac{1}{2}(b^2 - a^2)\omega B_0$$

Fig. 11-13

Alternatively we can say

$$\text{emf} = V_{BA} = \oint \mathbf{V} \times \mathbf{B} \cdot d\mathbf{l} - \int \frac{\partial \mathbf{B}}{\partial t} \cdot d\mathbf{A}$$

and taking a path through the fixed leads, disk, and axle, we get only a $\mathbf{V} \times \mathbf{B}$ contribution in the disk. It gives

$$V_{AB} = -V_{BA} = \int_a^b (r\omega)B_0\, dr = \tfrac{1}{2}(b^2 - a^2)\omega B_0$$

which agrees with the result obtained above.

11.2. What are the boundary conditions of the induced magnetic field at the wall of a flow channel?

Consider fully developed flow in a rectangular channel of constant area. The flow region near a wall is shown in Fig. 11-14. At a wall that is a perfect conductor, $\sigma = \infty$, the tangential electric field, E_y, is zero. Also, the fluid velocity is zero at the wall. Hence $J_y = \sigma(E_y + \mathbf{V} \times \mathbf{B}) = 0$ at the wall. But from $\nabla \times \mathbf{H} = \mathbf{J}$, we have $\partial H_x/\partial z = 0$ where z is the coordinate normal to the wall, and the flow is in the x direction. For an insulating wall, $J_z = 0$ at the wall, so that we find $\partial H_x/\partial y = 0$. Hence we conclude that at a perfectly conducting wall

$$\partial H_x/\partial n = 0$$

and at an insulating wall

$$\partial H_x/\partial t = 0$$

where t and n are the tangential and normal directions to the wall, and both are normal to the flow direction x.

In a finite conductivity wall, more complex relationships may be derived. The reader is referred to reference 2, page 225, for details.

Fig. 11-14

11.3. Calculate the terminal characteristics of the compressible vortex generator shown in Fig. 11-15.

m is the flow rate and v_b the inlet tangential velocity. B_0 is steady, uniform and applied along the z axis. Cylindrical screen electrodes are used. We assume: $v \gg u$ (where v is the θ component of velocity and u the radial component), no variations with z, and $R_m \ll 1$ (induced field negligible). The θ equation of motion is

$$\rho u(\partial v/\partial r + v/r) = -J_r B_0$$
$$= -\sigma(E_r + vB_0)B_0$$

Then, from $\nabla \cdot \mathbf{J} = 0$, $J_r = I/2\pi rh$ and $m = 2\pi u\rho rh$ so that the above equation reads

$$\frac{m}{2\pi rh}\left(\frac{dv}{dr} + \frac{v}{r}\right) = -\frac{IB_0}{2\pi rh}$$

which integrates to

$$\frac{v}{v_b} = \frac{b}{r} + \frac{IB_0 r}{2mv_b}\left(\frac{b^2}{r^2} - 1\right)$$

V_t is found from

$$V_t = -\int_a^b E_r \, dr$$

where E_r is given in terms of I from

$$I = J_r \cdot 2\pi rh = \sigma(E_r + vB_0)\, 2\pi rh$$

We find after integrating and setting $I = 0$,

$$V_{t_{oc}} = v_b b B_0 \ln(b/a)$$

and setting $V_t = 0$,

$$I_{sc} = 2\pi h\sigma v_b b B_0\left[1 - \frac{N}{2}\left(1 - \frac{b^2/a^2 - 1}{2(b/a)^2 \ln(b/a)}\right)\right]^{-1}$$

where N, the interaction parameter is

$$N = 2\pi\sigma B_0^2 b^2 h/m$$

m is a negative number since the flow is inward (u is negative) and r is positive outward.

Fig. 11-15

Supplementary Problems

11.4. Under what conditions is the body force $\mathbf{J} \times \mathbf{B}$ irrotational?

11.5. If $\mathbf{J} \times \mathbf{B}$ is irrotational, what can you say about the flow pattern? In two-dimensional incompressible flow when $\mathbf{J} \times \mathbf{B}$ is irrotational, show that the velocity distribution is exactly the same as for potential flow.

11.6. In the above problem, what are the restrictions on $\mathbf{B}_0$ such that the flow is potential? What is the orientation of $\mathbf{B}_0$?

11.7. In the Hartmann problem discuss the sign of E_z and I. Under open circuit conditions is $V_{t_{oc}}$ a positive or negative number?

11.8. In the Hartmann problem show that $\partial p/\partial x$ is a constant throughout the channel.

11.9. In the Hartmann problem solve for the pressure variation across the channel. ($\partial p/\partial y$ is not zero.)

11.10. Show that in two-dimensional flow where the velocity and $\mathbf{B}_0$ are coplanar, $\nabla^2\phi$ is proportional to the only component of $\nabla \times \mathbf{V}$, the vorticity vector. ϕ is the electric potential.

11.11. Consider a missile traveling through the ionosphere with velocity $\mathbf{V}_0$ in the presence of a magnetic field. What is the boundary condition on $\mathbf{E}$, relative to the missile, at infinity?

11.12. Show that if $\epsilon = \epsilon_0$ and $\mu = \mu_0$ for a conducting liquid, then in any frame of reference, we can write the constitutive equations as $\mathbf{B} = \mu_0\mathbf{H}$ and $\mathbf{D} = \epsilon_0\mathbf{E}$.

11.13. Show that the above equations can be written exactly in any frame only if both ϵ and μ are ϵ_0 and μ_0 respectively. (However, under the MHD approximation, $\mathbf{B} = \mu\mathbf{H}$ is valid in any frame.)

11.14. Find the dispersion equation for transverse waves in a fluid moving in the direction of propagation with speed V_0. The fluid is conducting and a magnetic field is applied.

11.15. Why is the magnetic transport equation not needed in the Hartmann problem? Could you use it to work the problem in a different manner?

11.16. If the transport equation is used instead of the Maxwell's equations and Ohm's law, how does the external electric circuit enter into the formulation? *Hint.* show how the boundary conditions of the induced field depend on the external electric circuit.

11.17. Solve the Couette MHD problem (which is the Hartmann problem with the top plate moving with velocity V_0 in the direction of flow).

11.18. Suppose the top and bottom insulating walls of the Hartmann problem have finite conductivity. Show that these walls just act as external resistances in parallel and do not change the solution.

11.19. How is the induced magnetic field affected in the above problem?

11.20. Is there such a thing as a moving field?

11.21. Calculate I_{sc} and R_i for the Faraday generator of Problem 11.1.

11.22. In Problem 11.2, under what conditions is $H_x = 0$ at the channel wall?

11.23. Solve the vortex generator for a radial field of the form $B_r = B_0/r$, (see Problem 11.3).

11.24. What is the appropriate energy equation for Problem 11.23? Can it be integrated to find $T(r)$? What about $p(r)$? *Hint.* assume $v^2/2 \gg u^2/2$.

NOMENCLATURE FOR CHAPTER 11

a = sonic velocity

a_s = shock velocity

A = Alfvén velocity; area

$\mathbf{B}$ = magnetic induction field

$\mathbf{B}_0$ = applied magnetic field

c = velocity of light

c_p = specific heat at constant pressure

$\mathbf{D}$ = displacement field

$\mathbf{E}$ = electric field

$\mathbf{H}$ = magnetic field

$\mathcal{J}$ = current per unit length of channel

I = total current for a device

I_{sc} = short circuit current

$\mathbf{J}$ = current flux

k = ratio of specific heats, c_p/c_v; propagation constant

L = characteristic length

m = mass rate of flow

$\mathbf{M}$ = magnetization vector

M = Hartmann number

M_m = magnetic Mach number

N_R = Reynolds number

N = Interaction parameter

p = pressure

P = power

$\mathbf{P}$ = polarization vector

P_m = magnetic Prandtl number

R_m = magnetic Reynolds number

T_{ij} = electromagnetic stress tensor

u = x component of velocity, internal energy

v = y component of velocity

v_p = phase velocity

$\mathcal{V}$ = volume

$\mathbf{V}$ = velocity vector

V_t = terminal potential

$V_{t_{oc}}$ = open circuit terminal potential

w = z component of velocity

β = $1/\sqrt{1 - V^2/c^2}$

ϵ = permittivity

ϵ_0 = permittivity of free space

ζ = second coefficient of viscosity

η = magnetic diffusivity

κ = relative permittivity

κ_m = relative magnetic permeability

κ_T = thermal conductivity

μ = magnetic permeability

μ_0 = magnetic permeability of free space

μ_f = fluid viscosity

ν = kinematic viscosity

ρ = fluid density

ρ_e = charge density

σ = electrical conductivity

τ = mechanical stress tensor

Φ = dissipation function

ϕ = electric potential

ψ = gravitational potential

ω = frequency

Chapter 12

Non-Newtonian Fluids

12.1 INTRODUCTION

There are fluids that do not obey the simple relationship between shear stress and shear strain rate given by equation (3.45), page 41, for a Newtonian fluid. These fluids have been given the general name non-Newtonian fluids. Many common fluids are non-Newtonian. Examples are: paints, solutions of various polymers, food products such as apple sauce and ketchup, emulsions of water in oil or oil in water, and suspensions of various solids and fibers in a liquid paper pulp or coal slurries and the drilling mud used in well drilling. It is not for lack of applications that many textbooks and courses have failed to give any consideration to non-Newtonian fluids. Although the properties of non-Newtonian fluids do not lend themselves to the elegant and precise analysis that has been developed for Newtonian fluids, the flow of non-Newtonian fluids does possess some interesting, useful and even exciting characteristics. For example: in the fracturing treatment of oil wells, materials have been developed which when added to water will make a fluid so thick that it will suspend sand, glass or metal pellets. Yet the same fluid can be pumped down a well through tubing at enormous rates with less than half the friction loss of water. In a typical fracturing job, over 100 barrels (4200 gallons) might be pumped per minute through several thousand feet of three-inch ID tubing. (Fracturing of oil and gas wells is a process used to increase the production of the well. A horizontal crack is initiated in the producing zone. Fluid pumped down the well under high pressure greatly extends this crack. The sand, or pellets act as propping agents to hold the fracture open after the treatment. Fluid must be delivered at a rapid rate to overcome the loss by diffusion of fluid within the pores of the fractured rock.)

Coal slurries having consistency of over 80% by volume of powdered or crushed coal in water possess non-Newtonian properties and can be pumped long distances with much less power requirements for pumping than pure water.

12.2 CHARACTERISTICS AND CLASSIFICATION OF NON-NEWTONIAN FLUIDS

(a) General.

As was illustrated in Section 3.3(d), page 41, the shearing stress τ for a Newtonian fluid is linearly related to the shearing rate $\dot{\gamma}$ by the viscosity μ,

$$\tau = \mu\dot{\gamma} = \mu\frac{\partial u}{\partial y} \qquad (12.1)$$

(where $\dot{\gamma}$ is the rate of shear strain)*; or conversely, the shearing rate is linearly related to shearing stress,

$$\dot{\gamma} = \frac{1}{\mu}\tau \qquad (12.2)$$

---

*In Chapter 3 we used the notation γ_{ij} for the shear strain rate. Here we use γ for shear strain and $\dot{\gamma}$ for shear strain rate, since both terms may be considered in a non-Newtonian fluid.

In what follows, non-Newtonian fluids which do not obey this linear relationship will be grouped and discussed in three general classifications:

(1) The simplest of these is the time independent non-Newtonian fluid in which the shear rate is a unique but non-linear function of the shear stress.

(2) Time dependent non-Newtonian fluids have more complex shearing stress strain rate relationships. In these fluids the shearing rate is not a single valued function of the shear stress. The shear rate depends on shearing time or on the previous shear stress rate history of that fluid.

(3) In viscoelastic fluids, shear strain as well as strain rate are related in some way to shear stress. Unlike a truly viscous fluid in which all its energy of deformation is dissipated, some of the energy of deformation of a viscoelastic fluid may be recoverable as it is in the deformation of an elastic solid.

(b) Time Independent Fluids.

For the time independent non-Newtonian fluid,

$$\dot{\gamma} = f(\tau) \tag{12.3}$$

A Newtonian fluid is simply a special case of the above where the function $f(\tau)$ is linear, and thus is also termed as being purely a viscous non-Newtonian fluid. The majority of the non-Newtonian fluids that we encounter probably fall into this category; and in some cases flow of fluids not in this category, such as time dependent fluids, may be approximated in this category for simple cases such as steady flow in a pipe or Couette flows.

The time independent non-Newtonian fluids have been commonly represented by three distinct types as shown by Fig. 12-1. These are:

(1) Bingham plastics, curve A

(2) pseudoplastic fluids, curve B

(3) dilatant fluids, curve C.

The Newtonian fluids are indicated by straight lines as shown by line D.

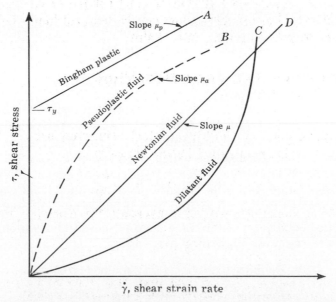

Fig. 12-1. Typical shear stress strain rate relationships for non-Newtonian fluids.

1. *Bingham Plastics.*

Bingham plastics exhibit a yield stress at zero shear rate, followed by a straight line relationship between shear stress and shear rate. The characteristics of these fluids are defined by two constants: the yield stress τ_y which is the stress that must be exceeded for flow to begin, and the plastic viscosity μ_p which is the slope of the straight line portion of curve A in Fig. 12-1. The equation for a Bingham plastic is then,

$$\tau = \tau_y + \mu_p \dot{\gamma} \qquad (12.4)$$

The Bingham plastic concept has been found to closely approximate the behavior of many real fluids such as slurries, plastics, emulsions such as paint, and suspensions of finely divided solids in a liquid. An important example of the latter are drilling muds, which consist primarily of clays suspended in water.

Because of its simple straight line relationship between shear stress and shear rate, the Bingham plastic concept is convenient for analysis.

2. *Pseudoplastic Fluids.*

Pseudoplastic fluids (curve B of Fig. 12-1), as well as dilatant fluids (curve C), do not have a yield stress. The pseudoplastic fluid is also characterized by a progressively decreasing slope of shear stress versus shear rate. This slope has been defined as apparent viscosity

$$\mu_a = \tau/\dot{\gamma} \qquad (12.5)$$

At very high rates of shear in real fluids the apparent viscosity becomes constant and equal to μ_∞, and the shear stress versus shear rate becomes linear.

There are a number of empirical relations that have been used to describe pseudoplastic fluids. The simplest of these is the power law due to Ostwald. It may be written as

$$\tau = k\dot{\gamma}^n \quad \text{where} \quad n < 1 \qquad (12.6)$$

k and n are constant for a particular fluid. k is a measure of the consistency of the fluid and n, the exponent, is a measure of how the fluid deviates from a Newtonian fluid. Note that for a Newtonian fluid $n = 1$ and $k = \mu$, the viscosity of the fluid.

Defining apparent viscosity as

$$\mu_a = \tau/\dot{\gamma} \qquad (12.7)$$

equation (*12.6*) gives

$$\mu_a = k\dot{\gamma}^{(n-1)} \qquad (12.8)$$

Note that when the shear rate is zero, the apparent viscosity is infinite. This is one of several objections that have been raised against the use of the power law model. Another is that for real fluids n is not constant over the entire flow range, and still another is that the constant k has dimensions which depend on n. As has been mentioned, n approaches 1, i.e. Newtonian flow, at very high rates of shear. Nevertheless the power law model has been found desirable because of its simplicity, as well as being adequate to analyze such flows as Couette flow and flow in pipes and channels.

Other empirical equations which have been proposed and which also overcome some of the objections to the power law fluid are

$$\text{Prandtl} \qquad \tau = A \sin^{-1}(\dot{\gamma}/C) \qquad (12.9)$$

$$\text{Eyring} \qquad \tau = \dot{\gamma}/B + C \sin(\tau/A) \qquad (12.10)$$

$$\text{Powell-Eyring} \qquad \tau = A\dot{\gamma} + B \sinh^{-1} C\dot{\gamma} \qquad (12.11)$$

$$\text{Williamson} \qquad \tau = A\dot{\gamma}/(B + \dot{\gamma}) + \mu_\infty\dot{\gamma} \qquad (12.12)$$

where A, B and C represent constants (different for each model).

Because the latter four equations lead to much greater complexity of analysis than the power law model which is adequate in many engineering applications, further discussion of the pseudoplastic fluids will be limited to the power law model. For cases where the power law model does not give an adequate representation of the fluid, it might be more practical to use a computer program that works from the actual measured properties of the fluid rather than resort to another empirical relationship.

3. *Dilatant Fluids.*

Dilatant fluids are similar to pseudoplastic fluids in having no yield stress. They differ from pseudoplastic fluids in that the apparent viscosity increases with increasing shear rate. These fluids are far less common than the pseudoplastic fluids. As with the pseudoplastic fluids, they may be represented by the power law model where the exponent n is now greater than unity.

The power law fluids can be represented graphically most simply by plotting the logarithms of shear stress versus the logarithms of shear rate, as illustrated in Fig. 12-2. Taking the logarithm of both sides of equation (12.6),

$$\log \tau = \log k + n \log \dot{\gamma} \qquad (12.13)$$

which is the equation of a straight line where the slope is n and the intercept of the curves with $\log \dot{\gamma} = 0$ or $\dot{\gamma} = 1$ gives the value of $\log k$, the consistency constant. A Newtonian fluid, $n = 1$, is just a special case of a power law fluid.

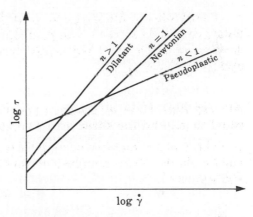

Fig. 12-2.   Log-log plot of power law fluids.

(c) Time Dependent Fluids.

Some fluids are more complex than those just described and the apparent viscosity depends not only on the shear rate but also on the time the shear has been applied. There are two general classes of such fluids:

    (1) thixotropic fluids

    (2) rheopectic fluids.

The shear stress decreases with time as the fluid is sheared for a thixotropic fluid and increases with time for a rheopectic fluid. A common example of a thixotropic fluid is printer's ink which is usually worked over several rolls before being applied to a plate.

1. *Thixotropic Fluids.*

The consistency or apparent viscosity of thixotropic fluids depends on the length of time of shearing as well as on the shear rate. As the fluid is sheared from a state of rest, it breaks down (on a molecular scale), but then the structural reformation will increase with time. An equilibrium situation is eventually reached where the breakdown rate is equal to the buildup rate. If allowed to rest, the fluid builds up slowly and eventually regains its original consistency. Thixotropy is then a reversible process.

Fig. 12-3 shows a plot of stress versus strain rate for a thixotropic fluid immediately after shearing and after the fluid has rested for varying times. The initial curve is shown as Newtonian in Fig. 12-3 but could well be non-Newtonian.

Fig. 12-3. Thixotropic fluid sheared at different times.

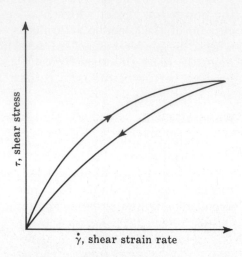

Fig. 12-4. Hysteresis loops for a thixotropic fluid.

If a thixotropic fluid is sheared at a constantly increasing rate, then at a constantly decreasing rate, a curve similar to a hysteresis loop is generated. In Fig. 12-4 is such a curve for a pseudoplastic type of thixotropic fluid. As the shear is decreased, the apparent viscosity is less than for the increasing shear.

Some Bingham plastic materials exhibit thixotropic behavior but, if the stress is high enough, will break down and behave like true liquids until the structure reforms. This behavior is indicated in Fig. 12-5(a). However, some materials, known as false-bodies, exhibit a yield stress even after shearing, although the yield stress value is decreased, as shown in Fig. 12-5(b). It generally takes a long time for a false-body to regain its original yield strength.

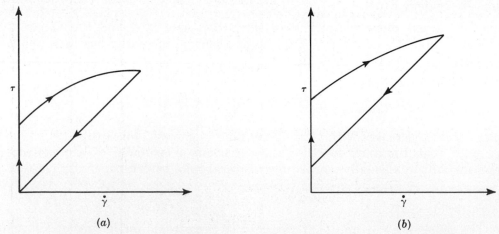

Fig. 12-5.   (a) True thixotropic Bingham plastic, (b) false-body behavior.

2. Rheopectic Fluids.

In rheopectic fluids, molecular structure is formed by shear and the behavior is opposite to that of thixotropy. A simple example of the formation of structure by shear is the beating and thickening of egg whites, although egg white is probably not a true rheopectic fluid. Many substances lose their rheopectic property at extremely high shear rates and may then even behave as thixotropic fluids.

(d) Viscoelastic Fluids.

A viscoelastic material exhibits both elastic and viscous properties. The simplest type of such a material is one which is Newtonian in viscosity and obeys Hooke's law for the elastic part. We can write

$$\dot{\gamma} = \tau/\mu_0 + \dot{\tau}/\lambda \qquad (12.14)$$

where λ is a rigidity modulus. Under steady flow then, $\dot{\gamma} = \dot{\tau}/\mu_0$ and the fluid behaves like a simple Newtonian fluid. However, if the shear stress is changed, an elastic effect is noticed.

Maxwell first proposed (12.14) in the form

$$\tau + (\mu_0/\lambda)\dot{\tau} = \mu_0\dot{\gamma} \qquad (12.15)$$

and liquids which obey this law are known as *Maxwell liquids*. The constant $(\mu_0/\lambda)^{-1}$ is known as the relaxation time and is, physically, the time constant for exponential decay of stress at a constant strain. If the motion is stopped the stress relaxes as $e^{-t\lambda/\mu_0}$.

Rather complex models of viscoelastic materials have been developed in which higher time derivatives of τ and γ appear. For time varying processes, the elastic constants may be complex functions of frequency. A very readable introduction to these models is given by Wilkinson (see reference 7, page 240).

12.3 LAMINAR FLOW IN PIPES

(a) Power Law Fluids.

To illustrate an application of the power law model, the equations for the velocity profile and pressure drop versus flow rate will be derived for fully developed laminar flow of a power law model fluid in a pipe.

The equation of shear stress for steady one dimensional flow in cylindrical coordinates (which is merely the steady state equation of motion for fully developed flow) is

$$\frac{d}{dr}(r\tau) = r\left(\frac{dp}{dz}\right) \qquad (12.16)$$

which for pipe flow integrates to

$$\tau = -\frac{r}{2}\left(\frac{dp}{dz}\right) \qquad (12.17)$$

where τ is the shearing stress defined positive when acting in the upstream direction on the surface of a cylindrical element, and dp/dz is the downstream pressure gradient as shown in Fig. 12-6.

Fig. 12-6.   One-dimensional flow in a pipe.

For a power law fluid, the rheological equation is

$$\tau = k\left(-\frac{du}{dr}\right)^n \qquad (12.18)$$

giving

$$k\left(-\frac{du}{dr}\right)^n = -\frac{r}{2}\left(\frac{dp}{dz}\right) \qquad (12.19)$$

or using the notation $-dp/dz = G$ and transposing $(12.19)^*$,

$$-\frac{du}{dr} = \left(\frac{G}{2k}\right)^{1/n} r^{1/n} \qquad (12.20)$$

Integrating (12.20),

$$\int_u^0 -du = \int_r^a \left(\frac{G}{2k}\right)^{1/n} r^{1/n}\, dr \qquad (12.21)$$

which gives

$$u = \frac{n}{n+1}\left(\frac{G}{2k}\right)^{1/n}(a^{(n+1)/n} - r^{(n+1)/n}) \qquad (12.22)$$

The total flow is

$$Q = \int_0^a 2\pi u r\, dr \qquad (12.23)$$

Substituting (12.22) into (12.23) and integrating,

$$Q = \frac{n\pi}{(3n+1)}\left(\frac{G}{2k}\right)^{1/n} a^{(3n+1)/n} \qquad (12.24)$$

The mean velocity is $V = Q/\pi a^2$, giving

$$V = \frac{n}{(3n+1)}\left(\frac{G}{2k}\right)^{1/n} a^{(n+1)/n} \qquad (12.25)$$

Setting $G = (\Delta p)/L$ for pipe flow (L = length of pipe, Δp = pressure drop and $D = 2a$, the pipe diameter), equation (12.25) can be written

$$\frac{2(3n+1)}{n}\frac{V}{D} = k^{-1}\left(\frac{D\,\Delta p}{4L}\right)^{1/n} \quad (12.26)$$

For a Newtonian fluid ($k = \mu$, $n = 1$), equation (12.26) reduces to the familiar equation for Poiseuille flow,

$$\frac{8V}{D} = \frac{D\,\Delta p}{4\mu L} \qquad (12.27)$$

Substituting $(G/2k)^{1/n}$ from (12.25) into (12.22) gives for the velocity profile in terms of the mean velocity,

$$\frac{u}{V} = \left(\frac{3n+1}{n+1}\right)\left[1 - \left(\frac{r}{a}\right)^{(n+1)/n}\right] \quad (12.28)$$

Fig. 12-7 shows velocity profiles given by (12.28) plotted for various values of n.

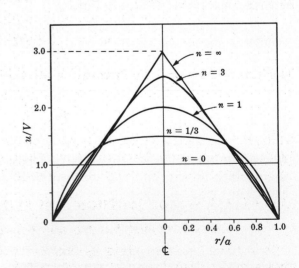

Fig. 12-7.   Velocity profiles in a circular pipe for a power law fluid for various values of n.

$^*G$ is taken as a positive number in what follows. Flow is taken positive in the positive z direction and dp/dz would be a negative value (and G positive) for positive flow.

The lower the value of n the flatter the velocity profile is, until eventually for very low values of n the flow assumes a plug-like form with only the fluid adjacent to the pipe walls being sheared, so that the velocity profile is almost indistinguishable from the profile for a Bingham plastic (see Fig. 12-8).

In some cases a fluid may be successfully treated as either a Bingham plastic or a power law fluid. This has been the case with certain drilling muds.

(b) Bingham Plastics

For the laminar flow of a Bingham plastic, the equation for shear stress to be substituted into equation (12.17) is

$$\tau = \tau_y + \mu_p \dot{\gamma} \qquad (12.29)$$

where $\tau > \tau_y$; if τ is less than τ_y, then $\dot{\gamma} = 0$ and the fluid moves as a plug of radius r_p, as shown in Fig. 12-8. We have for flow in a pipe of radius a,

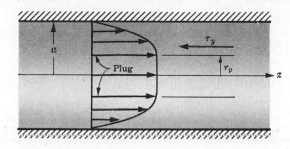

Fig. 12-8. Flow of a Bingham fluid in a circular pipe.

$$\tau = \tfrac{1}{2} r G = \tau_y - \mu_p \frac{du}{dr} \qquad (12.30)$$

for $r_p < r < a$; and for $r < r_p$, $du/dr = 0$. At $r = r_p$, $du/dr = 0$, giving

$$r_p = 2\tau_y/G \qquad (12.31)$$

Integrating (12.30) for velocity gives

$$\int_0^u du = \frac{1}{\mu_p} \int_a^r (\tau_y - \tfrac{1}{2} r G)\, dr \qquad (12.32)$$

so that for $r_p < r < a$, $\qquad u = \dfrac{G}{4\mu_p}(a^2 - r^2) - \dfrac{\tau_y}{\mu_p}(a - r) \qquad (12.33)$

Setting $r = r_p = 2\tau_y/G$, (12.33) gives

$$u_p = \frac{\tau_y^2}{\mu_p G}(a/r_p - 1)^2, \qquad r_p > r > 0 \qquad (12.34)$$

The flow rate found from integrating the velocity over the cross sectional area of the pipe is

$$Q = \frac{\pi a^4 G}{8\mu_p}\left[1 - \frac{4}{3}\left(\frac{2\tau_y}{aG}\right) + \frac{1}{3}\left(\frac{2\tau_y}{aG}\right)^4 \right] \qquad (12.35)$$

which reduces to the Poiseuille expression for $\tau_y = 0$. The above equation, called Buckingham's equation, gives the pressure gradient $G = (\Delta p/L)$ as an implicit function.

12.4 GENERALIZED METHOD FOR FLOW IN PIPES

(a) Generalized Reynolds Number and Friction Factor for Pseudoplastic Fluids.

A method has been given by Metzner and Reed (see reference 3, page 240) which defines a generalized Reynolds number which can be used to find friction factors for both laminar and turbulent flow of time independent fluids.

As in the case of a Newtonian fluid, the generalized Reynolds number can be defined as

$$N_R' = \frac{8\rho V^2}{\tau_{0L}} \qquad (12.36)$$

where τ_{0L} is the wall shearing stress corresponding to laminar flow, and V is the mean velocity.

Defining the Fanning friction factor* as

$$f = \frac{2\tau_0}{\rho V^2} \tag{12.37}$$

in laminar flow leads to the laminar flow relationship

$$f = \frac{16}{N_R'} \tag{12.38}$$

between the friction factor and Reynolds number for Newtonian fluids.

The next step in the method is to use measurements made in capillary tubes or other devices to determine rheological constants that can be used to evaluate the generalized Reynolds number.

The pressure drop Δp and mean velocity V are measured. Then two constants for the fluid are defined by the relation

$$\frac{\Delta p}{4L} = \tau_0 = K'(8V/D)^{n'} \tag{12.39}$$

where K' is the consistency index and n' is the flow behavior index. $8V/D$ would be the wall shear rate for Poiseuille flow of a Newtonian fluid. n' can be found from the tangent slope of $\log \tau_0$ plotted versus $\log 8V/D$:

$$n' = \frac{d(\log \tau_0)}{d(\log 8V/D)} \tag{12.40}$$

Equation (12.39) is based on an expression by Mooney for the wall shear rate at the pipe wall:

$$-\left(\frac{du}{dr}\right)_w = \left(\frac{3n'+1}{4n'}\right)\left(\frac{8V}{D}\right) \tag{12.41}$$

Equations (12.39), (12.40) and (12.41) are applicable to other fluids besides power law fluids, i.e. n' and K' are not necessarily constants. For the special case of power law fluids, $n = n'$ and we have

$$K' = k\left(\frac{3n+1}{n}\right)^n \tag{12.42}$$

Substituting τ_0 from (12.39) into (12.36), the expression for the generalized Reynolds number gives

$$N_R' = \frac{D^{n'}V^{(2-n')}\rho}{K'(8)^{(n'-1)}} \tag{12.43}$$

For a Newtonian fluid $n' = 1$ and $N_R' = \rho VD/K'$, so that $K' = \mu$, the viscosity.

(b) Turbulent Flow.

Dodge and Metzner (see reference 1, page 240) have produced a relationship based on the logarithmic resistance formula of von Karman for Newtonian fluids relating friction factor to the generalized Reynolds number N_R'. Analogous to this equation for Newtonian fluids, the equation proposed by Dodge and Metzner for a power law type of fluid flowing in smooth pipes is

$$\frac{1}{f} = \frac{4.0}{(n')^{0.75}} \log_{10}\left[N_R' f^{1-n'/2}\right] - \frac{0.4}{(n')^{1.2}} \tag{12.44}$$

---

*The Fanning friction factor differs from the one used previously, the Darcy friction factor (in Chapters 4 and 5), by a factor of 4: $(f, \text{Darcy}) = 4 \times (f, \text{Fanning})$.

Fig. 12-9 is a graph of this equation which does not give the friction factor f explicitly.

Fig. 12-9. Fanning friction factor f versus Reynolds number N'_R, equation (12.44).

The data of Dodge and Metzner show that the critical generalized Reynolds number corresponding to the onset of turbulence increases with decreasing values of the flow behavior index n', N'_R critical increasing from 2100 at $n' = 1$ to 3100 at $n' = 0.38$. However, no exact criterion has been established for the critical Reynolds number.

(c) Anomalous (Turbulent) Flow of Non-Newtonian Fluids.

While a great number of non-Newtonian fluids have been found to satisfy the generalized turbulent flow criteria of Metzner, solutions of certain high molecular weight organic compounds have been found that have friction factors much lower than those predicted by the type of relationship given by (12.44) for turbulent flow. Instead of the friction factor leveling out after the critical generalized Reynolds number is reached, the friction factor continues to drop almost as fast as the curve for laminar flow, making it appear that either turbulence has been suppressed or the onset of turbulence delayed. For certain fluids this trend may continue until friction factors are reached that are an order of magnitude lower than that for pure water.

Guar gum and certain polymers supplied commercially to reduce friction in pumping fluids possess these characteristics. One application of these fluids is in oil well treatment where huge quantities of fluid may have to be pumped down a well in a very short time. One unfortunate disadvantage of many of these high molecular weight compounds is their susceptibility to physical degradation i.e. tearing apart of the very large molecules due to high fluid shearing rates so that they lose their desirable friction reducing properties when fluid is reused.

Slurries of solids in water where the solid phase may not be tightly dispersed by the water, may also produce lower friction factor in turbulent flow than water in pipes. At the pipe walls the water or liquid phase separates from the solid phase to form a low viscosity layer. The more rigid core of the slurry tends to move as a plug. Because there is less turbulent momentum transfer from the boundary layer to the core, the laminar boundary layer is actually thicker and the friction factor less than it would be for the flow of pure water. Highly concentrated coal slurries show a much lower friction factor than water. The friction factor for turbulent flow of paper pulp in water also decreases below that of water as the concentration of pulp increases.

References

1. Dodge, D. W., and Metzner, A. B., Turbulent Flow of Non-Newtonian Systems, *A.I.Ch.E. Journal*, 5, pp. 189-204, 1959.

2. Fredricson, A. G. and Bird, R. Byron, Non-Newtonian Flow in Annuli, *Industrial and Engineering Chemistry*, 50, No. 3, pp. 347-352, March, 1958.

3. Metzner, A. B. and Reed, J. C., Flow of Non-Newtonian Fluids—Correlation of the Laminar Transition and Turbulent-flow Regions, *A.I.Ch.E. Journal*, 1, pp. 434-440, 1955.

4. Savins, J. G., Generalized Newtonian (Pseudoplastic) Flow in Stationary Pipes and Annuli, *Petrolium Transactions*, *A.I.M.E.*, 213, pp. 325-332, 1958.

5. Streeter, V. L., (Editor), *Handbook of Fluid Dynamics*, Chapter 7, by A. B. Metzner, McGraw Hill, 1961.

6. Vaughn, R. D. and Bergman, D., Laminar Flow of Non-Newtonian Fluids in Concentric Annuli, *Industrial and Engineering Chemistry—Process Design and Development*, 5, No. 1, pp. 44-47, 1966.

7. Wilkinson, W. L., *Non-Newtonian Fluids*, Pergamon Press, 1960.

Solved Problem

12.1. A clay slurry, $K' = 1.693$ (units of K' are in lb, ft and sec, the power depending on n') and $n' = 581$, is to be pumped at 1150 gallons per minute in 3.826″ ID pipe. What will be the pressure loss in the pipe?

1150 gal/min corresponds to 2.56 ft³/sec. The pipe cross sectional area is 0.0798 ft², giving a velocity of 32 ft/sec. From equation (12.43) the modified Reynolds number is $N'_R = 19,900$, well in the turbulent regime. From equation (12.44) the Fanning friction factor is found to be 0.00442. This value of f cannot be determined explicitly from (12.44) but may easily be found by assuming a trial value of f to substitute in the term $\log_{10}(N'_R f^{1-n'/2})$. Then (12.44) is solved for a new f to be used again in solving for f from (12.44), etc. f soon converges to the correct value to satisfy (12.44). Also, f can be found from Fig. 12-9. The pressure gradient $(\Delta p)/L$ is found in the usual way from the formula

$$\tau_0 = \frac{D\,\Delta p}{4L} = \frac{f\rho V^2}{2}$$

giving $(\Delta p)/L = 0.396$ psi/ft of pipe.

Supplementary Problems

12.2. Capillary tube rheometer measurements of a fluid have shown $\log \tau_0$ versus $\log 8V/D$ to be a straight line between $8V/D = 88$ sec⁻¹ and 5400 sec⁻¹ corresponding to τ_0 varying from $\tau_0 = 1.20$ to 2.50. What is the pressure drop for the fluid flowing through a 3.820″ ID tube at 400 gallons/minute? Is the flow laminar or turbulent?

12.3.   Show that the velocity profile for flow of a power law fluid between parallel plates can be expressed as

$$u \;=\; \frac{n}{1+n}\left(\frac{G}{k}\right)^{1/n}\left[h^{(n+1)/n} - y^{(n+1)/n}\right]$$

where h is the half width of the channel and y is the coordinate measured from the centerline.

12.4.   Derive the velocity profile for Bingham plastic flow between parallel plates.

NOMENCLATURE FOR CHAPTER 12

a	=	radius of pipe
A, B, C	=	constants used in various stress-strain rate relationships
D	=	diameter
f	=	friction factor (Fanning)
G	=	$-dp/dz$, pressure gradient in a pipe
k	=	proportionality constant for a power law fluid
K'	=	consistency index
L	=	length
n	=	exponent for a power law fluid
n'	=	flow behavior index
N_R'	=	generalized Reynolds number, $8\rho V^2/\tau_{0L}$
p	=	pressure
Q	=	volume flow rate
r	=	radial coordinate
r_p	=	radius of central plug in a pipe
u	=	velocity
u_m	=	maximum velocity
u_p	=	velocity of central plug in a pipe
V	=	average velocity
γ	=	shear strain
$\dot{\gamma}$	=	shear strain rate
λ	=	a rigidity modulus
μ	=	viscosity
μ_a	=	apparent viscosity
μ_0	=	viscosity at zero shear rate
μ_p	=	plastic viscosity
μ_∞	=	asymptotic value of apparent viscosity for high rates of shear
τ	=	shear stress
$\dot{\tau}$	=	shear stress rate
τ_0	=	wall shear stress
τ_{0L}	=	wall shear stress corresponding to laminar flow
τ_y	=	yield stress

Some Properties of Fluids

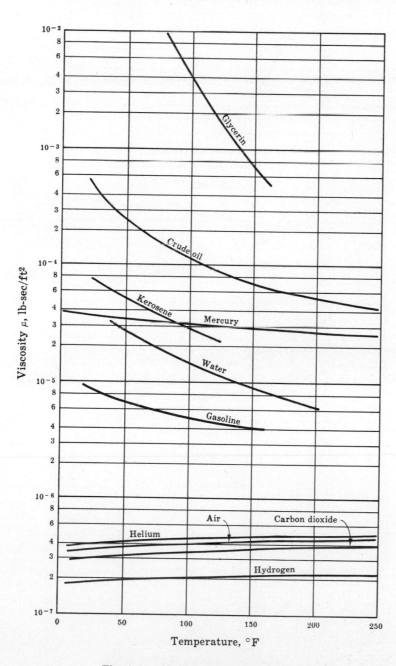

Fig. A-1. Absolute viscosity of some fluids.

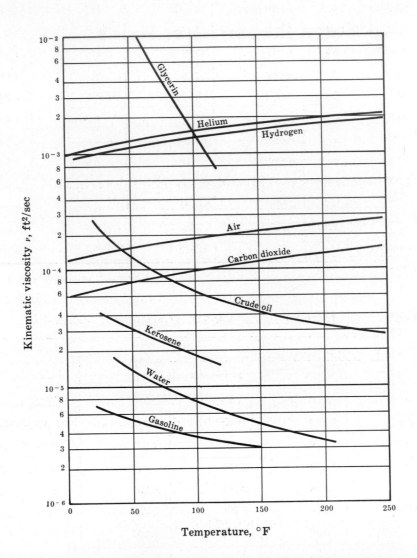

Fig. A-2. Kinematic viscosity of some fluids.

TABLE A.1. PROPERTIES OF WATER AT ATMOSPHERIC PRESSURE

Temperature		Density		Viscosity		Kinematic viscosity	
°C	°F	gm/cm³	slugs/ft³	dyne-sec/cm²	lb$_f$-sec/ft²	cm²/sec	ft²/sec
0	32	0.99987	1.940	1.794×10^{-2}	3.746×10^{-5}	1.794×10^{-2}	1.930×10^{-5}
4	39	1.00000	1.941	1.568	3.274	1.568	1.687
5	41	0.99999	1.941	1.519	3.172	1.519	1.634
10	50	0.99973	1.940	1.310	2.735	1.310	1.407
15	59	0.99913	1.940	1.145	2.391	1.146	1.233
20	68	0.998	1.937	1.009	2.107	1.011	1.088
30	86	0.996	1.932	0.800	1.670	0.803	0.864
40	104	0.992	1.925	0.654	1.366	0.659	0.709
50	122	0.988	1.917	0.549	1.146	0.556	0.598
60	140	0.083	1.907	0.470	0.981	0.478	0.514
70	158	0.978	1.897	0.407	0.850	0.416	0.448
80	176	0.972	1.885	0.357	0.745	0.367	0.395
90	194	0.965	1.872	0.317	0.662	0.328	0.353
100	212	0.958	1.858	0.284	0.593	0.296	0.318

TABLE A.2. PROPERTIES OF AIR AT ATMOSPHERIC PRESSURE

Temperature		Density		Viscosity		Kinematic viscosity	
°C	°F	gm/cm³	slugs/ft³	dyne-sec/cm²	lb$_f$-sec/ft²	cm²/sec	ft²/sec
0	32	1.293×10^{-3}	2.510×10^{-3}	1.709×10^{-4}	3.568×10^{-7}	0.1322	1.427×10^{-4}
50	122	1.093	2.122	1.951	4.074	0.1785	1.921
100	212	0.946	1.836	2.175	4.541	0.2299	2.474
150	302	0.834	1.619	2.385	4.980	0.2860	3.077
200	392	0.746	1.448	2.582	5.391	0.3461	3.724
250	482	0.675	1.310	2.770	5.784	0.4104	4.416
300	572	0.616	1.196	2.946	6.151	0.4782	5.145
350	662	0.567	1.101	3.113	6.500	0.5490	5.907
400	752	0.525	1.019	3.277	6.842	0.6246	6.721
450	842	0.488	0.947	3.433	7.168	0.7035	7.570
500	932	0.457	0.887	3.583	7.481	0.7840	8.436

Units and Dimensions

In fluid mechanics we must deal with measurable quantities such as pressure, velocity, density and viscosity. These quantities are related through equations derived from laws or definitions. Each contains some or all of the basic dimensions of force (F), mass (M), length (L), time (T) and temperature (θ). For quantitative purposes a set of units must be established for these basic dimensions. (In electromagnetic theory there is one additional basic dimension (which is arbitrary). It is often convenient to take this dimension as charge which is measured, in mks units, in coulombs. Thus in magnetohydrodynamics there are five basic dimensions.)

Equations expressing relationships among physical quantities must be dimensionally homogeneous. That is, each term of an equation must have the same dimensions.

A difficulty arises when the units of mass and force are established independently. The different disciplines related to fluid mechanics, such as aerodynamics, thermodynamics and heat transfer, all have their own well developed system for handling this problem — the one which best serves their specific needs.

From Newton's law we find that force and mass are not independent dimensions. Force is proportional to the product of mass and acceleration; that is,

$$\mathbf{F} \propto m\mathbf{a}$$

And by requiring dimensional homogeneity, we find that

$$(F) = \left(\frac{ML}{T^2}\right) \quad \text{or} \quad (M) = \left(\frac{FT^2}{L}\right)$$

The actual choice of basic dimensions then is somewhat arbitrary. One may use an F, L, T, θ system or an M, L, T, θ system. Then all other dimensions may be expressed in terms of the chosen independent basic dimensions by means of laws and definitions.

Now we may use Newton's law to define the unit of mass in terms of force and acceleration. We write

$$\mathbf{F} = m\mathbf{a} \quad \text{or} \quad m = \frac{F}{a}$$

If the unit of force is lb_f and the unit of acceleration is ft/sec², then the unit of mass is

$$\frac{lb_f \, sec^2}{ft}$$

This is the amount of mass which is accelerated at the rate of 1 ft/sec² when acted upon by 1 lb_f. This unit of mass is called a *slug*.

Another unit of mass established independently of Newton's law is also used. The pound mass (lb_m) is defined as the amount of mass which would be attracted toward the earth's surface by a force of one pound (at a particular location). When units of force and mass are defined independent of Newton's law, we must write the equation with a conversion factor, k, in order to make the equation dimensionally homogeneous. We have

$$\mathbf{F} = km\mathbf{a} \quad\text{or}\quad \mathbf{F} = \frac{1}{g_c}m\mathbf{a}$$

and

$$g_c = \frac{ma}{F}$$

The quantity g_c has a numerical value and units which depend on the particular units chosen for force, mass and acceleration. Some particular sets of values are

$$g_c = \frac{1(\text{slug})\,(\text{ft/sec}^2)}{lb_f} \qquad g_c = \frac{1(\text{gm})\,(\text{cm/sec}^2)}{\text{dyne}}$$

$$g_c = \frac{32.2(\text{lb}_m)\,(\text{ft/sec}^2)}{lb_f} \qquad g_c = \frac{1(\text{kg})\,(\text{m/sec}^2)}{\text{newton}}$$

where we see that

$$1 \text{ slug} = 32.2 \text{ lb}_m$$

and we note that 1 lb_m will be accelerated at the rate of 32.2 ft/sec² when acted upon by 1 lb_f. The slug is the unit of mass implied through most of the book and thus g_c does not appear in the equations.

Some physical quantities and their dimensions are listed in Table B.1. Some conversion factors are given in Table B.2.

The method of making the proper conversions is illustrated in the following example. Solve numerically for h_0 in ft lb_f/lb_m where the numerical value of each quantity of the right side is given in terms of the units shown.

$$h_0 = u + pv + \frac{V^2}{2}$$

$$u = A\,\frac{\text{Btu}}{\text{lb}_m} \qquad p = B\,\frac{lb_f}{\text{in}^2} \qquad v = C\,\frac{\text{ft}^3}{\text{lb}_m} \qquad V = D\,\frac{\text{ft}}{\text{sec}}$$

We substitute the numerical values into the equation along with the units and conversions.

$$h_0 = A\,\frac{\text{Btu}}{\text{lb}_m} \times \frac{778 \text{ ft lb}_f}{\text{Btu}} + B\,\frac{lb_f}{\text{in}^2}\,C\,\frac{\text{ft}^3}{\text{lb}_m} \times \frac{144 \text{ in}^2}{\text{ft}^2} + \frac{D^2}{2}\,\frac{\text{ft}^2}{\text{sec}^2} \times \frac{\text{sec}^2\,lb_f}{32.2 \text{ lb}_m \text{ ft}}$$

$$= \left(778\,A + 144\,BC + \frac{D^2}{2(32.2)}\right)\frac{\text{ft lb}_f}{\text{lb}_m}$$

Thus we see that g_c is treated as a conversion factor.

In summary, it is useful to write the equation $F = ma$ in various systems of units. The following equations indicate the relationships among the dimensions and units.

CGS System: F (dynes) $=$ m (grams) $\times$ a (cm/sec²)

MKS System: F (newtons) $=$ m (kilograms) $\times$ a (m/sec²)

FPS System: F (poundals) $=$ m (lb_m) $\times$ a (ft/sec²)

FSS System: F (lb_f) $=$ m (slugs) $\times$ a (ft/sec²)

TABLE B.1. DIMENSIONS AND UNITS

Physical Quantity	Dimensions		Units			
			Metric		English	
	MLT System	FLT System	CGS System	MKS System	FPS System	Engineering System
Length	L	L	cm	m	ft	ft
Mass	M	$FL^{-1}T^2$	gm	kg	lb_m	slug
Time	T	T	sec	sec	sec	sec
Velocity	LT^{-1}	LT^{-1}	cm/sec	m/sec	ft/sec	ft/sec
Acceleration	LT^{-2}	LT^{-2}	cm/sec²	m/sec²	ft/sec²	ft/sec²
Force	MLT^{-2}	F	gm cm/sec² = dyne	kg m/sec² = newton	lb_m ft/sec² = poundal	slug ft/sec² = lb_f
Momentum, Impulse	MLT^{-1}	FT	gm cm/sec = dyne sec	kg m/sec = nt sec	lb_m ft/sec = pdl sec	slug ft/sec = lb_f sec
Energy, Work	ML^2T^{-2}	FL	gm cm²/sec² = dyne cm = erg	kg m²/sec² = nt m = joule	lb_m ft²/sec² = ft pdl	slug ft²/sec² = ft lb_f
Power	ML^2T^{-3}	FLT^{-1}	gm cm²/sec³ = dyne cm/sec = erg/sec	kg m²/sec³ = joule/sec = watt	lb_m ft²/sec³ = ft pdl/sec	slug ft²/sec³ = ft lb_f/sec
Density	ML^{-3}	$FL^{-4}T^2$	gm/cm³	kg/m³	lb_m/ft³	slug/ft³
Angular velocity	T^{-1}	T^{-1}	rad/sec	rad/sec	rad/sec	rad/sec
Angular acceleration	T^{-2}	T^{-2}	rad/sec²	rad/sec²	rad/sec²	rad/sec²
Torque	ML^2T^{-2}	FL	gm cm²/sec² = dyne cm	kg m²/sec² = nt m	lb_m ft²/sec² = ft pdl	slug ft²/sec² = ft lb_f
Angular momentum	ML^2T^{-1}	FLT	gm cm²/sec	kg m²/sec	lb_m ft²/sec	slug ft²/sec
Moment of inertia	ML^2	FLT^2	gm cm²	kg m²	lb_m ft²	slug ft²
Pressure, Stress	$ML^{-1}T^{-2}$	FL^{-2}	gm/(cm sec²) = dyne/cm²	kg/(m sec²) = nt/m²	pdl/ft²	lb_f/ft²
Viscosity (μ)	$ML^{-1}T^{-1}$	$FL^{-2}T$	gm/(cm sec) = dyne sec/cm²	kg/(m sec) = nt sec/m²	lb_m/(ft sec) = pdl sec/ft²,	slug/(ft sec) = lb_f sec/ft²
Kinematic viscosity (ν)	L^2T^{-1}	L^2T^{-1}	cm²/sec	m²/sec	ft²/sec	ft²/sec
Surface tension	MT^{-2}	FL^{-1}	gm/sec² = dyne/cm	kg/sec² = nt/m	lb_m/sec² = pdl/ft	slug/sec² = lb_f/ft

TABLE B.2. CONVERSION OF UNITS

Length

1 kilometer (km)	= 1000 meters	1 inch (in.)	= 2.540 cm
1 meter (m)	= 100 centimeters	1 foot (ft)	= 30.48 cm
1 centimeter (cm)	= 10^{-2} m	1 mile (mi)	= 1.609 km
1 millimeter (mm)	= 10^{-3} m	1 mil	= 10^{-3} in.
1 micron (μ)	= 10^{-6} m	1 centimeter	= 0.3937 in.
1 millimicron (mμ)	= 10^{-9} m	1 meter	= 39.37 in.
1 angstrom (A)	= 10^{-10} m	1 kilometer	= 0.6214 mile

Area

1 square meter (m^2) = 10.76 ft^2
1 square foot (ft^2) = 929 cm^2

Volume

1 liter (l) = 1000 cm^3 = 1.057 quart (qt) = 61.02 in^3 = 0.03532 ft^3
1 cubic meter (m^3) = 1000 l = 35.32 ft^3
1 cubic foot (ft^3) = 7.481 U.S. gal = 0.02832 m^3 = 28.32 l
1 U.S. gallon (gal) = 231 in^3 = 3.785 l;   1 British gallon = 1.201 U.S. gallon = 277.4 in^3

Mass

1 kilogram (kg) = 2.2046 lb_m = 0.06852 slug;   1 lb_m = 453.6 gm = 0.03108 slug
1 slug = 32.174 lb_m = 14.59 kg

Speed

1 km/hr = 0.2778 m/sec = 0.6214 mi/hr = 0.9113 ft/sec
1 mi/hr = 1.467 ft/sec = 1.609 km/hr = 0.4470 m/sec

Density

1 gm/cm^3 = 10^3 kg/m^3 = 62.43 lb_m/ft^3 = 1.940 slug/ft^3
1 lb_m/ft^3 = 0.01602 gm/cm^3;   1 slug/ft^3 = 0.5154 gm/cm^3

Force

1 newton (nt) = 10^5 dynes = 0.1020 kg_f = 0.2248 lb_f
1 pound force (lb_f) = 4.448 nt = 0.4536 kg_f = 32.17 poundals
1 kilogram force (kg_f) = 2.205 lb_f = 9.807 nt
1 U.S. short ton = 2000 lb_f;   1 long ton = 2240 lb_f;   1 metric ton = 2205 lb_f

Energy

1 joule = 1 nt m = 10^7 ergs = 0.7376 ft lb_f = 0.2389 cal = 9.481×10^{-4} Btu
1 ft lb_f = 1.356 joules = 0.3239 cal = 1.285×10^{-3} Btu
1 calorie (cal) = 4.186 joules = 3.087 ft lb_f = 3.968×10^{-3} Btu
1 Btu = 778 ft lb_f = 1055 joules = 0.293 watt hr
1 kilowatt hour (kw hr) = 3.60×10^6 joules = 860.0 kcal = 3413 Btu
1 electron volt (ev) = 1.602×10^{-19} joule

Power

1 watt = 1 joule/sec = 10^7 ergs/sec = 0.2389 cal/sec
1 horsepower (hp) = 550 ft lb_f/sec = 33,000 ft lb_f/min = 745.7 watts
1 kilowatt (kw) = 1.341 hp = 737.6 ft lb_f/sec = 0.9483 Btu/sec

Pressure

1 nt/m^2 = 10 dynes/cm^2 = 9.869×10^{-6} atmosphere = 2.089×10^{-2} lb_f/ft^2
1 lb_f/in^2 = 6895 nt/m^2 = 5.171 cm mercury = 27.68 in. water
1 atmosphere (atm) = 1.013×10^5 nt/m^2 = 1.013×10^6 dynes/cm^2 = 14.70 lb_f/in^2
        = 76 cm mercury = 406.8 in. water

Angle

1 radian (rad) = 57.296°;   1° = 0.017453 rad

Appendix C

Some Basic Equations
in Various Coordinate Systems*

1. NAVIER-STOKES EQUATIONS OF MOTION FOR
AN INCOMPRESSIBLE FLUID WITH VISCOSITY CONSTANT

These equations may be used with a high degree of accuracy for problems involving viscosity variations if the viscosity gradient is not too large. In most physical problems this assumption is adequate and the Navier-Stokes equations may be used in most incompressible flow problems. The following symbols are used:

p = Pressure

$\mathbf{F}$ = Body force density

μ = Viscosity

$\dfrac{D}{Dt}$ = Material derivative (not the same on a component as on a vector).

(a) Vector.

$\mathbf{V}$ is the velocity vector.

$$\rho \frac{D\mathbf{V}}{Dt} = \rho\left[\frac{\partial \mathbf{V}}{\partial t} + (\mathbf{V}\cdot\nabla)\mathbf{V}\right] = -\nabla p + \mathbf{F} + \mu\nabla^2\mathbf{V} \tag{A.1}$$

The term $(\mathbf{V}\cdot\nabla)\mathbf{V}$ is actually a pseudo-vector expression and care must be used in its expansion in other than Cartesian coordinates. It is convenient to express this acceleration term in true vector form, and the equation of motion may be written in the alternative form:

$$\rho\left[\frac{\partial \mathbf{V}}{\partial t} + \nabla\left(\frac{V^2}{2}\right) - \mathbf{V}\times(\nabla\times\mathbf{V})\right] = -\nabla p + \mathbf{F} + \mu\nabla^2\mathbf{V} \tag{A.2}$$

Care must be taken in expanding $\nabla^2\mathbf{V}$ and $D\mathbf{V}/Dt$, since the operation on a vector is not the same as the operation on a scalar component. The following vector identity is useful:

$$\nabla^2\mathbf{V} = \nabla(\nabla\cdot\mathbf{V}) - \nabla\times(\nabla\times\mathbf{V})$$

(b) Cartesian Tensor.

w_i is the velocity in the x_i direction.

$$\rho\left[\frac{\partial w_i}{\partial t} + w_j\frac{\partial w_i}{\partial x_j}\right] = -\frac{\partial p}{\partial x_i} + F_i + \mu\frac{\partial^2 w_i}{\partial x_j\,\partial x_j} \tag{A.3}$$

(c) Cartesian.

u, v, and w are the velocities in the x, y, and z directions respectively. In the following section:

*For a more complete listing of useful equations see: Hughes, W. F., and Gaylord, E. W., *Basic Equations of Engineering Science*, Schaum Publishing Co., New York, 1964.

250

$$\frac{D}{Dt} = \frac{\partial}{\partial t} + u\frac{\partial}{\partial x} + v\frac{\partial}{\partial y} + w\frac{\partial}{\partial z}, \qquad \nabla^2 = \frac{\partial^2}{\partial x^2} + \frac{\partial^2}{\partial y^2} + \frac{\partial^2}{\partial z^2}$$

$$\rho\frac{Du}{Dt} = F_x - \frac{\partial p}{\partial x} + \mu\nabla^2 u$$

$$\rho\frac{Dv}{Dt} = F_y - \frac{\partial p}{\partial y} + \mu\nabla^2 v \qquad \textbf{(A.4)}$$

$$\rho\frac{Dw}{Dt} = F_z - \frac{\partial p}{\partial z} + \mu\nabla^2 w$$

Written out in full, these become:

$$\rho\left(\frac{\partial u}{\partial t} + u\frac{\partial u}{\partial x} + v\frac{\partial u}{\partial y} + w\frac{\partial u}{\partial z}\right) = -\frac{\partial p}{\partial x} + F_x + \mu\left(\frac{\partial^2 u}{\partial x^2} + \frac{\partial^2 u}{\partial y^2} + \frac{\partial^2 u}{\partial z^2}\right)$$

$$\rho\left(\frac{\partial v}{\partial t} + u\frac{\partial v}{\partial x} + v\frac{\partial v}{\partial y} + w\frac{\partial v}{\partial z}\right) = -\frac{\partial p}{\partial y} + F_y + \mu\left(\frac{\partial^2 v}{\partial x^2} + \frac{\partial^2 v}{\partial y^2} + \frac{\partial^2 v}{\partial z^2}\right) \qquad \textbf{(A.5)}$$

$$\rho\left(\frac{\partial w}{\partial t} + u\frac{\partial w}{\partial x} + v\frac{\partial w}{\partial y} + w\frac{\partial w}{\partial z}\right) = -\frac{\partial p}{\partial z} + F_z + \mu\left(\frac{\partial^2 w}{\partial x^2} + \frac{\partial^2 w}{\partial y^2} + \frac{\partial^2 w}{\partial z^2}\right)$$

(d) Cylindrical.

v_r, v_θ, and v_z are the velocities in the r, θ, and z directions respectively. In the following section:

$$\frac{D}{Dt} = \frac{\partial}{\partial l} + v_r\frac{\partial}{\partial r} + \frac{v_\theta}{r}\frac{\partial}{\partial \theta} + v_z\frac{\partial}{\partial z}$$

$$\nabla^2 = \frac{\partial^2}{\partial r^2} + \frac{1}{r}\frac{\partial}{\partial r} + \frac{1}{r^2}\frac{\partial^2}{\partial \theta^2} + \frac{\partial^2}{\partial z^2}$$

$$\rho\left[\frac{Dv_r}{Dt} - \frac{v_\theta^2}{r}\right] = F_r - \frac{\partial p}{\partial r} + \mu\left[\nabla^2 v_r - \frac{v_r}{r^2} - \frac{2}{r^2}\frac{\partial v_\theta}{\partial \theta}\right] \qquad \textbf{(A.6)}$$

$$\rho\left[\frac{Dv_\theta}{Dt} + \frac{v_r v_\theta}{r}\right] = F_\theta - \frac{1}{r}\frac{\partial p}{\partial \theta} + \mu\left[\nabla^2 v_\theta + \frac{2}{r^2}\frac{\partial v_r}{\partial \theta} - \frac{v_\theta}{r^2}\right]$$

$$\rho\frac{Dv_z}{Dt} = F_z - \frac{\partial p}{\partial z} + \mu\nabla^2 v_z$$

Written out in full, these become:

$$\rho\left[\frac{\partial v_r}{\partial t} + v_r\frac{\partial v_r}{\partial r} + \frac{v_\theta}{r}\frac{\partial v_r}{\partial \theta} + v_z\frac{\partial v_r}{\partial z} - \frac{v_\theta^2}{r}\right]$$

$$= F_r - \frac{\partial p}{\partial r} + \mu\left[\frac{\partial^2 v_r}{\partial r^2} + \frac{1}{r}\frac{\partial v_r}{\partial r} + \frac{1}{r^2}\frac{\partial^2 v_r}{\partial \theta^2} + \frac{\partial^2 v_r}{\partial z^2} - \frac{v_r}{r^2} - \frac{2}{r^2}\frac{\partial v_\theta}{\partial \theta}\right]$$

$$\rho\left[\frac{\partial v_\theta}{\partial t} + v_r\frac{\partial v_\theta}{\partial r} + \frac{v_\theta}{r}\frac{\partial v_\theta}{\partial \theta} + v_z\frac{\partial v_\theta}{\partial z} + \frac{v_r v_\theta}{r}\right] \qquad \textbf{(A.7)}$$

$$= F_\theta - \frac{1}{r}\frac{\partial p}{\partial \theta} + \mu\left[\frac{\partial^2 v_\theta}{\partial r^2} + \frac{1}{r}\frac{\partial v_\theta}{\partial r} + \frac{1}{r^2}\frac{\partial^2 v_\theta}{\partial \theta^2} + \frac{\partial^2 v_\theta}{\partial z^2} + \frac{2}{r^2}\frac{\partial v_r}{\partial \theta} - \frac{v_\theta}{r^2}\right]$$

$$\rho\left[\frac{\partial v_z}{\partial t} + v_r\frac{\partial v_z}{\partial r} + \frac{v_\theta}{r}\frac{\partial v_z}{\partial \theta} + v_z\frac{\partial v_z}{\partial z}\right]$$

$$= F_z - \frac{\partial p}{\partial z} + \mu\left[\frac{\partial^2 v_z}{\partial r^2} + \frac{1}{r}\frac{\partial v_z}{\partial r} + \frac{1}{r^2}\frac{\partial^2 v_z}{\partial \theta^2} + \frac{\partial^2 v_z}{\partial z^2}\right]$$

(e) Spherical.

v_r, v_θ, and v_ϕ are the velocities in the r, θ, and ϕ directions respectively.   In the following section:

$$\frac{D}{Dt} = \frac{\partial}{\partial t} + v_r \frac{\partial}{\partial r} + \frac{v_\theta}{r} \frac{\partial}{\partial \theta} + \frac{v_\phi}{r \sin \theta} \frac{\partial}{\partial \phi}$$

$$\nabla^2 = \frac{1}{r^2} \frac{\partial}{\partial r} \left(r^2 \frac{\partial}{\partial r} \right) + \frac{1}{r^2 \sin \theta} \frac{\partial}{\partial \theta} \left(\sin \theta \frac{\partial}{\partial \theta} \right) + \frac{1}{r^2 \sin^2 \theta} \frac{\partial^2}{\partial \phi^2}$$

$$\rho \left[\frac{Dv_r}{Dt} - \frac{v_\theta^2 + v_r^2}{r} \right]$$

$$= F_r - \frac{\partial p}{\partial r} + \mu \left[\nabla^2 v_r - \frac{2v_r}{r^2} - \frac{2}{r^2} \frac{\partial v_\theta}{\partial \theta} - \frac{2v_\theta \cot \theta}{r^2} - \frac{2}{r^2 \sin \theta} \frac{\partial v_\phi}{\partial \phi} \right]$$

$$\rho \left[\frac{Dv_\theta}{Dt} + \frac{v_r v_\theta - v_\phi^2 \cot \theta}{r} \right] \tag{A.8}$$

$$= F_\theta - \frac{1}{r} \frac{\partial p}{\partial \theta} + \mu \left[\nabla^2 v_\theta + \frac{2}{r^2} \frac{\partial v_r}{\partial \theta} - \frac{v_\theta}{r^2 \sin^2 \theta} - \frac{2 \cos \theta}{r^2 \sin^2 \theta} \frac{\partial v_\phi}{\partial \phi} \right]$$

$$\rho \left[\frac{Dv_\phi}{Dt} + \frac{v_\phi v_r}{r} + \frac{v_\theta v_\phi \cot \theta}{r} \right]$$

$$= F_\phi - \frac{1}{r \sin \theta} \frac{\partial p}{\partial \phi} + \mu \left[\nabla^2 v_\phi - \frac{v_\phi}{r^2 \sin^2 \theta} + \frac{2}{r^2 \sin^2 \theta} \frac{\partial v_r}{\partial \phi} + \frac{2 \cos \theta}{r^2 \sin^2 \theta} \frac{\partial v_\theta}{\partial \phi} \right]$$

Written out in full, these become:

$$\rho \left[\frac{\partial v_r}{\partial t} + v_r \frac{\partial v_r}{\partial r} + \frac{v_\theta}{r} \frac{\partial v_r}{\partial \theta} + \frac{v_\phi}{r \sin \theta} \frac{\partial v_r}{\partial \phi} - \frac{v_\theta^2 + v_\phi^2}{r} \right]$$

$$= F_r - \frac{\partial p}{\partial r} + \mu \left[\frac{1}{r^2} \frac{\partial}{\partial r} \left(r^2 \frac{\partial v_r}{\partial r} \right) + \frac{1}{r^2 \sin \theta} \frac{\partial}{\partial \theta} \left(\sin \theta \frac{\partial v_r}{\partial \theta} \right) \right.$$

$$\left. + \frac{1}{r^2 \sin^2 \theta} \frac{\partial^2 v_r}{\partial \phi^2} - \frac{2v_r}{r^2} - \frac{2}{r^2} \frac{\partial v_\theta}{\partial \theta} - \frac{2v_\theta \cot \theta}{r^2} - \frac{2}{r^2 \sin \theta} \frac{\partial v_\phi}{\partial \phi} \right]$$

$$\tag{A.9}$$

$$\rho \left[\frac{\partial v_\theta}{\partial t} + v_r \frac{\partial v_\theta}{\partial r} + \frac{v_\theta}{r} \frac{\partial v_\theta}{\partial \theta} + \frac{v_\phi}{r \sin \theta} \frac{\partial v_\theta}{\partial \phi} + \frac{v_r v_\theta}{r} - \frac{v_\phi^2 \cot \theta}{r} \right]$$

$$= F_\theta - \frac{1}{r} \frac{\partial p}{\partial \theta} + \mu \left[\frac{1}{r^2} \frac{\partial}{\partial r} \left(r^2 \frac{\partial v_\theta}{\partial r} \right) + \frac{1}{r^2 \sin \theta} \frac{\partial}{\partial \theta} \left(\sin \theta \frac{\partial v_\theta}{\partial \theta} \right) \right.$$

$$\left. + \frac{1}{r^2 \sin^2 \theta} \frac{\partial^2 v_\theta}{\partial \phi^2} + \frac{2}{r^2} \frac{\partial v_r}{\partial \theta} - \frac{v_\theta}{r^2 \sin^2 \theta} - \frac{2 \cos \theta}{r^2 \sin^2 \theta} \frac{\partial v_\phi}{\partial \phi} \right]$$

$$\rho \left[\frac{\partial v_\phi}{\partial t} + v_r \frac{\partial v_\phi}{\partial r} + \frac{v_\theta}{r} \frac{\partial v_\phi}{\partial \theta} + \frac{v_\phi}{r \sin \theta} \frac{\partial v_\phi}{\partial \phi} + \frac{v_\phi v_r}{r} + \frac{v_\theta v_\phi \cot \theta}{r} \right]$$

$$= F_\phi - \frac{1}{r \sin \theta} \frac{\partial p}{\partial \phi} + \mu \left[\frac{1}{r^2} \frac{\partial}{\partial r} \left(r^2 \frac{\partial v_\phi}{\partial r} \right) + \frac{1}{r^2 \sin \theta} \frac{\partial}{\partial \theta} \left(\sin \theta \frac{\partial v_\phi}{\partial \theta} \right) \right.$$

$$\left. + \frac{1}{r^2 \sin^2 \theta} \frac{\partial^2 v_\phi}{\partial \phi^2} - \frac{v_\phi}{r^2 \sin^2 \theta} + \frac{2}{r^2 \sin^2 \theta} \frac{\partial v_r}{\partial \phi} + \frac{2 \cos \theta}{r^2 \sin^2 \theta} \frac{\partial v_\theta}{\partial \phi} \right]$$

2. SOME USEFUL VECTOR OPERATIONS

The operations $\frac{D}{Dt}$ and ∇^2 listed below are for operations on a scalar. These are not the same as operation on a vector except in cartesian coordinates.

(a) Cartesian.

$$\frac{D}{Dt} = \frac{\partial}{\partial t} + u \frac{\partial}{\partial x} + v \frac{\partial}{\partial y} + w \frac{\partial}{\partial z}$$

$$\nabla \cdot \mathbf{V} = \frac{\partial u}{\partial x} + \frac{\partial v}{\partial y} + \frac{\partial w}{\partial z} \tag{A.10}$$

$$\nabla^2 = \frac{\partial^2}{\partial x^2} + \frac{\partial^2}{\partial y^2} + \frac{\partial^2}{\partial z^2}$$

(b) Cylindrical.

$$\frac{D}{Dt} = \frac{\partial}{\partial t} + v_r \frac{\partial}{\partial r} + \frac{v_\theta}{r} \frac{\partial}{\partial \theta} + v_z \frac{\partial}{\partial z}$$

$$\nabla \cdot \mathbf{V} = \frac{1}{r} \frac{\partial}{\partial r} (r v_r) + \frac{1}{r} \frac{\partial v_\theta}{\partial \theta} + \frac{\partial v_z}{\partial z} \tag{A.11}$$

$$\nabla^2 = \frac{\partial^2}{\partial r^2} + \frac{1}{r} \frac{\partial}{\partial r} + \frac{1}{r^2} \frac{\partial^2}{\partial \theta^2} + \frac{\partial^2}{\partial z^2}$$

(c) Spherical.

$$\frac{D}{Dt} = \frac{\partial}{\partial t} + v_r \frac{\partial}{\partial r} + \frac{v_\theta}{r} \frac{\partial}{\partial \theta} + \frac{v_\phi}{r \sin \theta} \frac{\partial}{\partial \phi}$$

$$\nabla \cdot \mathbf{V} = \frac{1}{r^2} \frac{\partial}{\partial r} (r^2 v_r) + \frac{1}{r \sin \theta} \frac{\partial}{\partial \theta} (v_\theta \sin \theta) + \frac{1}{r \sin \theta} \frac{\partial v_\phi}{\partial \phi} \tag{A.12}$$

$$\nabla^2 = \frac{1}{r^2} \frac{\partial}{\partial r} \left(r^2 \frac{\partial}{\partial r} \right) + \frac{1}{r^2 \sin \theta} \frac{\partial}{\partial \theta} \left(\sin \theta \frac{\partial}{\partial \theta} \right) + \frac{1}{r^2 \sin^2 \theta} \frac{\partial^2}{\partial \phi^2}$$

3. THE DISSIPATION FUNCTION

The mechanical or viscous dissipation function Φ is defined in generalized orthogonal coordinates as (in terms of the strain rate tensor e_{ij})

$$\Phi = \mu[2(e_{11}^2 + e_{22}^2 + e_{33}^2) + (2e_{23})^2 + (2e_{31})^2 + (2e_{12})^2] + \lambda(e_{11} + e_{22} + e_{33})^2 \qquad \textbf{(A.13)}$$

(In some texts, the definition of Φ differs by a factor of μ from the one defined here.) λ is the second coefficient of viscosity defined in Chapter 3.

(a) Cartesian Tensor in terms of the stress tensor.

$$\Phi = \sigma_{ij}' \frac{\partial w_i}{\partial x_j} \qquad \textbf{(A.14)}$$

(b) Cartesian.

$$\Phi = 2\mu\left[\left(\frac{\partial u}{\partial x}\right)^2 + \left(\frac{\partial v}{\partial y}\right)^2 + \left(\frac{\partial w}{\partial z}\right)^2 + \frac{1}{2}\left(\frac{\partial u}{\partial y} + \frac{\partial v}{\partial x}\right)^2 + \frac{1}{2}\left(\frac{\partial v}{\partial z} + \frac{\partial w}{\partial y}\right)^2\right.$$
$$\left. + \frac{1}{2}\left(\frac{\partial w}{\partial x} + \frac{\partial u}{\partial z}\right)^2\right] + \lambda\left[\frac{\partial u}{\partial x} + \frac{\partial v}{\partial y} + \frac{\partial w}{\partial z}\right]^2 \qquad \textbf{(A.15)}$$

(c) Cylindrical.

$$\Phi = \mu\left[2\left\{\left(\frac{\partial v_r}{\partial r}\right)^2 + \left(\frac{1}{r}\frac{\partial v_\theta}{\partial \theta} + \frac{v_r}{r}\right)^2 + \left(\frac{\partial v_z}{\partial z}\right)^2\right\} + \left(\frac{1}{r}\frac{\partial v_z}{\partial \theta} + \frac{\partial v_\theta}{\partial z}\right)^2\right.$$
$$\left. + \left(\frac{\partial v_r}{\partial z} + \frac{\partial v_z}{\partial r}\right)^2 + \left(\frac{1}{r}\frac{\partial v_r}{\partial \theta} + \frac{\partial v_\theta}{\partial r} - \frac{v_\theta}{r}\right)^2\right] \qquad \textbf{(A.16)}$$
$$+ \lambda\left[\frac{\partial v_r}{\partial r} + \frac{1}{r}\frac{\partial v_\theta}{\partial \theta} + \frac{v_r}{r} + \frac{\partial v_z}{\partial z}\right]^2$$

(d) Spherical.

$$\Phi = \mu\left[2\left\{\left(\frac{\partial v_r}{\partial r}\right)^2 + \left(\frac{1}{r}\frac{\partial v_\theta}{\partial \theta} + \frac{v_r}{r}\right)^2 + \left(\frac{1}{r\sin\theta}\frac{\partial v_\phi}{\partial \phi} + \frac{v_r}{r} + \frac{v_\theta\cot\theta}{r}\right)^2\right\}\right.$$
$$+ \left\{\frac{1}{r\sin\theta}\frac{\partial v_\theta}{\partial \phi} + \frac{\sin\theta}{r}\frac{\partial}{\partial \theta}\left(\frac{v_\phi}{\sin\theta}\right)\right\}^2 \qquad \textbf{(A.17)}$$
$$\left. + \left\{\frac{1}{r\sin\theta}\frac{\partial v_r}{\partial \phi} + r\frac{\partial}{\partial r}\left(\frac{v_\phi}{r}\right)\right\}^2 + \left\{r\frac{\partial}{\partial r}\left(\frac{v_\theta}{r}\right) + \frac{1}{r}\frac{\partial v_r}{\partial \theta}\right\}^2\right]$$
$$+ \lambda\left[\frac{\partial v_r}{\partial r} + \frac{1}{r}\frac{\partial v_\theta}{\partial \theta} + \frac{2v_r}{r} + \frac{1}{r\sin\theta}\frac{\partial v_\phi}{\partial \phi} + \frac{v_\theta\cot\theta}{r}\right]^2$$

Answers to Selected Problems

CHAPTER 2

2.15. (a) 111 in., (b) 8.14 in.

2.16. 3.78 psi

2.17. 0.747 psi

2.18. 0.0205 psi

2.19. 0.00419 psi

2.20. 585 lb_f

2.22. $8.47(10)^4$ lb_f; $F_N = 0$

2.23. The same as if the container were at rest.

2.24. 6.94 ft

2.25. $p_B - p_A = \gamma$ psf; $p_D - p_A = 1.61\gamma$ psf; $p_C - p_A = 0.61\gamma$ psf

2.26. $\dfrac{\Delta a}{\Delta p} = \dfrac{D}{4t\gamma}$ where D is the mean diameter of the cup, and t is the wall thickness of the cup.

2.30. Water surface is parallel to the inclined plane.

2.31. Same as for rotation of an open container with its minimum depth equal to the height of the container with the lid.

2.32. $p = \frac{1}{2}\rho r^2 \omega^2$, independent of vertical position.

2.33. $p_{top} + \rho a (H - h)$

2.34. $p - p_0 = \frac{1}{2}\rho_1 \omega^2 r^2 + \rho_1 g (z_{01} - z)$ for $z_{01} > z - \dfrac{\omega^2 r^2}{2g} > z_{02}$

$p - p_0 = \frac{1}{2}\rho_2 \omega^2 r^2 + \rho_2 g (z_{02} - z) + \rho_1 g (z_{01} - z_{02})$ for $z_{02} > z - \dfrac{\omega^2 r^2}{2g}$

Free surface: $z = z_{01} + \frac{1}{2}\rho\omega^2 r^2$

Interface: $z = z_{02} + \frac{1}{2}\rho\omega^2 r^2$

2.35. Shape is unimportant. L and h are relevant parameters.

2.37. If the balloon is filled with helium it will slant forward as the car accelerates.

2.38. $\sigma = \dfrac{\pi D^2}{4NA}(p_c + \rho\omega^2 D^2/16)$ where ρ = density of oil, σ = tensile stress, N = number of bolts, A = cross-sectional area of a bolt, p_c = pressure from charging pump, ω is measured in radians per sec.

CHAPTER 3

3.14. 0.0119 ft³/sec

3.15. $F = \frac{1}{3}\pi\rho a^2 V_0^2 + \pi a^2 (p_2 - p_1)$

3.16. $p_1 = p_2 + 2\tau_0 L/a + \rho V_0^2/3$

3.18. 10.6 fps

3.19. 16.21 psi

3.20. (a) $Q = \pi a^2 V_c/2$, (b) $\frac{1}{3}\pi\rho a^2 V_c^2$, (c) $\frac{1}{8}\pi\rho a^2 V_c^3$

3.21. 47.0 horsepower

3.22. 18.0 ft³/sec; 4760 lb_f

3.23. 437 ft/sec

3.27. 0.361 psi/ft

3.31. 2.32 ft/sec²

3.32. $Q = A_2 \sqrt{2gh_1}$ if $A_2 \ll A_1$ and $h_2 < \dfrac{p_{atm}}{\rho g}$

3.33. $-\rho U^2 h/6$

3.34. $D = -0.63\rho U^2 D$

3.35.   76.5 rpm

3.36. $\omega = \sqrt{p_0/x_0\,\rho H}$ where p_0 is atmospheric pressure.

CHAPTER 4

4.11.   Lift = 2150 lb

4.12. $f = 0.028$.   Pressure drop per mile = 168 psi = 484 ft oil = 387 ft water,   assuming sp. gr. 0.8.

4.14. $C_D = 0.18$. D = 20 lb, the same as for the model test.

4.18. Π's are $\rho DV/\mu$ and $\omega D/V$

4.19. $\omega D/V$ modeling can be achieved but not $\rho DV/\mu$ which is less important.

4.20.   Froude modeling requires $V_m = \sqrt{20}$ mph and is independent of the fluid viscosity. Reynolds number modeling is impractical here since for $V_m = 5$ mph, say, $\nu = 1.36 \times 10^{-7}$ and such a liquid is not available.

4.22.   Efficiency = 57%, $Q = 135$ ft³/sec, $H = 90$ ft,   power = 6075 hp

4.24.   11.25°F

CHAPTER 5

5.13.   0.305 in.

5.14.   0.00151 lb$_f$/ft²

5.15.   0.125 lb$_f$; 0.000705

5.19. $1.29(UL/\nu)^{-1/2}$

5.22. $\dfrac{0.075\,h^2 V_1^2}{[h - 0.1\sqrt{x}/8]^3\,\sqrt{x}}$;   32.5 ft/sec²

5.23. $\rho U^2/12$

5.24. $p - p_{\text{entrance}} = -1.03(10)^{-3}$ psi

5.26.   0.338 lb$_f$/ft

5.27. $p - p_{\text{entrance}} = -6.67(10)^{-3}$ psi

5.28.   3.43 lb$_f$

5.31.   0.460 lb$_f$

5.32.   0.0735 horsepower

5.33. $\mu = 1.16(10)^{-4}$ lb$_f$ sec/ft²

5.34.   7270 rpm

5.35. $\pi\mu(\omega_1 - \omega_2)(R_2^4 - R_1^4)/2T_{\text{in}}$

5.36.   1.12 ft/sec

5.37.   23.0 ft

5.38.   23.6 ft/sec

5.40.   12.6 ft/sec

5.41.   0.0923 psi

5.42.   0.216 psi

5.43. $T = \dfrac{A}{a}\sqrt{\dfrac{2}{g}}\left[\sqrt{h_0 + h_1} - \sqrt{h_0}\,\right]$

5.46. $F = \dfrac{\pi D L \mu V}{h}\left[1 + \dfrac{3}{h^2}\left(\dfrac{d^2}{4} - h^2\right)\right] \approx \tfrac{3}{4}(d/h)^3\pi L\mu V$ where $h = \dfrac{D_c - D}{2}$

CHAPTER 6

6.13.   26.6 lb$_f$/ft

6.16.   Force = $2m^2\rho \displaystyle\int_0^\infty \dfrac{(x^2 - a^2)^2}{(x^2 + a^2)^4}\,dx = \dfrac{3\pi m^2\rho}{16a^3}$

6.17. Force $= \dfrac{m^2\rho}{a^3}\left(\dfrac{3\pi}{16}\cos^2\alpha + \dfrac{\pi}{4}\sin^2\alpha - \dfrac{1}{3}\sin 2\alpha\right)$

6.18. No difference since F depends on m^2.

6.20. $F = -m \ln (\sinh \pi z/2d)$

6.21. $\phi = A(x^2 - y^2)$, $\psi = (A)(2xy)$

6.23. $F = -\dfrac{Q}{2\pi} \ln (\sinh \pi z/d) - U_0 z$

6.24. $F = \dfrac{i\Gamma}{2\pi} \ln \left(\dfrac{z - id}{z + id}\right)$, streamlines are nested circles.

6.31. $u - iv = -\dfrac{Q}{2\pi}\left[\dfrac{z - (b + ia)}{z - (b - ia)} + \dfrac{z + (b - ia)}{z - (b + ia)} + \dfrac{z + (b + ia)}{z + (b - ia)} + \dfrac{z + (b - ia)}{z + (b + ia)}\right]$

6.32. $F = -\dfrac{Q}{2\pi} \ln \left\{\displaystyle\prod_{n=0}^{7}\left[z - ae^{i(\pi/4)(1/2 + n)}\right]\right\}$

6.34. $ry = \Gamma^2/4\pi^2 g$, where y is measured downward from the level of the free surface at infinity to the free surface at r.

CHAPTER 7

7.26. 4880 ft/sec

7.27. 0.313; 1.11

7.28. 0.182

7.29. 16.1 psi

7.30. 72.5 psi; 179.2 Btu/lb; 822°R

7.31. 0.00256 ft²

7.32. 18.1 lb$_m$/sec

7.33. (a) 0.00806 ft²; 0.01385 ft². (b) 2.01

7.34. 0.222 lb/sec; 1590 ft/sec

7.35. 1.40

7.36. 1198 ft/sec

CHAPTER 8

8.6. $M_2 = 2.6$; $T_2 = 381°R$; $p_2 = 5.5$ psia

8.7. $M_2 = 1.45$; $T_2 = 638°R$; $p_2 = 31$ psia

8.8. β (bottom) $= 15°$; β (top) $= 19.5°$

8.9. $M_2 = 2.6$; $T_2 = 437°R$; $p_2 = 3.93$ psia

8.10. $D_2 = 0.68D_1$

8.11. $D_2 = 1.75D_1$

8.13. For the nth half wavelength, $\dfrac{\Delta p}{p_1} = \dfrac{(-1)^n \epsilon}{\lambda\sqrt{M_1^2 - 1}}$

8.14. $L = 1.03cp_1$ per unit length (shock expansion theory).

8.15. $G = \dfrac{c}{2\sqrt{M_1^2 - 1}}$

8.17. $C_L = \dfrac{4\bar{\alpha}}{\sqrt{M_1^2 - 1}}$, $\quad C_D = \dfrac{4}{\sqrt{M_1^2 - 1}}\left[\dfrac{\pi^2}{2}\left(\dfrac{H}{c}\right)^2 + \bar{\alpha}^2 + 2\pi^2\left(\dfrac{Y}{c}\right)^2\right]$

8.20. $|\theta| = 53°$

8.22. Velocity of shock before reflection $= 1160$ ft/sec.

INDEX

Catalog

If you are interested in a list of SCHAUM'S
OUTLINE SERIES in Science, Mathematics,
Engineering and other subjects, send your name
and address, requesting your free catalog, to:

SCHAUM'S OUTLINE SERIES, Dept. C
McGRAW-HILL BOOK COMPANY
1221 Avenue of Americas
New York, N.Y. 10020